Date Due

JUL 21 '68 Engl			
GB	PRINTED	IN U. S. A.	

FOUNDATIONS OF INFERENCE IN NATURAL SCIENCE

FOUNDATIONS OF INFERENCE
IN NATURAL SCIENCE

by

JOHN OULTON WISDOM, Ph.D.

Lecturer in Logic and Scientific Method at
the London School of Economics. Formerly
of the Philosophy Department at Farouk I
University, Alexandria.

METHUEN & CO., LTD., LONDON
36 Essex Street, Strand, W.C.2

First published in 1952

CATALOGUE NO. 5351 /U

PRINTED IN GREAT BRITAIN

Science is most significant as one of the greatest spiritual adventures that man has yet known.

K. R. Popper

May we venture to hope that . . . Inductive Reasoning, which has long been the glory of Science, will have ceased to be the scandal of Philosophy?

C. D. Broad

PREFACE

THE title of this book is not intended to convey that there are fundamental principles of scientific inference here set forth; what is meant is more mundane—that principles have been proposed from time to time and that the book is about these.

The subject-matter is what used to appear in the second half of logic books under the heading "inductive logic". The overt assumption was that scientific inference is inductive. The 'hypothetical method', it is true, received a mention—but with the expressed or implied rider that induction assimilated it.

When setting out to write this book, part of which was drafted and used for lectures to honour students at Farouk I University, Alexandria, I wished to stress the independence of the rôle played by hypotheses, and to show that a certain kind of hypothesis could not be assimilated by induction at all, namely those embodying concepts that have no observable instances. Thus induction was still allowed a rôle. But even this change of emphasis concedes too much to induction. Professor Popper has convinced me that induction plays no part whatever in science—that there is no inductive method and that nothing approximating to inductive inference is used. What appears to be inductive is assimilated by the method of hypothesis and deduction—the hypothetico-deductive system. Thus the traditional view is completely reversed.

It is hoped that by this re-orientation the account offered of scientific procedure will be as faithful as possible to science as it is practised.

The reader will find almost no historical discussion and almost no mention of Aristotle, Bacon, or Mill. The book is largely a critical survey of the views of scientific inference that have been developed over the last thirty years or so, from the time at the end of World War I when the late Lord Keynes and Professor C. D. Broad broke new ground. It contains some detailed exposition of ideas introduced by Keynes that were cryptically put forward, often quoted, but nowhere explained.

The framework of the book is this. First comes the hypothetico-deductive approach, illustrated by concrete examples; then examination of 'induction'; and thirdly aspects of probability that have been held to have a bearing on the 'problem of induction'; with a concluding outline of the shape this problem takes if transformed by the hypothetico-deductive approach, and of a way in which it may be tackled.

Chapter XI with slight alterations originally appeared in *Mind* (1945) and parts of Chapter IX in the *Proceedings of the Aristotelian Society* (1944). I wish to thank the Editors for permission to utilise these papers. I am indebted also for permission to quote from an English draft of Professor K. R. Popper's *Logik der Forschung*. Moreover I have made use of some of Professor Popper's ideas, which have gained a certain currency but which have not appeared in print. I wish to express my thanks to him, to Professor Gilbert Ryle, and to Professor W. J. H. Sprott for helpful suggestions, and to Professor Sprott further for kindly reading the greater part of the proofs.

J. O. WISDOM

The London School of Economics
London, W.C.2
July, 1951

CONTENTS

PART I

PART II

PART III

PART IV

N.B. In order to distract the reader's eye as little as possible, footnotes merely containing references are indicated by numbers, while those containing comment are distinguished by an asterisk or other sign.

Quotations are printed in smaller type than the rest of the text, and without quotation marks. Double quotation marks are used when words, phrases, expressions, or statements are spoken about. Sometimes words, phrases, and expressions are enclosed in single quotation marks, even though these verbal forms are not spoken about but are used to speak about other matters. The purpose of using single quotation marks is to draw attention to the verbal form, indicating that it is technical, obscure, or noteworthy for some reason.

PART I

CHAPTER 1

SCIENTIFIC OUTLOOK

Conviction is belief in the possession of absolute truth on any matter of knowledge. This belief takes it for granted, therefore, that there are absolute truths; also, that perfect methods have been found for attaining to them; and finally, that every one who has convictions makes use of these perfect methods. All three notions show at once that the man of convictions is not the man of scientific thought.—Nietzsche.

In this book we shall be concerned with the study of *scientific procedure*. It is made up of the study of *scientific inference* and the study of *scientific practice*. In addition to inference, certain other general features of method play an indispensable part in science. Indeed it cannot be overstressed that scientific inference and scientific method are interwoven and inseparable. The subject is commonly described as "methodology" or as "the study of scientific method". Either description is, however, at once too wide and too narrow. On the one hand either would allow us to include minute details concerning the techniques used in making experiments—but the methodologist is not interested in whether it is better to seal a joint in a piece of glass-tubing by means of plasticine or rubber. On the other hand the word "method" draws the stress away from processes of inference, which play an enormous part in science. We may, however, conveniently reserve "methodology" or "scientific method" for the study of the general features of *scientific practice* in which the rôle of inference is not stressed. In this book scientific inference is much more extensively discussed than methodology. It will be convenient, therefore, to introduce the word "metascience" as a name for the study of scientific inference. It should be observed, moreover, that in this book metascience is being restricted to scientific procedure in natural science; mathematics is a science in a different sense; the corresponding metascientific study of it is deductive logic; but this study will not be included.

Apart from Jevons, logicians in the past have been more concerned with what scientific inference ought to be than with what it actually is. It is most important to begin by finding out what kind of inference scientists do use before proceeding to discuss the nature of their inferences. A word must be said, however, about actual scientific inference. We start from the work of good scientists; but we are not concerned with their mistakes, and on the other hand an occasional instance of good inference by a poor scientist will serve our purpose. Our data are therefore instances of good inference. Whatever the criteria of this may be, any pattern of supposedly good inference we consider should be subjected to the test of seeing whether it is actually found in or implied by some scientific example. While it might be possible to think of a pattern that is not found in or implied by any example, such a pattern must be treated with caution; it is only too easy, as logicians' mistakes show, to put forward a pattern that appropriate scientific examples or sufficiently careful scrutiny would show to be unusable. Thus when we speak of actual scientific practice, we mean what is found in or implied by good scientific practice.

Very little reflection suffices to show that there is something peculiar about scientific inference. We shall be mistaken if we suppose that all inference is alike simply because, by a mental process consisting of a train of thought, we begin at one point and end at another, begin with something we know and end with something we did not know. Many have regarded mathematics and deductive (or formal) logic as providing the pattern of inference. Yet even pure mathematicians hardly use these in ordinary life. The syllogism of ancient deductive logic has often been regarded as the ideal pattern of inference—how much ink has left its well in the service of

> All men are mortal;
> Socrates is a man;
> Therefore Socrates is mortal!

But if you take the trouble to study a carefully argued discourse from the law courts, the leading article of a newspaper, or a university-lecture (scientific, philosophical, or otherwise) you will be able to express in syllogistic form only a minute fraction of it. The idea has long held sway that any pattern diverging from the time-honoured pattern was inferior. On this we should for the present keep an open mind; first it is necessary to study the scientific pattern.

If we tend to regard deduction (whether in mathematics or in formal logic) as the only 'true' form of inference, we may be inclined to prescribe to science how it shall conduct itself. This kind of approach is often visible in other spheres. Thus in music it is often possible to find critics condemning a new composer for having broken the rules of harmony. But there are no such rules that hold for all time. It does not occur to many of us that Mozart's music was revolutionary in his day and may have given his contemporaries something of the shock that Wagner's did to those of a later time or that Sibelius' did to others not long ago. Each broke the rules; the rules meant only the grammar that was to be found in the work of a certain composer or group of them—and grammar is derived from the composition and not the composition from grammar. The reader can provide himself with the illustration that suits him best. He may think that the 'correct' way to hold a golf-club is with the 'overlapping grip'; but this is no more than the practice of the vast majority of the best players of the present—it used not to be so and it may not be so in the future. But, lest it should appear that scientific inference can be nothing but a vogue, it may be remarked that even the criterion of strict mathematical inference has continually undergone changes.

Metascientists have sometimes held that science breaks the rules of deductive logic. Whether or not this is true must be investigated. But, even if it is, then we cannot deny to science its right to do so; and it would be for the metascientist to accept the scientific pattern of inference and adjust himself to it as best he may. In short, we must examine the *scientist in action*, note the general features of his methods, and detach from these the principle of inference involved—and then we may permit ourselves the liberty of asking whether his pattern of inference is reasonable.

We may turn now to the metascientific view of scientific concepts. For the scientific outlook, the natural world can be explored by means of the five senses (more, if we subdivide the sense of touch) aided by the intellect. No entity that is incapable of being related to some kind of perception is admitted into science. The scholastics bequeathed the saying: *Nihil in intellectu quod non prius fuerit in sensu.* This it is now realised is too narrow for scientific purposes; for science allows entities other than those that are directly open to inspection. This does not mean that the criterion adopted by science is far from stringent; the stringency is very great. Entities and concepts are admitted if relatable, *directly or indirectly*, to perception—but related they must be. The nearest scholastic dictum expressing this is the celebrated Ockham's razor, for some unknown reason attributed to William of Ockham: *Entia non sunt multiplicanda praeter necessitatem.* That entities are not to be needlessly increased in number may be taken to mean that concepts bearing no relation, direct or indirect, to perception are useless. Thus many regard as suspect the concept of *collective mind*. It may serve as a short way of drawing attention to certain likenesses between individuals and groups of people; but, so far, it does not enable us to do anything of a scientific kind that we could not do without it, beyond expressing certain facts in a different form of language.

Though at various times scientists have indeed introduced unneeded concepts, such as the æther, this was never done wittingly, and progress was later achieved by eliminating such concepts—or, perhaps it would be more accurate to say, they disappeared and were recognised to be needless as a result of progress. Thus the above interpretation of Ockham's razor constitutes the chief principle of the scientific outlook. It is simple in nature, but the comprehension of it may require a reorientation of the mind gained by seeing the principle at work in scientific procedure.

Another important feature of the scientific outlook is the disbelief in *absolutes*. First of all it is to be emphasised that *absolute exactitude* is impossible—not only in practice but in principle. Results are always *approximate*—remarkably fine approximations, it is true, but not absolutely exact. It is known that the next total eclipse of the sun visible from England will take place on August 11, 1999; the hour and the minute are also known; and so is the second, *more or less*; but in all predictions of this sort there is a slight discrepancy between the calculated time and the observed time, perhaps a second or an appreciable fraction of a second. Such discrepancy is not trivial, but discussion of its significance may be postponed. Suffice it to say, that the scientists knows he will never attain absolute precision, yet he spends a good part of his time seeking ways of gaining more and more precision—the Astronomer Royal has lately scrapped his clocks, which measured the day correctly only to one-hundredth of a second, because it has become possible to produce clocks that measure the day to one-thousandth of a second. Some scientific achievement depends upon such refinement, but not all; a great deal of progress has been achieved without it.

Moreover, there is a widespread tendency to speak of carrying out projects mathematically or scientifically. Thus bombs have been dropped with 'mathematical precision' and war has been waged 'scientifically'. The fact is that bombs have been dropped with accuracy, but there is nothing mathematical about this; and that war-activities have been methodically planned, but there is nothing scientific about this. No doubt mathematics and science have been applied at some stage of the proceedings, just as have commonsense, economics, and psychology; but it is an immense confusion to identify mathematics or science with methodicality. One needs to be methodical to be efficient at mathematics and science, as one does at packing, running a business, and many other things, but that does not make these activities science.

If these things are not understood, fallacious philosophical edifices are all too easily constructed upon the misunderstanding; and those that boldly restrict their cultural interests exclusively to what are sometimes called the humanities owe their lack of insight into the nature of science in some degree to these confusions (though these would result from deeper psychological factors): the mathematician becomes thought of as a sort of accountant, and the scientist as a mechanic, mistakes analogous to that of regarding a landscape painter as a sort of house decorator.* On the contrary, mathematical and scientific discovery has its æsthetic qualities; it is difficult to assign these their place in metascience but they play their part nonetheless. Mathematicians are not given to talking about this unless they are alone, but among themselves they take the æsthetic qualities of mathematics for granted and do not seem to disagree particularly about what theorems or branches of the subject are 'elegant' or 'beautiful'. It is scarcely too much to say that a new development will not be given much attention by mathematicians unless it has these

---

* Mr. Rowse has been rightly pressing the claims of history as a necessary part of a cultivated man's equipment. Unfortunately, though wishing to be fair to science, he falls into the above confusions: "One may be a cultivated man without knowing mathematics or chemistry or engineering, for these are specialisms. We expect the technicians in question to know them and to do our sums and sanitation for us". (A. L. Rowse, *The Use of History*, London, 1946, p. 191.)

qualities. And, in a somewhat different way perhaps, the same applies to physics and chemistry. The æsthetic factor makes nonsense of the distinction between science and the humanities, but it is a very real factor and one that should not be perpetually concealed if the point of view of the mathematician and scientist is to be grasped. Appreciation of the beauties of the arts is fairly widespread; less so with mathematics. Unfortunately one cannot show to another the beauty of a painting; and likewise one cannot show to another the beauty of a theorem.

The disbelief in absolutes has an even more important place in the scientific outlook, in that scientific results are never certain. A law of science may be accepted for hundreds of years and then be found to stand in need of alteration. There is nothing self-contradictory in supposing that a well-confirmed hypothesis may prove false. Accordingly the scientific attitude is that a well-attested hypothesis is to be accepted until some conflicting fact is discovered; and with this goes the willingness to relinquish a hypothesis and bow to facts.

This does not mean that scientific truth is unreliable. The usual occurrence is to find, not that an old hypothesis is wholly false and must be discarded, but that some modification is needed. More precisely, the advantage of knowledge enables us to state the conditions in which an old hypothesis does not hold and the conditions in which it does hold. Thus Newton's law of gravitation holds for relatively isolated bodies that are not too small and that do not move too fast. The Boyle-Mariotte law of gases holds provided the temperature is not too low. And there is a further fact about an old hypothesis that is retained in spite of defects: it may be shown to be 'a particular case' of a newer and more satisfactory hypothesis. That is to say, if we combine with the Einstein law of gravitation, for example, certain particular conditions, such as that bodies are not too small or do not move too fast, the Newtonian law can be shown deductively to be approximately equivalent to the newer law. This is a vital point in scientific progress; and in view of it we must not grossly assert, as is sometimes done, that the Newtonian law is discarded and superseded by the Einstein law.

On the other hand the frailty of hypotheses does not imply that we should be slow to form any. On the contrary the procedure of science is to form them and improve upon them. This practice does not mean that the scientist, using partially tested hypotheses, is guilty of having preconceived opinions. In the usual sense of this phrase, a preconceived opinion is one that a person is going to cling to through thick and thin no matter what the evidence is that tells against it. But a hypothesis, at any stage from a 'working hypothesis' to one that is very highly tested, is one that is entertained for as long as no adverse evidence is forthcoming.

This is a very different procedure from the method of 'induction', which has hitherto been the main theme of the second half of textbooks on logic. Broadly speaking, induction is usually conceived as a procedure for obtaining a general conclusion from a set of particular observations. It must of course be a matter for discussion whether there is a pattern of inductive *inference*. In the past the distinction was not drawn between induction as a method and as a form of inference; but it is an important distinction, because the practice of science makes it clear that, whether or not there is a pattern of inductive inference, there is no *method* of induction. It must be stressed, therefore, that the actual procedure of science is to work with hypotheses. Put like this, one may feel that at some stage observations must precede the formation of hypotheses. Without pressing the application of this point to the beginnings of human life, we can see that priority of hypotheses holds of the beginnings of science; for the beginnings of science occur just because some observation conflicts with some attitude or expectation. The attitude is not a hypothesis: it may not have been recognised to exist, far less formulated as a general statement, until the discrepant observation was made. Thus the scientist brings to bear on his work numbers of explicit hypotheses and also expectations, perhaps unvoiced. For the set of hypotheses and attitudes brought to bear at any time Popper, who introduced the idea, has coined the happy phrase "horizon of expectations". Progress is made by finding some fact that makes a hole in this, necessitating the formation of a new horizon. And even chance discoveries, like penicillin, fit in with this conception; for the chance observation that bacteria died in the presence of a mould is one that only a bacteriologist could have made; and only a bacteriologist who had the expectation that the mould would *not* interfere with the culture of the bacteria would have made the observation—another would have thrown out the contents of his test tube and begun afresh. Probably no one ever formulated the hypothesis that moulds do not interfere with bacteria; but that hypothesis became explicit when refuted by the 'chance observation'. And if it had been felt to be in no way surprising that the mould should kill bacteria, the significance of the observation would still have related to a hypothesis. Many substances will kill bacteria; that is not the problem: the problem is to find something that will not harm human beings. Hence the important feature of the situation was that someone, making the observation about the mould, should have formed the hypothesis that such moulds are harmless to human beings, against a background attitude to the contrary.

We have seen, then, that we must be prepared to accept the possibility of there being patterns of inference not prescribed by deductive logicians. In these patterns occur hypotheses, and it is a mark of a hypothesis of science that it should contain only concepts that relate to experience, whether directly or indirectly. Such hypotheses are never absolutely verified, nor is absolute exactness attainable even in principle. Hypotheses are used until proved false, and we must always be willing to sacrifice them. This does not mean that they are discarded when an aberrant fact is discovered, for we learn more precisely the conditions in which they hold; and old hypotheses are often found to be 'particular cases' of new ones. Moreover, hypotheses must always be used; there is no *method* of induction as an alternative. The purpose of hypotheses is, of course, to explain. There are three great spheres that arouse our scientific curiosity and need for explanation: the inanimate world, organic life, and the human mind. The three corresponding groups of sciences, the physical, biological, and psychological and social, aim at understanding the processes that take place in their respective spheres. What kind of thing this understanding is and whether the scientist ever attains the understanding he hopes for are questions that must be deferred.

CHAPTER II

EXPERIMENTS AND METHOD

IT will be convenient to have some experiments in front of us.

EXPERIMENT No. I. (Vegetable Mould).

Darwin's[1] attention became drawn to two facts: cinders, stones, and the like, which had been thickly strewn over several meadows were found after some years some centimetres below the surface but still in a layer; and undisturbed fields are found to be covered with what is known as vegetable mould, which is blackish and is composed of particles of uniform fineness. Such facts would be contrary to one's expectations. It seemed to him that the two facts were connected: he entertained the hypothesis that the stones were covered by the mould which was brought to the surface by earthworms in the form of castings. Accordingly he set out to answer the question whether this was so.

He records numerous instances of the following type:[2]

In the spring of 1835, a field, which had long existed as poor pasture and was so swampy that it trembled slightly when stamped on, was thickly covered with red sand so that the whole surface appeared at first bright red. When holes were dug in this field after an interval of about $2\frac{1}{2}$ years, the sand formed a layer at a depth of $\frac{3}{4}$ in. beneath the surface. In 1842 (i.e., 7 years after the sand had been laid on) fresh holes were dug, and now the red sand formed a distinct layer, 2 inches beneath the surface, or $1\frac{1}{2}$ inches beneath the turf; so that on an average, ·21 inch of mould had been annually brought to the surface. Immediately beneath the layer of red sand, the original substratum of black sandy peat extended.

He points out:[3]

The specific gravity of the objects does not affect their rate of sinking, as could be seen by porous cinders, burnt marl, chalk and quartz pebbles, having all sunk to the same depth within the same time.

[1] Charles Darwin, *The Formation of Vegetable Mould through the Action of Worms*, London, 1945, p. 20 and Chapter III.
[2] *Id.*, p. 73.
[3] *Id.*, p. 83.

9

Darwin now turned his attention to large stones, which in general he found also sank into the ground. He seems to suggest, however, that he found some huge boulders that had not sunk at all; the explanation is that if the boulder is sufficiently large the earth underneath it will remain dry and will therefore not be inhabited by worms.

Under one large stone that had sunk he found almost no worms; but he did find large colonies of ants; there may formerly have been worms later driven out by the ants.

Darwin cites a great variety of instances. He also notes any apparent exception. This is valuable not merely because of its candour but because it affords the possibility of further confirmation of the conclusion. The apparent exception concerning large boulders, where because of the dryness of the soil worms do not burrow, clinches the argument.

EXPERIMENT No. II (Spontaneous Generation)

It was thought that some organisms were spontaneously generated: for the known facts were that worms and maggots breed on putrefying flesh; maggots are sometimes found at the core of soft fruit and at the core of apples where the skin is unpierced; and with the discovery of the microscope, tiny organisms known as *infusoria* were seen in rain water which is a *putrescible* liquid.

Scientific work had, however, shown that the first two facts were not due to spontaneous generation. Thus Redi, an Italian scientist, put gauze over meat, which did not exclude the smell; larvae were hatched on the gauze and not on the meat; and this confirmed his impression that worms in putrefying flesh were larvae of eggs of flies. Again, another Italian scientist showed that the grub in fruit was hatched from eggs deposited by insects before the fruit had matured. There remained the problem of infusoria in putrescible liquids. It was then that Pasteur[1] carried out a great series of experiments. The question he asked of nature was specifically: do the infusoria come from the air?

(*a*) On the hypothesis that they do, it would be necessary to examine dust particles from the air. Pasteur filtered air by passing

---

[1] René Valléry-Radot, *The Life of Pasteur*, London, 1919, pp. 87–114; W. C. D. Whetham and M. D. Whetham, *Cambridge Readings in the Literature of Science*, Cambridge, 1924, "Memoir on the Organised Corpuscles which Exist in the Atmosphere."

it through a tube containing gun cotton. He dissolved the latter in alcohol and æther and dust particles remained. Studying these with a microscope he found that they were organic.

(b) He half filled a flask with some sugared yeast water, which is highly putrescible, and boiled it for two or three minutes after sealing the flask. After allowing the liquid to cool he introduced into it some heated air and kept the flask at 30°C. for a long time. No organisms appeared. Thus a putrescible liquid is unaltered by heated air, and it could not be dust that causes putrescence—an important hypothesis to refute.

(c) To test ordinary air, i.e. to test the hypothesis that air carries infusoria, he procured two flasks, one with a long thin neck, which was partly filled with putrescible liquid. After boiling this, he bent the neck so as to point more or less downwards and drew it out to a small open point. After boiling the other flask he left it open. The liquid in the first flask remained pure but in the second developed infusoria. On account of the smallness of the hole in the neck of the first flask, though air could enter, dust could not. Hence infusoria are not the same as dust, but come from the air, and are carried on dust particles. The last point was further substantiated by shaking the flask, when infusoria developed in it—for the shaking allowed the dust to enter through the small hole.

(d) Not content with this, Pasteur substituted asbestos for gun cotton in order to collect dust particles, without affecting the result. And he used specimens of air taken from cellars, mountains, the country, the city, and so on, again without affecting the result.

(e) An exception appeared to have been discovered when Needham, an English priest, found infusoria in boiled liquid. But it was ascertained by the Abbé Spallanza that he had used cork stoppers for sealing his flasks, through which infusoria could eventually penetrate. This apparent exception adds cogency to Pasteur's conclusion once it has been satisfactorily explained.

This great series of experiments falsified the hypothesis of spontaneous generation.

EXPERIMENT No. III. (Bump of Location)

Rabaud[1] has produced a fascinating study of orientation in bees, ants, and birds.

Let us first of all state the problem.

[1] Etienne Rabaud, How Animals Find their Way about, London, 1928.

A bee comes out of the hive; it flies away, and then at some distance, often at a great distance, alights on a cluster of flowers and forages. It goes from one flower to another, and works about in divers directions, describing many turns and meanderings, without any fixed order; at the end of a certain time, it flies off, and almost immediately takes the direction of the hive, which it regains by the shortest route.[1]

Ants and birds do the same. What is the explanation? It is easy to suppose, as most students have done in the past, that the phenomenon is due to a special supersensory faculty, but Rabaud set himself to find out whether the question can be answered by means of the ordinary senses and sensory memory alone, and thus refute the hypothesis of an extra faculty.

A bee is captured, removed some distance, even as far as a couple of kilometres, and set free; it goes in a 'bee-line' for its nest. Three factors have to be examined separately: (i) immediate departure in the correct direction; (ii) recognition of the site of the nest; and (iii) recognition of the nest itself.

(i) (a) A hive was moved 7 kilometres from its original site, and before the bees emerged they were taken to various points from 40 to 80 metres away. When an obstacle, such as a house, intervened, the bees failed to find their way back. But such bees as had escaped and been able to reconnoitre were able subsequently to find their way after being captured, placed with a house between them and the nest, and released. Moreover, with hives that were not moved, young bees that had never been outside could not, when taken out of sight of their hive, find their way home. These facts suggest that bees make use of visual cues. They falsify a hypothesis of a special homing faculty—or at any rate require it to be greatly modified.

(b) A solitary bee, *Osmia rufohirta*, which nests in the shells of snails, moved its nest to one side. After foraging, it returned *via* the original position of the nest. The observer moved the nest, and the bee, even after learning the new position, returned by a zig-zag route bordering the first two positions. Then the bee itself replaced its nest in the first position, and after foraging it skirted this place, went to the others, and only then back to the nest. The conclusion is that the bee registers local landmarks, visual in kind. The alternative hypothesis is that of muscular memory, but the

[1] *Id.*, p. 1.

experimenter ruled this out by removing certain landmarks at the angles of the zig-zag route and then the bee returned straight to its nest without making a zig-zag.

(c) Nonetheless a contrary wind makes the insect seek its destination too early. This suggests that muscular memory can play a part and in fact in familiar surroundings gradually displaces the use of visual cues.

(ii) (d) As regards the location of the site, the insect finds the site even if the nest is removed. Thus the nest itself is not in general a landmark.

(e) If the nest is unmoved, but the appearance of the site is altered, e.g. by mowing the grass, the bee is baffled. Thus, not only is the nest not a landmark, but recognition of the site must be based upon visual cues.

(iii) (f) It is harder to pin down the factors upon which recognition of the nest depends. Sense of touch may play a part, but primarily it is probably sense of smell, for if a nest is suspended in a wind, insects that are down-wind are attracted to the nest.

Rabaud concludes that sensory memory based upon sensory cues is sufficient to account for the behaviour of the bee. The hypothesis that direction-finding depends on visual cues was unfalsified. That site recognition likewise depended on them was also unrefuted by a clever attempt to do so.

It is interesting to compare these results with those for the ant. The solitary ant, for instance, takes its direction by the direction of light. Thus if sunlight is deflected by means of mirrors, the ant will take its booty in a direction opposite to that of the nest. Again, the location of the site of the nest is largely due to muscular memory. Thus if an ant crawls on to a piece of paper, which is then pulled some distance towards the nest, the ant will then pass the nest by. Such experiments are obviously planned in the light of hypotheses.

EXPERIMENT No. IV (Mistakes).

Freud conducted a famous investigation into the causes of slips of the tongue, of the pen, of reading, of seeing, of hearing, of faulty action, and of faulty remembering (including mislaying).[1]

[1] J. O. Wisdom, "The Methodology of the Psycho-Analytical Law of Mistakes," *The Egyptian Journal of Psychology*, Vol. I, No. 1, Cairo, 1945.

The old explanation was that these were due to feeling tired or unwell, excited, or having one's attention distracted; but it is easy to find mistakes in circumstances where none of these feelings is present.   Accordingly Freud's specific question was: is there a purely mental factor involved in causing mistakes?

(a) Some slips were meaningful in the sense of expressing a wish.   Thus a professor of anatomy who, after lecturing to his students about the nostril, said that the number of people who could understand it properly could be counted "on one finger"— he immediately corrected this to the fingers of one hand.   The meaning (or form of wish) is obvious.   It is clear from introspection* that some slips, therefore, have a meaning and that the meaning is a factor in causing the slip.

(b) Can the explanation be extended to mistakes where no one can see a meaning?   This is not a valid analogy unless a meaning can be found in cases where there does not appear to be a meaning, i.e. where there is no introspectible meaning.   Frink gives an example of such a kind.

He forgot a name, which he ascertained was "Pond", and collected free associations to this.   It reminded him of a Dr. Pond, a baseball pitcher; and of an Indian Pond where he fished as a child and where he threw stones.   Then it reminded him of Pond's extract, which contains a product baseball pitchers sometimes use; this suggested a fat young friend, known as "Piggy", who had fallen head first into the mud during a game; and he remembered that his own nickname was "Pig".   Then "Pond" reminded him of ponder, think, "sicklied o'er with the pale cast of thought", Hamlet, a certain village and a farmer there, one of whose neighbours had maliciously killed two pigs and thrown them into his well. The significance of all this is not difficult to see; but here the interesting fact is that Frink thereupon remembered a forgotten experience that had upset him when he was six: he used to throw stones for his dog Gip to catch when swimming in the pond; unluckily the dog was stunned by one stone and was drowned.   Thus an auto-analysis made by collecting free associations led to the meaning of the mistake of memory; whereas no meaning was in evidence before, now it was found and introspectible.   Thus a universal law is confirmed; for even circumstances unfavourable to the hypothesis do not in fact falsify it.

* This word is convenient but it is not used here in its strict psychological sense.

EXPERIMENT No. V (Argon).

When Rayleigh and Ramsay[1] discovered the new element, the gas argon, the only relevant known fact was that the density of atmospheric nitrogen was $\frac{1}{2}\%$ heavier than that of chemically prepared nitrogen.

(a) It was supposed that the latter became contaminated with some light gas, such as hydrogen; but the introduction of hydrogen into nitrogen had no perceptible effect upon the density. Thus a serious hypothesis was falsified.

(b) The new question was whether the atmosphere contains an unknown heavy gas. This hypothesis required the elimination of the known gases from a specimen of the atmosphere, including nitrogen. A spark was passed through air with oxygen in the presence of an alkali, and a small residue was left.

(c) Because of the high temperature and restricted space in the apparatus, this residue might be hydrogen or nitrogen; but it was found that the residue was proportional to the amount of air used.

(d) Atmospheric nitrogen was passed over red-hot magnesium and a residue was left. The residue was found to be heavier than nitrogen.

(e) Atmolysis of air—a process in which a mixture of gases leaks through a porous pot, the various gases passing through at different rates according to their densities—left some gas that was heavier than nitrogen.

(f) These two experiments refute the hydrogen hypothesis. The hypothesis of a new gas was formed. The new gas, argon, was found to have a different spectrum from that of nitrogen.

(g) Argon was found to be $2\frac{1}{2}$ times as soluble in water as nitrogen.

(h) This suggests that there should be more argon than nitrogen in rainwater. Tests bore this out quite closely.

(i) The melting and freezing points of argon were found to be different from those of nitrogen.

These experiments refute the hypothesis that the gas was nitrogen.

It was noteworthy that Cavendish had passed electric sparks through air, over potash and mercury, in an inverted U-tube, and had recorded that a small bubble of air remained unabsorbed.

[1] *Enc. Brit.*, 14th ed., Art. "Argon"; R. J. Strutt, *John William Strutt, 3rd Baron Rayleigh*, London, 1924.

His careful description had been overlooked subsequently. Only an expert would have been surprised and felt his expectations upset.

EXPERIMENT No. VI (Electric Acid and Impurities).

In the above experiment and in Needham's version of Pasteur's, we have seen something of the misleading consequence of un-suspected interference factors counteracting the true effect of some process. The following is a beautiful example of this.

In the early days of electrolysis, considerable quantities of acid and alkali collected at the poles, and this was attributed to some sort of electric acid. The simplest example of electrolysis is of water. Two closed vertical glass tubes connected by a hori-zontal tube are filled with water; one pole of a battery is connected to each vertical tube and a current passed; this breaks down the water into hydrogen and oxygen which accumulate separately in the tubes; but what puzzled the early experimenters was the unexpected presence of acid and alkali as well. They would have been quite justified in suggesting that probably an unknown factor, 'electric acid', was a factor that in conjunction with the electric current caused the hydrogen and oxygen and also the acid and alkali. In fact the hypothesis was not very far wrong, because there was an unknown factor, though not of the kind supposed, and it did not play a part in causing the breakdown of the water. By pursuing more thoroughly the policy of varying the conditions one by one, and guided by the hypothesis that im-purities were present rather than electric acid, Davy resolved the question: he changed the glass apparatus to gold or agate and the amount of acid and alkali decreased; he used distilled water and there was a further decrease; he avoided contaminating the liquid with his fingers and there was a further decrease; finally he conducted the experiment under an exhausted receiver and the acid and alkali ceased to appear. Thus the disturbing factor con-sisted of 'impurities'. By removing them part of the total effect was eliminated, leaving the gases alone, without the acid and alkali, connected with the electrolytic process.[1]

In this connexion Jevons reminds us of the procedure of 'blind experiment'.[2] If we are testing a substance for the presence of arsenic, we should take the precaution of testing the vessels con-taining the substance for arsenic.

[1] W. S. Jevons, *The Principles of Science*, London, 1924, pp. 428–9.
[2] *Id.*, p. 433.

These records are necessarily over-brief and originals should be consulted; still we may hope to learn something from them. We will consider them straightaway before passing on to further experiments of a different kind.

Stebbing gives the following six maxims of technique,[1] which can be discerned in scientific practice and seem to be essentially sound.

(i) *Investigate to answer a definite question.* This is obvious from the examples given. For discovery, the important thing is to ask the right questions and to ask them precisely.

(ii) *Analyse the situation.* It is necessary to assemble the known facts (*observation*) that are likely to be relevant and to scrutinise their features. *Classification* may then play a part. For instance, the experiment on bump of location cannot be performed without a classification of species.* A careful *description* is then required. This is the special sense in which "description" is used in books on inductive logic; but in fact it is no more than part of the descriptive process of stating accurately the various features of the facts to be investigated. It may be noted that observation and experiment scarcely differ in principle. Experiment is more efficacious because an experiment is devised to give the observations most likely to be useful, and we may have to wait a long time before the facts required to be observed turn up of their own accord. In astronomy we have no alternative, however, but to wait.

(iii) *Relevant conditions should be noted.*

(iv) *Take care to avoid introducing unnoticed factors.* These two go together. Thus Needham (Experiment No. II) introduced an unnoticed factor when he used a cork to seal a flask; but it is also a relevant condition that the method of sealing should be extremely reliable.

(v) *Vary the supposedly irrelevant factors one at a time.* This is shown in Pasteur's investigation of spontaneous generation by his substituting asbestos for gun cotton and repeating his experiment. It is beautifully illustrated by Davy's experiment on 'electric acid'.

(vi) *Vary the relevant factors one at a time.* This is clearly in

---

[1] L. Susan Stebbing, *A Modern Introduction to Logic*, London, 1933, p. 325.
*Evidently the very act of classifying presupposes that scientific method is fruitful; but there is nothing circular in working upon this assumption.

evidence in Pasteur's experiment and also in the work described
by Rabaud on bump of location. This is the most important
maxim of all. If more than one factor is varied, it is difficult to
draw an accurate conclusion.

A word should be added on the 'control experiment', somewhat
the same as seeking a 'negative instance'. When Pasteur inocu-
lated a group of sheep with a prophylactic against rabies, later
giving them the infection, to show they did not develop the disease, he also infected a 'control' group that had not been inocu-
lated, with the result that they died; this ruled out the possibility
that the first group had not been properly infected, and the possibility that the prophylactic really had nothing to do with immunity, for the sheep might conceivably have been immune without
the prophylactic. This, however, is merely a matter of varying
the factors one at a time. It may also be expressed in terms of
seeking a negative instance to the supposed connexion between
inoculation and immunisation: *i.e.* seeking an instance where the
prophylactic was not accompanied by immunity. Failure to find
a negative instance after thorough search for one is the scientist's
aim.

It is easy enough to obtain results when all the factors can be
varied singly. But it is not always possible to do this. All that can
be done then is to vary as many factors as possible in as small
groups as possible. It is important in such circumstances to study
the subsequent results with care.

These maxims of technique are not all on the same level. (iii),
(iv), and (v) are required for efficiency and accuracy—relatively
particular maxims of tactics. (vi) is the chief characteristic of
scientific *method*. It leads to the elimination of the irrelevant and
transforms vague hypotheses into more precise ones. This maxim
has the character of *general tactics*. By contrast, the first two
maxims, which might appear to be no more than conditions for
the likelihood of success, amounting to maxims of *methodicality*,
are in fact of greater significance. It is impossible to 'investigate
to answer a definite question' without having a hypothetical
answer in mind, impossible to 'analyse the situation', *i.e.* to
'observe', 'clarify', and 'describe', absolutely fully and objectively;
it can be done only in relation to some attitude determining a
selection to be observed, classified, and described, *i.e.* it can be
done only in relation to some hypothesis. Consequently these
maxims imply the existence of a working hypothesis, which has a

strategic character. The most important distinction to be made here is thus between (vi), a maxim of general tactics, and (i) and (ii), maxims of strategy. It is easy to see that both play a fundamental rôle in all the experiments described: hypotheses were used at every stage, and these were tested by varying the conditions one at a time. *Moreover the result of the experiments was not that a conclusion was inferred from them but that a hypothesis passed tests.*

These experiments and the maxims found in them have to do with factors changeable as a whole, *i.e.* with *qualitative* change. This alone is enough to show the falsity of the belief, to which some scientists periodically revert, that science is essentially *quantitative*. Still, important as is qualitative science, quantitative science is probably more important. Here the method consists in varying factors not one at a time but in varying one factor in degree only, *i.e.* the change is *quantitative*. Examples will now be given. One of them will deal with the degree of expansion of a solid when heated, but for purposes of contrast it will be prefaced by a similar experiment giving the corresponding qualitative result only.

EXPERIMENT No. VII (The Ball and Ring).
A smooth metal ball just slides through a metal ring. When the ball is heated, it sticks; when cooled, it passes through the ring again. The hypothesis that the metal in question expands when heated survives test.

EXPERIMENT No. VIII (Coefficient of Linear Expansion).
A hollow brass rod is mounted with a micrometer screw gauge, capable of measuring to a thousandth of a centimetre, at one end. The rod is measured and the room temperature noted. Steam is then passed through the rod, which raises the temperature to a convenient figure, namely 100°, and the rod is again measured. By subtracting the original length from the expanded length we get the actual expansion. Dividing this by the original length we get the proportion of expansion, or the expansion per centimetre. Now the change in temperature of the heat absorbed in the course of expanding is found by subtracting the room temperature from 100. Dividing by this quantity also we get the expansion per centimetre per degree rise of temperature. This is known as the coefficient of expansion. For brass it is ·000019 which means that

this fraction of a centimetre would be the expansion if a rod of one centimetre in length were heated through one degree; and, of course, if a metre rod were heated from ice cold to boiling point, the expansion would be ·19 centimetres or about 2 millimetres. In this experiment it is assumed and not demonstrated by further experiment that the expansion is uniform, or more roughly that for given changes of temperature there are corresponding changes of length.

EXPERIMENT No. IX (Charles's Law).

Apparatus is set up in such a way that the volume of some gas can be measured and the temperature of it taken. The gas expands when heated, provided its pressure is always kept constant. In this way we can get the volume of the gas at various temperatures. If v is volume in cubic centimetres and t the temperature in degrees centigrade, suppose we get the following pairs of readings:

$v = 10\cdot0$	$10\cdot8$	$11\cdot5$	$12\cdot1$	$12\cdot6$
$t = 17$	37	57	77	97

Let us draw a graph by plotting these points, taking the v-axis horizontal and the t-axis vertical, O being the origin or point where the axes cross each other. The graph is a straight line, or rather that is the simplest way of joining the points obtained. The points sum up the results of experiment; but the graph asserts more—the straight line asserts something about the points in between the points resulting from observation. The line expresses Charles's Law: changes in volume are proportional to changes of temperature. If this law is supposed to hold for points on the curve anywhere *between* the extreme points plotted, the new ones constitute *interpolations*. Thus, if a volume is assigned *within* the range investigated, the corresponding temperature can be predicted by means of the graph, or algebraically from an equation, and the prediction can be verified by further experiment. If the law is supposed to hold for points *beyond* the extreme points plotted, the new ones constitute *extrapolations*. Thus if a volume is assigned *outside* the range investigated, the corresponding temperature can be predicted in the same way, and with Charles's Law the prediction can be confirmed for an enormous range. The traditional practice has been to assume that there is no limit to the extrapolation that holds good with Charles's Law. This is equivalent to producing the graph, which will be found to meet the v-axis to the left of O at the point where $t = -273$. This has a curious meaning: at the temperature $-273°$ the value of v is zero, *i.e.* the gas has ceased to exist. In fact a temperature as low as $-272·9°$ has been achieved and matter has shown no sign of vanishing. Actually the law is only approximate at any temperature and is very rough indeed when extrapolated to very low temperatures. However, for convenience of description, the straight line is accepted, and $-273°$ is regarded as the absolute zero of temperature. Thus the melting point of ice is $273°$ absolute and the temperature of steam is $373°$ absolute. This way of measuring temperature has the advantage that we may express Charles's Law as follows: *The volume of a fixed mass of gas at constant pressure is proportional to its absolute temperature.*

This is a good example of varying one factor in degree only and connecting it with the variation of another factor in degree only. It must not, of course, be thought that we always get straight-line graphs from such experiments; this will be seen from the following.

EXPERIMENT No. X (The Boyle-Mariotte Law).*

To a metre scale is fixed a J-shaped tube, open at the top of the J and closed at the end of the shorter arm of it. So as to alter levels of the contents of the tube, the bend of the J is not glass but a rubber tube. A small volume of gas is trapped in the closed end with mercury in the rest of the tube up to near the top of the open end. The long part of the J may be moved up and down, thus altering the levels of mercury; this alters the pressure on the gas and consequently its volume. The difference between the two mercury levels gives the mercury pressure; if we add to this the atmospheric pressure, which we may take to be 76, we get the total pressure p exerted on the gas. For various positions we take readings of the pressure and the volume. Suppose we get the following pairs of readings:

$p =$	110	90	80	70	60	50	40	30
$v =$	10·0	12·2	13·8	15·7	18·3	22·0	27·5	36·7

The graph of p against v is *not* a straight line but a curve. It happens, however, that the graph of v against the reciprocal of p does

---

* This is known as Boyle's Law in Britain and as Mariotte's Law in France. Mariotte discovered the law later than Boyle but independently. It is in keeping with a good deal of scientific usage to bracket the names.

give a straight line, and thus the law is that *the volume is inversely proportional to the pressure.*

The foregoing quantitative hypotheses are tested by applying them to interpolated and extrapolated values.

In these last two experiments there is a sort of smooth relation between the varying factors; there is a *perfect correlation* between them.   Now it often happens that the variation of two factors cannot be represented by a smooth curve.   Thus, suppose we measure the heights of a group of men and take their weights; the graph of height against weight will not be smooth, and we cannot find any law connecting them by drawing simple graphs. Such variation is found in sociological and other data, but not in the field of elementary physics.

In such circumstances statistical methods have to be used, and as a result of them statistical hypotheses can be formed.   There is no space to describe this procedure in detail, and the interested reader must be referred to any elementary textbook on the subject.   One of the important purposes of statistics, however, must be mentioned.   We often require a way of obtaining the central tendency of a set of numbers, which may be done by taking their average or *mean*.   Thus we may need the mean height of the male population.   But such a measure is of little value unless we also can form some estimate of the way in which the various heights are scattered round the mean.   We might find that all men varied between five feet five inches and five feet six inches in height; but they might also vary between four feet and seven feet, and yet the mean height might be the same.   The most important way of measuring this dispersion or scatter is by the 'standard deviation' denoted by σ.   It is calculated by taking the square root of the mean of the squares of the deviations of each height, say, from the mean of all the heights.

There are many other aspects of statistics, such as the theory of correlation; but they will not be needed in this book.

CHAPTER III

THE CONTRAST BETWEEN GENERALISATION AND NON-INSTANTIAL HYPOTHESIS

I PROPOSE to introduce a sharp distinction between 'generalisations and 'non-instantial hypotheses'. All the experiments described in Chapter II, to which may be added Kepler's three laws of planetary motion, are examples of the one and Newton's law of gravitation is an example of the other. We may notice that Newton's law subsumes the three due to Kepler, but this is not exactly the point where the difference lies. The difference may be brought out by contrasting this subsumption with a different one in which certain generalisations are subsumed by another generalisation.

Consider Charles's Law, according to which the volume v of a fixed mass of gas at constant pressure p is proportional to the absolute temperature T (Experiment No. IX); and consider the Boyle-Mariotte Law according to which the volume v at constant temperature T is inversely proportional to the pressure p (Experiment No. X). What happens if the volume, pressure, and temperature are all allowed to vary? And how is the pressure related to the absolute temperature if the volume is kept constant? The latter is answered by a simple experiment, which yields a law—also due to Charles. But both questions can be answered by means of a little mathematics alone. If all three vary, a little algebra shows that the volume v is proportional to the quotient of the absolute temperature divided by the pressure T/p, which is equivalent to the statement that the product pv is proportional to T.* To deal with the second question: from the

---

* I append the algebraic proof of this, deducing it however from the two laws of Charles instead of using the Boyle-Mariotte law, because of a slight simplication this affords.

Let p, v, T be corresponding values of the pressure, volume, and absolute temperature at any given moment and let p_1, v_1, T_1 be corresponding values at a later time when all three have been allowed to vary. Now instead of allowing this variation to take place, let p be kept constant and allow v to move to v_1. Then T will assume a value corresponding to v_1, which may be called T′. From Charles's Law and the nature of proportion we have $v/v_1 = T/T'$.

v has now moved the whole way to its final value; let it now be kept constant and allow p to move to its final value p_1; then T′ must move correspondingly and must

result just mentioned it follows that if v is kept constant the pressure p is proportional to the absolute temperature T; and this law can be confirmed directly by means of a constant-volume apparatus which allows us to compare pressure and temperature. This new law could be found independently with such apparatus, without knowing the other two laws; but it is instructive to deduce it from previous knowledge.

We now have three generalisations subsumed under one that is more general. But this more general one, that the product of the pressure and the volume of a fixed mass of gas is proportional to the absolute temperature, remains a generalisation.

What is meant may be explained as follows. Laws of nature or accepted generalisations may be described as "general facts". To call them "facts" may be misleading, because it suggests that they can be immediately observed in the sense in which we observe particular facts such as the fact that the sun is shining. It is, however, justified by ordinary usage: not only may a scientist say that it is a fact that salt is soluble in water, but the plain man may say that it is a fact that sugar dissolves in tea. This usage has the advantage of stressing the close connexion such 'facts' have with observation. What is characteristic of such 'facts' or laws is that *instances* of them, particular facts, can be observed and therefore also the elements that constitute them can be observed. The law that salt is soluble is not observable, but any instance of salt dissolving is observable.* We may put it otherwise by saying that we can perceive *any* instance of the law but not *all* the instances of it. Similarly, while it is false that Charles's Law is something that can be observed, instances can be, just as with an instance of solubility when a lump of salt melts. And it is the same with the more general gas law deduced above, that the product of the volume and pressure of a given mass of gas is proportional to the absolute temperature, which subsumes the Boyle-Mariotte Law and the two due to Charles; for, if an apparatus is set up in which the volume, pressure, and temperature may all be varied, in-

assume its final value T_1. Hence from Charles's other law and the nature of proportion we have

$$p/p_1 = T'/T_1.$$

If we multiply together these two equations, the intermediate value T' cancels out and we get

$$pv/p_1v_1 = T/T_1$$

i.e., the product pv is proportional to T.

* Certainly this statement may require further logical scrutiny, but there is a common usage of "observable", adequate for present purposes, that justifies the statement that an instance of salt dissolving is "observable".

stances of the general law may be observed. Thus this law, like those it subsumes, expresses a 'general fact'. A salient feature, then, of accepted generalisations is that instances of them can be observed.

It is this feature that differentiates a generalisation from what is here called a "non-instantial hypothesis". The point may be briefly illustrated by Newton's law of gravitation, which includes the notion of force of attraction. Now "attraction" does not stand for anything that can be observed; hence no instances of the law are observable. In what way, then, can it be brought into relation with perception and tested? By combining it with certain known facts, to do with the weights of the sun, moon, and earth, and the distances between them, it is possible to deduce (mathematically) after some intermediate steps that these three bodies will occupy certain places at a certain time (for instance that there will be a total eclipse of the sun visible from England on August 11, 1999); this conclusion can then be tested by observation. Another example is Schrödinger's concept of the wave-function ψ. It denotes no *kind* of entity; it has no instances. It is only remote conclusions deduced from it that are of an observable kind.

The scientific procedure for attaining a law of this type, then, consists in *framing a hypothesis*, instances of which cannot be observed, in *deducing* from it, after some intermediate steps and after combining with it certain known facts, a conclusion that is of an observable kind, and in testing this conclusion by actual observation to find out whether it is confirmed or falsified.

This procedure in itself suggests, though it does not establish, that non-instantial hypotheses are different in kind from generalisations. The traditional view of scientific procedure was that generalisations are obtained from particular instances by induction—the generalisation being a conclusion. Thus from the particular premisses that brass, zinc, and copper expand when heated, the generalisation that all metals expand when heated was induced. But, even if this is the procedure of science where generalisations are concerned, it is inapplicable to non-instantial hypotheses. They cannot be induced; we must start with them and test consequences derived from them—the hypothetico-deductive procedure.

Another way of making the distinction would be to point out that all the *concepts* involved in a generalisation have instances, whereas this is not true of non-instantial hypotheses. The latter may indeed embody some concepts that are instantial, but they must contain at least one non-instantial concept.

Let us now compare the non-instantial hypothesis of gravitation with the generalisation about gases in which the volume, pressure, and temperature all vary. Clearly the hypothesis contains a non-instantial concept, whereas the generalisation contains only instantial concepts. It might seem that the hypothesis and the generalisation are alike in subsuming instantial laws; but there is an important difference in the subsumption. The gas laws subsumed can be deduced without additional assumptions from the general one; but from the hypothesis of gravitation the three laws discovered by Kepler do not follow without the introduction of factual or instantial premises and the process of approximation. It is necessary to note, as Popper has pointed out, that the weight of the sun is vast compared with that of the earth, and that we must therefore make an approximation by neglecting the weight of the earth. One would hesitate, however, to regard this process of approximation as being a general feature distinguishing between a non-instantial hypothesis and a generalisation; the introduction of instantial premises would seem to be the important factor.

A most instructive example of the formation of a non-instantial hypothesis is afforded by the following construction of Newton's Second Law of Motion, built up from experiments with a single piece of apparatus known as Fletcher's Trolley. This law is concerned with the force that is at work when a body moves; it states that the force acting is proportional to the acceleration (both being measured in the same direction). The details are as follows:

EXPERIMENT No. XI

In order to measure acceleration it is necessary to find a way of measuring distances travelled and the times taken; force is measured by means of weights.

The form of moving body used is a trolley; this consists of a piece of wood about 30 cm. long mounted on wheels. To pull it along a table a thread is attached to it and passed over a pulley placed at the end of the table on a level with the trolley; the thread then hangs down and weights may be attached to it. Since there is bound to be some friction, which would interfere with the motion of the trolley, the table is tilted very slightly towards the pulley, so that when the trolley is given a small push, without any weight attached to the thread, it will travel at a uniform rate; the tilt must be sufficient to prevent the trolley from slowing down, but not so great as to increase its speed; at such a tilt the trolley will remain at rest unless some force is applied. In this way the apparatus is subject to *no forces*.

At the other end of the table, away from the pulley, held firmly in a clamp in a horizontal position is a long piece of thin steel, which must be at least as long as the trolley. It is held in the clamp at one end and it stretches over the length of the trolley, so that the other end is free; if the free end is drawn slightly to one side and released, the steel will vibrate. The number of vibrations it makes per second must first be ascertained, and we will suppose that this is *five*. Further, to the free end is attached in a vertical position a paint-brush with a thin point, so adjusted as to touch the trolley. The brush is dipped in ink and a piece of paper is pinned to the trolley; then, if the trolley is made to move by means of a weight attached to the thread over the pulley, the brush will trace out a wavy line on the paper; at first the waves will be close together, but as the trolley moves faster, the waves will separate from one another. If we measure the distance between the first ink mark and the fifth wave, we shall have found the distance covered in the first second of motion—provided we have taken care to set the trolley in motion and the brush vibrating at the same moment. We now have a mechanism for measuring distance and time. Now the *motive force*, which moves the trolley, is simply the pull of the weight attached to the thread. We can therefore compare the distance covered in a certain time with the force bringing this about.

We will suppose that the trolley weighs 1000 gm. Let s represent the distance travelled in centimetres and t the time taken in seconds; let the motive force be denoted by P. The experiment will now be conducted in three phases:

(*a*) Let P be a weight of five-grammes, and set the apparatus working as described. The wave trace is as shown in the diagram. The distances travelled from the beginning in one second, two seconds and so on, are now measured; we get the following table:

$s = 0$	2·4	9·8	22·0	39·0
$t = 0$	1	2	3	4

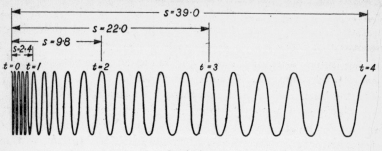

Scale 1:4

As usual an attempt is made to arrange these figures on a graph which shall be a straight line; we find eventually that the graph of s against t^2 is straight as required, so that s/t^2 is constant. Now from the definition of "uniform acceleration" it follows that $s/t^2 = \frac{1}{2}f$, where f denotes acceleration in centimetres per second per second. Hence *the acceleration due a falling weight is uniform.* This may seem to be trivial; but it is of supreme importance; if it were not so, the motive force would not bear the relation of simple proportion to the acceleration, which will be established below, but would depend in a complicated way upon some quantity vastly more complicated than uniform acceleration. The result here obtained is in fact the discovery of Galileo; though he is usually supposed to have given the formula for a falling body, this really follows from the definitions of velocity and acceleration, if the acceleration is uniform.

(*b*) P is a weight of five grammes as before, but the trolley is loaded with successive additions of 200 gm. It must be borne in mind that the weight moved is not only that of the trolley but also of the motive force itself. Hence the initial weight is 1005 gm., then 1205, and so on. In this phase of the experiment we get several wave-traces from each of which only one pair of measurements is taken—one distance and one time. From this pair, the acceleration is calculated from the fact that $f = 2s/t^2$. We are then in a position to compare the weight moved with the acceleration with which it moves. We get:

W =	1005	1205	1405	1605	1805
f =	4·9	4·1	3·5	3·1	2·7

Here it turns out that the graph of f against $1/W$ is a straight line, so that f is proportional to $1/W$, subject of course to the condition that P is constant.

(*c*) In the final phase of the experiment, the weight of the trolley is kept constant and the motive force is varied (this in fact introduces a slight error into the total weight W; but it may be neglected). Five grammes may be added at a time, giving us several wave-traces, from each of which as before we take but one pair of readings and calculate the acceleration in each case. We get:

P = 5	10	15	20	25
f = 4·9	9·7	14·5	19·2	23·9

Here the graph is f against P is straight, so that f is proportional to P.

Combining the results of (*b*) and (*c*) we have that, since f is proportional to $1/W$ when P is constant and proportional to P when W is constant, therefore f is proportional to their product P/W when P, W both vary.

It is easy to get rid of the relation of proportion in this and to replace this result by an equation: in the particular case where the weight falls freely, the motive force P is equal to the weight moved W, so that if the uniform acceleration due to a falling weight is denoted by g, we get

$$P/W = f/g*$$

which is one of the mathematical forms of Newton's Second Law of Motion.

To get simply the verbal expression of the law given above, which referred to a given body and not to a variable weight, we could have omitted (*b*) and need not have concerned ourselves about the mathematical equation; we should simply have had that P was proportional to f as required. But it is worth giving the whole thing, to bring out once more how conditions are varied

---

* The algebraic proof of this is as follows: Since f is proportional to P/W, then from the nature of proportion

$$f = kP/W$$

where k is a constant. Now when, as here, P is equal to W, then f is equal to g. Hence the above equation becomes

$$g = kW/W$$

so that k is equal to g. Substituting this value of k in the original equation we get

$$f = gP/W$$

which is equivalent to the required result

$$P/W = f/g.$$

one at a time, to throw the law into its general form, and to express it in the mathematical way in which it is actually serviceable.

Now that this experiment is concluded, it is necessary to ask what kind of testing of the result is needed. This turns on whether the entities involved, P, W, f, g, have instances of an observable kind. There is no difficulty about f and g. It is true that acceleration is not observable in the same way a body is; but that is only because of its complicated nature—all its constituents can be observed in the ordinary sense. Weight is also of an observable kind. We are familiar with it as the feeling of pressure when we support something. Equal weights are defined by a balance. If two weights balance when placed in opposite scale-pans and continue to balance if each is put in the pan of the other, then they are equal. It is easy to build up multiple and fractional weights. But with the motive force P matters are different. We know the experience of weight and we can observe bodies fall; but force we do not perceive at all. To put the matter more carefully, we experience force when we are pushed or when we support a weight or when we push something, but not the force of a falling body. It is true we feel force when a body falls on us, but this would entitle us to attribute force to the body only if it were thrown at us. With a weight that falls we might suppose that something hurled it, which is to say that we think of inanimate bodies as acquiring their force from outside themselves; and this would be granted by Newton himself in virtue of his own law of gravitation, according to which falling bodies acquire their force from the 'attraction' of the earth. Whether we regard force as an innate quality of bodies or an adventitious entity due to the presence of other bodies at a distance, it is equally a hypothesis without observable instances.

It is therefore necessary to consider *how to test* the hypothesis that force is proportional to acceleration. Here is one of the many ways in which this can be done.

From the mathematical expression of the hypothesis it follows that $g = Wf/P$; this can be calculated from any of the tables given; in fact from the tables in (a), (b), (c) g can be calculated many times over, from different sets of figures. These values centre round 980, and this is in fact their average. We now apply the mathematical hypothesis to a simple pendulum, which is a heavy bob at the end of a long thin string, about a metre in length. By means of a little mathematics it can be *deduced* from the hypothesis that the time that the pendulum takes to swing through a complete amplitude (*i.e.* to swing from one side to the other and return) is given by

$$t = 2\pi\sqrt{l/g}$$

where l is the length of the pendulum. Now l can be measured; π is known to have the value 3·142; and t can be found by means of a stop-watch, by timing the pendulum as it swings for about a minute and dividing the time in seconds by the number of amplitudes. Hence g can be calculated from the above equation or from the following equivalent:

$$g = 4\pi^2 l/t^2$$

since π, l, t are all known. In practice the value works out at about 981, which closely conforms to the value based upon the hypothesis *i.e.* closely conforms to the predicted value, so that the hypothesis is confirmed.

We are so accustomed to reading of scientific hypotheses that are true that we are apt to forget the existence of false ones; and, since a false hypothesis is equally significant from the metascientific point of view, it is desirable to have an example.

EXPERIMENT No. XII

One of the most interesting false hypotheses that had a vogue in physics was that of the æther. It was conceived that a stream of æther flowed through space like water down a river. It could not be observed, but that was no reason against it because the concept of it might have served as a useful hypothesis in the same way as that of the unobservable attraction between stars.

One of the purposes of the æther was to provide a medium in which light could travel. Given the notion, then, of an æther-stream though which light made its way, we have the hypothesis: *The velocity of light travelling through the æther depends upon the velocity of the æther.*

This we seek to test in the following way. We send out a light-ray along a measured distance, have it reflected by a mirror, so that it returns to its starting point, and we measure the total time taken; we also send out another ray for the same distance in a perpendicular direction, have it reflected in the same way, and measure its total time. Now if this is carried out at different times of the year, so that the earth is moving in direct directions, we should at some time or other have our apparatus so placed that one of the rays will be travelling *along* the æther drift and the other ray *across* it.

It is easy to prove that the times taken by the two rays should be different. The situation is exactly like that of a swimmer, who is capable of a certain speed, first swimming downstream in a river and returning, and then swimming across and returning; it turns out that his first swim takes longer than the second.

Let s be the measured distance, c the velocity of light when propagated (analogous to the speed of a swimmer in still water), and v the velocity of the æther.

When going down the æther-stream, the ray of light has a velocity of $c + v$, and when going upstream it has a velocity of $c - v$. The times taken for the two journeys are respectively $s/(c + v)$, and $s/(c - v)$, so that the total time is

$$s/(c + v) + s/(c - v)$$
$$= s.(c - v + c + v)/(c^2 - v^2)$$
$$= 2sc/(c^2 - v^2).$$

When going across the stream, if the ray is to go straight across it must be directed slightly upstream to allow for the current; consequently its velocity across the stream will be a little diminished, and it will in fact be $\sqrt{c^2 - v^2}$ (this follows from the 'triangle of velocities' which every airman knows and which will be found in every book on elementary dynamics). The time taken for the distance s will be $s/\sqrt{c^2 - v^2}$ so that the total time for the journey across and back will be

$$2s/\sqrt{c^2 - v^2}$$

It is clear that the two expressions for the two total times are not equal, for the time down and up is equal to

$$2s/(c - v^2/c)$$
$$= 2s/c(1 - v^2/c^2)$$

while the time across and back is equal to

$$2s/c\sqrt{1 - v^2/c^2}.$$

In these two forms it is obvious that the two times are unequal.

All this constitutes a deduction of a prediction. We therefore set about the task of testing this by measuring the times, and this was the famous experiment carried out by Michelson and Morley. The result was that even with apparatus of great delicacy, sufficiently delicate to reveal any difference if there was one, no difference in time could be observed.

The conclusion is that the hypothesis of the æther is false; but it should be stressed that the hypothesis, though falsified and not confirmed, was in the metascientific sense testable, for it led by the deduction-mechanism to an observable situation.

It is clear, then, that the scientific procedure of building up some scientific law consists of forming a hypothesis, which is not perceptual, and of testing it, *i.e.* combining with this suitable known facts, and deducing from the combination either a fact, which is confirmed by observation, or an accepted generalisation, which may be already known or may have instances that can be confirmed. It is important to stress that the deduction is made from a combination of the hypothesis with known facts, which are essentially perceptual, and not with other hypotheses. A harmless ambiguity should perhaps be noted: the process of testing sometimes refers to the act of confirmation, but sometimes to the process of prediction plus confirmation.

Some mention should be made of the use of the word "theory". There is nothing hard and fast about it. Sometimes it is used for a hypothesis, sometimes for a confirmed hypothesis; sometimes for a train of thought; sometimes for a wild guess at some fact, or for a reasoned claim about what some fact is—or even for a philosophical speculation. It seems to me that colloquial usage wastes a useful word; for most of the examples just given there is a familiar alternative. One may mean hypothesis, generalisation, guess, prediction (of fact future or present), speculation; there is no need to use "theory" for any of these. This leaves only two possible candidates, of which one is a confirmed hypothesis. This is the usage when we speak of the Newtonian theory, the Einstein theory, the evolution theory, the psycho-analytic theory. It is important to notice, however, that this usage does not imply that a theory is absolutely true or even that it is almost certain, for it means only that good confirmation has been forthcoming. Thus when a hypothesis reaches the stage of being called a theory, it has had confirmation sufficiently good to make it acceptable; but this is not the same as certainty, and in fact a theory may later be proved false. In this way it is possible to speak of rival theories, as well as of rival hypotheses. For example there were the corpuscular and wave theories of light, both of which were highly credible. There is no hard and fast line to determine how much confirmation is needed to warrant a hypothesis being regarded as a theory. For this recommendation to conform with ordinary practice a slight modification is needed. Newton's Laws of Motion are theories in the sense described but would not ordinarily be called such. Perhaps this is because they are thought of as forming part of a wider body (together they form a body of theory), for it is not usual to speak of constituents of a theory as being theories. According to the sense suggested then, a theory is a very general body of confirmed hypothesis.

There is also the usage in which "theory" covers both the basic laws of a subject and their development. Thus if a particle is moving under the influence of an attractive force that is inversely proportional to the distance of the particle from the centre of attraction, then the development that shows what the motion of the particle must be, that its orbit for instance must be elliptical, may be called the 'theoretical' account of its motion.

CHAPTER IV

THE PRINCIPLE OF TESTABILITY[1]

THAT hypotheses should be testable is, we have seen, a cardinal principle of science. It is necessary, however, to distinguish between testability in scientific practice and testability as a meta-scientific principle. In the Newtonian experiment described in the previous chapter, the scientist is concerned that the testing should result in *confirmation* of the hypothesis or in the refutation of rival hypotheses: the scientist is concerned in his test to establish his hypothesis and not to prove it false.*

This is the objective of his practice; but there is also the principle *underlying* his practice, which is that a hypothesis must be either confirmable *or* falsifiable—if it is neither it is not a hypothesis.† That is to say, from a hypothesis, which is non-instantial, it must be possible to *deduce* something is instantial—else we are not dealing with a hypothesis. Thus, if we deduce from the hypothesis of gravitation that there will be an eclipse of the sun or from that of motion that the acceleration, g, of a falling body has the value 980, the respective hypotheses are confirmed if the eclipse is observed or if g is found actually to have approximately this value, and the hypotheses are false if the eclipse does not take place or if g is found to have some other value. But, confirmable or falsifiable, the hypotheses can be tested by observation.‡

Since what cannot be tested in this way is not a hypothesis, it may be described as "transcendental". The *collective mind*, for instance, is not a hypothesis because from it no deductions can be obtained of a perceptual kind. It might even appear that hypotheses are foreign to science because of Newton's apparent

---

[1] For fuller treatment see J. O. Wisdom, *The Metamorphosis of Philosophy*, Cairo, 1947, Chapter V.

* Confirmation, as indicated in Chapter I and as will be shown further in Chapter VI, is the result of failure to falsify; but the final aim of confirmation is not belied by this.

† We shall consider later the sense of "falsifiability" in which falsifiability alone is sufficient.

‡ In metascientific contexts it has been an unfortunate custom to speak of "verification" to include both confirmation and falsification; *i.e.*, it has had the wide sense of testing. This custom will not be followed here.

opposition to them—the reader will, no doubt, think of his famous phrase, *"Hypotheses non fingo"*. This I have heard aptly called Newton's little joke, because he owed his achievements to the daring hypotheses he framed; but he plainly had in mind transcendental judgments and not hypotheses in the sense now used.

Historically testability may be regarded as the child of 'the descriptive interpretation of science', according to which words like "gravitation" did not describe anything in the universe, but provided ways of describing in a short way endless numbers of perceptual events. We ought, too, to recognise that the child had another parent, the Empiricism of Berkeley and Hume. Here, however, we need be concerned only with the recent form of the doctrine, framed in terms of "verifiability", or, it is better to say, "testability". It is due to certain philosophers, who were influenced by Wittgenstein;[1] it was enunciated by Schlick,[2] Carnap,[3] Ayer,[4] and others. Refinements arose not only from publications but also from numerous discussions; no attempt will be made, therefore, to disentangle the several contributions and do historical justice to the various authors.

Because of the influence that Positivism has had on metascientific thought, the following account of the principle has been put together to depict the positivist approach, though it does not aim at being a faithful picture of any one form of the doctrine. Afterwards what is sufficient for metascience will be separated from its unnecessary positivist clothing.

The basic positivist contention is that testability of statements is a criterion of *significance* or *meaningfulness*; what cannot be tested is *non-significant* or *without meaning*.

The original form of the principle was that the meaning of a statement is determined by the method of verifying it (to this scientists under the influence of the descriptive interpretation of science often subscribe); for, if a word like "gravitation" denotes nothing, there is no way by which it can derive a meaning except from the method of testing it. That this is misleading will become clear.

First it is necessary to ask why the concept of verifiability must

[1] Ludwig Wittgenstein, *Tractatus Logico-Philosophicus*, London, 1922.
[2] Moritz Schlick, "Meaning and Verification", *Philosophical Review*, Vol. XLV, No. 268, New York, 1936, p. 176.
[3] Rudolf Carnap, *The Unity of Science*, London, 1934; *Philosophy and Logical Syntax*, London, 1935, and *The Logical Syntax of Language*, London, 1937.
[4] A. J. Ayer, *Language, Truth and Logic*, London, 1936.

be replaced by that of testability. Most, if not all, statements that are susceptible of confirmation in some degree are incapable of being verified, *i.e.*, of being absolutely or completely confirmed. We can obtain increasing confirmation of the solubility of salt, but the confirmation can never be complete. Hence the concept of verifiability is inapplicable. "Testable", then, is to be equated not with "verifiable or falsifiable" but with "confirmable or falsifiable".

In what follows different kinds of statement will be taken in turn and the method of testing them inquired into.

(I) First of all there are statements, such as "There is a book on my desk", which when true express what it is humanly possible to observe at some particular time. This statement expresses something observable. But if it is false it does not. However, it is convenient to say that its contradictory does, which we may say if we agree that "There is no book on my desk" expresses what is observable when in fact there is no book there. We may then say that, true or false, "There is a book on my desk" expresses something of an *observable kind*. Now such a statement may be either true or false and it must be one of the two; and this is what is meant by "significant" in its basic sense. Clearly, then, "expressing something of an observable kind" and "significant" are equivalent. With other kinds of statement that are obviously significant in some sense without expressing what is of an observable kind, it is necessary to define their significance in terms of this fundamental sense.

It is desirable that "observable" should be understood in a wide sense. There is no need to restrict it to observations made here and now; it may refer to those that have been made by anyone at any time, and also those that could be made if we took the trouble; but it may in addition refer to those that we could not make with the means now at our disposal, provided we could make them with a suitable improvement of scientific or other apparatus. Thus we can accept as significant, in the same sense as before, statements about the past that no one is now in a position to check, not to mention statements of the same fundamental kind made by other scientists, and also statements that tell us for instance that there are mountains on the other side of the moon; for we could check a colleague's statement if necessary and we could test the existence of mountains on the other side of the moon with a suitable improvement of interstellar communications. The common characteristic of these kinds of statement is that of *resembling* in an obvious way those of the fundamental kind.

"Observable" will therefore be understood to include what has been, is being, could at present be, and with suitable developments could in the future be observed. We are clearly concerned with observing in the sense in which one observes a table and not with any philosophical sense in which one does not observe a table but only one surface of it. The kind of statement here described is the kind in terms of which all scientific statements are in fact tested.

(II) There is in the second place the kind of statement that purports to express a generalisation; it may be illustrated by Charles's Law or by "Arsenic is poisonous". A false example would be "All metals contract when heated". An example of a true statement that does not, though it purports to, express a generalisation is "Gravitation causes planetary motion".

Obviously what is here expressed cannot be observed, because of the feature of generality: it is not only a physical impossibility but a logical one to observe all the possible instances that could come under such a generalisation. But *any* instance, if there is one, is observable, and it is in this that the significance of the present type of statement lies. Naturally certain refinements must be made about the details. Thus if a statement expressing a generalisation is false, there may be no observable instances at all. But then the contrary of the statement, which would also express a generalisation, would, though it might also be false, refer to some instances. Alternatively, the contradictory of a false statement that expresses a generalisation must be true and therefore express what is observable. The criterion of significance involved, then, may be put as follows:

A statement purporting to express a generalisation is significant, if what either it or its contrary expresses has instances;

or

A statement purporting to express a generalisation is significant, if what it expresses has instances or its contradictory is true.

Thus "Arsenic is poisonous", which purports to express a generalisation, is significant because there are instances of what it expresses. "All gases contract when heated", which purports to express a generalisation, does not express what has instances, because it is always false; but it is significant because what its contrary expresses has instances and also because its contradictory is true. "Gravitation causes planetary motion", which purports to express a generalisation, fails to do so, not because it is false, but because neither it nor its contrary expresses what has instances; it is therefore not significant in the present sense.*

This criterion, which I was stimulated to construct by a proposal made by Stace[1], may be called the *Principle of Observable Instances*. Other suggestions were previously made. Thus it was thought that such a statement as those being considered was significant if it was 'strongly falsifiable', *i.e.* if a single observable instance could confute it.[2] Clearly, however, this criterion is essentially the same as the present one—if elaborated it would come to the same thing. Another proposal was that such a statement was significant if it was 'weakly confirmable'. This arose from the impossibility of ever getting complete confirmation of a natural law—any test could provide only some confirmation which was therefore incomplete or 'weak', and nothing else could be expected.[3] Again, there is nothing new in essence, because all that is relevant is the possibility of observable instances—if elaborated it, too, would come to the same thing.

It may be mentioned here that logical positivists have in general (though the tendency is dying out) equated meaning with significance, *i.e.* with testability; but a distinction should be drawn. A test, real or imagined, does not necessarily tell us what a statement means; it does not prescribe, confer, or contain the meaning; nor does it render the statement of a natural law true, for it confers no more than probability or acceptability upon the statement; but it certainly shows once and for all whether or not the statement *has* a meaning or *is* significant. There is an equivalence between 'having meaning', 'being significant', and 'being testable'; 'significance' is the same as 'existence of meaning' but not the same as 'meaning'; a test, real or imagined, may show the existence of meaning but not what the meaning is. While this,

---

*The mode of formulation employed, concerning "a statement expressing what has instances", is not only cumbrous but not wholly satisfactory. There is the difficulty of saying what it is that a general statement or a false statement states. This problem is neither solved nor dealt with here; the issues under discussion do not require a solution. Unfortunately the problem is touched in a subsidiary way, though the terminology adopted appears to slide over it.

[1] W. T. Stace, "Positivism", *Mind*, N. S. Vol. LIII, No. 211, London, 1944, p. 218.
[2] See Ayer, *op. cit.*, p. 25.
[3] *Id.*, p. 22.

it is hoped, will clarify the positivistic approach, it should be constantly borne in mind that the positivistic sense of "meaning" is arbitrary.

The chief point of the present section, then, is this: the significance of a statement of natural law or generalisation is definable in terms of the fundamental sense of (I), according to which a statement to be significant must express what is of an observable kind.

(III) There remain statements of scientific hypotheses, such as those about gravitation, the Schrödinger function, or the æther. For these the method of testing has already been described: a statement purporting to express a hypothesis must lead in a deductive way to a prediction that is of an observable kind. Naturally, in order to perform the deduction, the statement must be combined with other premisses, and it is important to note that these must express what is of an observable kind, as described in (I).* But the formulation must be made wider, because it is not essential to predict something of an observable kind; *it will suffice to deduce a natural law*. In other words, it is not essential to test by means of a statement of the type (I); a statement of the type (II) will serve. This can happen in science: thus we can test the hypothesis of gravitation for significance either by confirmation of an eclipse, for example, or by deducing (approximately) one of Kepler's natural laws. We may, then, set up the following criterion of significance, which may be called the *Principle of Testability by Deduction*:

A statement purporting to express a non-instantial law or hypothesis is significant if and only if, in combination with other statements that express what is of an observable kind, it is possible to deduce from it either a statement purporting to express a natural law that satisfies the Principle of Observable Instances or a statement that itself expresses what is of an observable kind.

An important point about, say, the hypothesis of the æther should be noted: it is in a definable sense a false hypothesis, but the statement of it is nonetheless significant. There is a common and convenient form of the Principle, which runs that a concept that cannot be related to any perceptual experience or that cannot be used is non-significant. Now this might easily lead us

---

* This has not been made very clear in the literature.

to suppose that statements about the æther are non-significant. But this is untrue; for, from the æther-statement we can deduce a prediction of a perception that would be experienced if the æther-statement were true—it is the sort of statement that could quite well be true—while with a really non-significant statement it is not that we deduce a prediction that turns out untrue to fact but that there is no way of deducing a prediction of a perceptual situation at all. It is desirable not to overlook the existence and significance of false hypotheses and to show how they differ from non-significant statements that might purport to express hypotheses.

Three kinds of statement have now been distinguished and illustrated. It is now necessary to make some supplementary remarks about them.

(i) Concerning the status of the criteria offered, it is clear that they offer definitions of the significance of certain kinds of statement. Taken together the two criteria and the concept of observable kind mark out a class of statements which the positivist would regard as *meaningful*; and what does not come under one of the three headings he would class as *meaningless*. Now this is a much stronger assertion than is relevant to the theme of this book. If, in the criteria, we replace 'significant' by 'scientific', we have, I believe, an acceptable way of distinguishing scientific statements from non-scientific ones. But to go further and assert that non-scientific statements are *meaningless*, while it might conceivably be true, is to go beyond what is required by metascientific enquiry.

Thus Positivism has contributed to a metascientific question, but fused with its answer a philosophical contention, which has no bearing on that question and which goes beyond the empirical outlook associated with science.

(ii) Occasionally one comes across a supposedly scientific statement such as "Opium induces sleep because of its soporific qualities"; or, if we carry out an archæological excavation and find a bronze axe, we may say "This axe belongs to the Bronze Age". The former is a well-known example of a tautology that is based upon a trick of terminology; the latter, as Daniel points out, "is almost saying no more than that it is made of bronze, which is perilously near saying nothing at all."[1] Ignoring the

[1] G. E. Daniel, *The Three Ages: An Essay on Archæological Method*, Cambridge, 1943, p. 40.

qualification "almost" (which seems unnecessary) let us take this to be a tautology. It masquerades as a statement like those of (I), expressing what is of an observable kind; and the opium-example masquerades like those of (II), appearing to be a causal law; is there any difficulty, then, about subjecting them to the threefold classification containing criteria of significance? We ask if they express what is of an observable kind (we seek the meaning of "Bronze Age" and find it means a period when bronze was used), we ask if they satisfy the Principle of Observable Instances, and we ask if they satisfy the Principle of Testability by Deduction; we find that all three answers are negative, and we conclude that the statements are not scientific ones. Metaphysical statements, which by their very nature transcend experience, are treated in the same way.

(iii) The Principle of Observable Instances can be put in the deductive form of the Principle of Testability by Deduction; for, if we seek to test the statement, "Arsenic is poisonous", we shall need the premiss that here is a sample of arsenic and that it is being absorbed by an animal, and then the conclusion will follow that the animal will get ill. There is therefore an important feature in common between the two Principles; yet, though that of Testability can apply to generalisations, that of Observable Instances cannot apply to non-instantial hypotheses. It would seem that the latter principle is simply *a particular case* of the other, which arises when a non-instantial concept is replaced by one that is instantial.

Further, there are differences between the two deductive forms. If it is a generalisation that is being tested, all the concepts of the minor premiss and conclusion are instantial concepts occurring also in the major premiss, *i.e.* in the generalisation itself; but if a non-instantial hypothesis is being tested, the concepts of the minor premiss and conclusion, which are all instantial, will not all occur in the major premiss. Again, all the concepts in the major premiss, if this is a generalisation, will occur among the concepts of the minor premiss and conclusion; but, if the major premiss is a non-instantial hypothesis, at least one (non-instantial) concept will not be found anywhere in the minor premiss or conclusion. Another, rather interesting, difference is in the complexity of the two types of deduction. Where the major premiss is a generalisation the inference has the simple form of a general major premiss, a particular minor, and a particular conclusion that follows at once from the two premisses. Where the major is a non-instantial hypothesis, however, though the minor is again particular, a conclusion can be derived only after certain logical (usually mathematical) operations have been carried out.

Thus, if the test operations of both Principles are put in deductive form, certain resemblances and differences appear; but it is desirable to keep the two Principles separate because of the instantial nature of one and the non-instantial nature of the other.

(iv) Positivists would refuse to recognize this difference for a special reason. They would deny that a generalisation can have instances of an observable kind, on the grounds that arsenic is unobservable in the same sense as gravitation. The reason for this lies in the phenomenalist account of perception.[1] With this as a basis, they would also hold that the statements of (I) are significant not in a fundamental sense but in a derivative one requiring a criterion; they would also deny the Principle of Observable Instances, and deny its equivalence with the alternative of weak confirmability.

In accordance with Phenomenalism they would seek a test for a statement such as "I am seeing a book". Part of the test would be given by "I am seeing a patch of colour", or, in technical language, by "I am seeing a certain sense-datum". The rest of the test, in accordance with the deduction-prediction criterion, would be given by statements to the effect that if I moved my position I should see a second sense-datum related in a certain way to the first one; the characteristic relation involves continuity or the gradual transition that could be found between the first sense-datum and the second, for we could see a more or less continuous series of sense-data by moving from the first position to the second.

An important consequence of this is that the test, since it does not refer to the book, consists entirely of sense-data and their mutual relations, so that the book no more 'literally' exists than does gravitation—just as there is no instance in the universe denoted by "gravitation", so there is no instance denoted by "book".

This goes beyond scientific practice; and it would seem that positivists are thus using the scientific criterion of testability outside science in such a way as to construct a metaphysic of sense-data—though it was to demolish metaphysics that they adopted

[1] A. J. Ayer, *The Foundations of Empirical Knowledge*, London, 1940, pp. 229–43.

the criterion. According to the present view, Phenomenalism is an *additional* part of the positivist thesis, an *application* of the principle of testability, an application, moreover, that could be rejected while retaining this principle; but they would regard Phenomenalism as a *consequence* of the criterion. From the metascientific standpoint, however, this philosophical thesis is not needed: with metascience, what is essential is to establish the criterion actually found in scientific practice together with its applications; but the application of testing statements about natural objects, such as books, is not known in science.

The relevance of Phenomenalism here is that it would deny the equivalence between the Principle of Observable Instances and that of weak confirmability. The latter was proposed not only to deal with statements of natural law but also those like "I am seeing a book", which it should be noticed are also incapable of being completely tested.[1] Hence the principle of weak confirmability can have a wider field of application that that of Observable Instances. However, if the phenomenalist account of perception is not admitted, the fields are the same.

The subject of the scientific outlook may be taken up again. For positivists it consists of the need to relate all statements to sense-data; here, however, we will confine ourselves to the outlook that is to be found animating scientific practice.

In the first chapter it was mentioned that the scholastic dictum, "*Nihil est in intellectu quod non prius fuerit in sensu*", was too narrow; it is in fact equivalent to Hume's criterion that for a word to have meaning it must denote something with instances.

It is now clear exactly why this is too narrow; there is no instance denoted by the word "gravitation", and gravitation can be in the intellect even though it cannot be sensed. It is perhaps noteworthy that among early philosophers Berkeley, who was much against the use of words without a corresponding idea, conceded that there was a legitimate use of words like "gravitation".[2]

In that chapter it was indicated that for the scientific outlook a concept must be capable of being related to perception, *directly or indirectly*; it is now clear what is the precise way in which a concept is *indirectly* related to perception—it is by the mechanism of testability by deduction. We may also say that Ockham's

---

[1] *Id.*, pp. 239-40.
[2] George Berkeley, *Works*, ed. by Sampson, Vol. II, *De Motu*, § 17

razor expresses this: entities that cannot be related to perception even indirectly are unnecessary and not to be introduced. And Newton's "*Hypotheses non fingo*" has the same import.

The scientific outlook, then, is expressed in the Principle of Testability by Deduction.

CHAPTER V

INDUCTION AND THE
HYPOTHETICO-DEDUCTIVE SYSTEM

THE problem presented by induction is that on the one hand no justification of the process of forming generalisations seems to be possible, while on the other it seems irrational to trust them in the absence of all guarantee that they will continue to hold. The problems presented by the method of hypothesis are (i) that likewise there seems to be no explanation of its success, yet it continues to give satisfactory service, and (ii) that non-instantial statements of hypotheses do not by themselves state anything about anything, and yet they can be used. Traditional treatment of induction and hypothesis asserted an 'inner necessity' to account for their 'truth', an assertion that cannot be tested; Logical Positivism has claimed that there is no problem of induction and Operationalism that there is no problem of non-instantial concepts, which is evading the issue.

In this chapter we seek to know whether the two kinds of procedure are fundamentally distinct. In this book the difference has been particularly emphasised. Traditionally the method of hypothesis has tended to be included under induction. We have to ask whether this is right, whether the reverse is possible, or whether the two must be regarded as fundamentally distinct.

Shall we regard a generalisation from instantial premisses as a hypothesis from which a conclusion (interpolation or extrapolation) may be deduced and tested? Certainly we may do so. Indeed this is the actual *method* of science. Undoubtedly the *method* of science is for the scientist to jump, by some imaginative means, to a generalisation or to a non-instantial hypothesis, which he must then proceed to test. The method of hypothesis certainly exists and its framework is often referred to by Kraft's phrase, "the hypothetico-deductive system". By contrast there is no such thing as a *method* of induction, for there is no machinery by which a general conclusion can be inferred from particular premisses in an inductive argument. Indeed every premiss used in induction is introduced in the light of the conclusion already conceived as a hypothesis.

It might appear, however, that non-instantial hypotheses presuppose induction, on the ground that many inductive conclusions are needed before we can begin to frame a non-instantial hypothesis—we cannot speak about gravitation, for example, without having made numbers of inductions about objects of all kinds, such as that a given piece of matter will have in the future the same weight as it had in the past. But this means only that these 'inductive' conclusions have to be interpreted as previously tested generalisations.

Nonetheless, though there is no method of induction, we should consider whether it is possible to throw the framework of premisses (one of which is a generalisation), deduction, and testing into *the form of induction*. Is it possible to do this in the way in which an inference may be expressed in syllogistic form? It is rare in ordinary discourse for anyone to put an argument in syllogistic form; but it is a form in which some arguments can be expressed. Can we do the same here? Though there is no method of induction, may there not be a form of inductive inference? This possibility should be borne in mind because there are some writers who hold that a genuine form of inductive inference can be constructed with the aid of the theory of probability (it will be argued in Part III that this cannot be done). It should also be borne in mind because there may exist an inductive problem about the use of hypotheses; this will be discussed in the final chapter.

Whether or not a generalisation in the hypothetico-deductive system can be expressed as the conclusion of an induction, a non-instantial hypothesis certainly cannot be expressed in this way. Thus induction can be expressed in the hypothetico-deductive system; it is not certain that the latter when embodying a generalisation can be put in inductive form; but there is no doubt that non-instantial hypotheses cannot be put in this form.

But can a generalisation be put as the conclusion of an inductive inference? Obviously we can write it in this position if we wish. The question of whether or not there exists an inductive form of inference then turns on the relative value of the two ways of proceeding. But I hope to show that the inductive form cannot be justified and is useless, whereas the hypothetico-deductive framework shows several signs of being fruitful.

An important difference between a generalisation and a non-instantial hypothesis, over and above those discussed in Chapter IV, should be mentioned.   Non-instantial hypotheses are connected with explanation, whereas generalisations merely state 'general facts'.   Otherwise expressed, a generalisation asserts interconnectedness, but a non-instantial hypothesis asserts the interconnectedness of interconnectednesses.   Thus non-instantial hypotheses imply something more in the nature of a system.

CHAPTER VI

HYPOTHETICO-DEDUCTIVE EXPLANATION

THE focus of the main problem of scientific inference has been altered with far-reaching effect by Popper[1] from the justification of induction to the analysis of explanation. Central in this is the hypothetico-deductive system. This schema is not of course new in methodology, but it is new to metascientific discussion. Popper has made a much more extended methodological use of it than has been done in the past and appears to be the first to give it serious attention in metascience—placing it at the centre of metascientific inquiry, developing the ideas it contains, and showing its form. The present chapter is devoted to those parts of his treatment of the subject that bear on the present work.

In the previous chapter I have stressed that induction is never a method. Popper, however, makes an important additional point. So far as the previous chapter is concerned, I have simply said that there is no rational machinery for passing from observational premisses to an inductive generalisation but that a hypothesis* is attained by some mental jump. Now this way of putting the matter would suggest that the observations recorded in the premisses are made first and that only subsequently does there arise the question of how a conclusion is obtained. But Popper points out that this is not the actual procedure of science, because the hypothesis or at any rate some hypothesis is entertained in mind before the observations are made. The time factor is important, for it finally disposes of the possibility of induction as a method. If the reader will consult any example of 'inductive' discovery, he will see at once that at all points of an investigation some hypothesis precedes experiment and observation, and that experiments are planned in the light of a hypothesis in order to test it. Here Darwin's famous reflexion comes to mind:

---

[1] K. R. Popper, *Logik der Forschung*, Wien, 1935, § 12; "The Poverty of Historicism (III)", *Economica*, N.S. Vol. XII, No. 46, London, 1945, pp. 75–6; *The Open Society and its Enemies*, Vol. II, London, 1945, pp. 249, 342–3.

* In this chapter the distinction between "instantial generalisation" and "non-instantial hypothesis" will not be required and it will therefore be convenient to use "hypothesis" indifferently for either.

How odd it is that anyone should not see that all observation must be for or against some view if it is to be of any service![1]

Thus Pasteur tested the hypothesis that the material used for filtering air was relevant to his enquiry (and found that it was not); a piece of paper on which an ant had crawled was pulled along so that the ant travelled beyond its objective, and this refuted the hypothesis that the ant relies mainly upon visual cues.

In general, observations are made only because of some interest or expectation—however dim, unvoiced or unverbalised this may be—and expectations are such that if they were verbalised they would be expressions of hypotheses. In a laboratory there are myriads of facts that could be observed but are never noticed. As Darwin said in the same context,

About thirty years ago there was much talk that geologists ought only to observe and not to theorise; and I well remember someone saying that at this rate a man might as well go into a gravel-pit and count the pebbles and describe the colours.

One makes an observation only because something discordant or surprising is felt—an expectation is jolted. Thus on walking off an escalator that has been temporarily stopped one makes the observation that one has leaned backwards, which is not done on walking away from an ordinary staircase; one has leaned backwards because of a bodily expectation, conditioned by previous experience of moving escalators, that this adjustment preserves one's balance. As Russell has put it,

Our life is full of expectations of which, as a rule, we only become aware when they are disappointed.[2]

For this sum of expectations Popper has introduced the useful phrase "horizon of expectations", where there is no fast line to be drawn between pre-scientific or commonsense expectations and hypotheses. Progress in gaining knowledge of the world, commonsense or scientific, occurs when some hole is made in this horizon, i.e., when something occurs that conflicts with some expectation; this necessitates constructing a new expectation or

---

[1] *More Letters of Charles Darwin*, ed. by Francis Darwin, Vol. I, London, 1903, p. 195. I am indebted to Lady Barlow for this reference.

[2] Bertrand Russell, *Human Knowledge : Its Scope and Limits*, London, 1948, p. 65.

hypothesis, which then forms part of a new horizon; and this
persists so long as it is not in its turn falsified by experience. Progress in gaining knowledge thus covers the falsification of expectations whether commonsense or scientific. All this, it should be
noted, belongs to methodology rather than to metascience.

In scientific practice, then, hypotheses precede observations,
which in induction would be expressed as premises. Subsequent
procedure, as Russell remarks, is this:

Scientific method . . . consists mainly in eliminating those beliefs
which there is reason to think a source of shocks, while retaining those
against which no definite argument can be brought.[2]

The rôle of observations, selected in the light of our hypotheses,
is changed: instead of leading to a hypothesis, their function is to
test it, and the only way of continuing scientific activity is by
means of the hypothetico-deductive system. The hypothesis is
expressed in a general statement, some relevant observations
are made and expressed in a particular statement, and a conclusion, which is sometimes a prediction, is *deduced* and finally
tested by experience. The requirements of the system are, then,
(*a*) a general expectation, (*b*) an observation, and (*c*) a valid
deduction.

Popper now proceeds to say that the conclusion is to be interpreted as the fact to be 'explained' and the hypothesis as the
'scientific explanation' of it. Hence a fact is explained if a description of it can be placed as the conclusion of a valid deductive inference, and the scientific explanation of a fact is found if a statement expressing it can be made a premiss of that inference. This
schema is so well known in mathematical physics that some connecting links should be mentioned. If the fact to be explained is
an eclipse, the explanation is the law of gravitation, and the
particular observations constituting the other premiss are, say,
the present positions or the positions at 11 o'clock on November
11, 1918, of the sun, moon, and earth. In science these observations are known as "initial conditions". Thus the schema is

> Hypothesis
> Initial conditions
> —————————————
> Prediction (or given fact).

Here it is the first of the two premisses that is the 'explanation'.

[2] *Id.*, p. 201.

By contrast, Popper points out that the initial conditions constitute a 'historical explanation'; for one explanation of the historical fact that a state of war was proclaimed to exist on September 3, 1939 between Great Britain and Germany is that Hitler had not agreed to the terms of the British ultimatum—a particular fact or set of facts. But what has not hitherto been realised is that the fact about Hitler cannot be said to 'explain' the fact about the proclamation of a state of war without an auxiliary premiss of the type, "Whenever the terms of an ultimatum are not accepted, war follows." The reason why this was not noticed is that the general auxiliary premiss required in historical contexts is of so trivial a kind that no one—except a metascientist— would think it worth mentioning.

The importance of this contrast between scientific and historical explanation is that it affords Popper a way of defining "causal explanation". In some contexts, mainly historical, the 'causal explanation' is identified with the historical explanation just described, and in such a context the causal explanation is *relative*—relative to a hypothesis. But in scientific explanation the search for causes is identified with the search for a hypothesis. Thus the explanation of the expansion of a piece of brass when heated is the general causal hypothesis that all brass expands when heated. But here, too, the explanation is *relative*—relative to initial conditions. The 'effect' is in both cases what is expressed in the conclusion. Thus a reasonable usage of "cause" and "effect" is provided.

It is desirable at this point to enter a correction. To say that a historical cause is relative to a law might suggest that there exists an absolute legal connection inherent in nature—which would be entirely discordant with the point of view adopted. This implication does not arise if a little care is exercised in expressing the position. To say that one event is the historical cause of another event is to be equated with saying that the *statement* of the supposed connexion between these events is relative to a *statement* of a law. That is to say, one event E is explained by another event X, if E is described in a statement that is the conclusion of a valid inference in which one of the premisses is a statement describing the other event X and the other premiss is a general statement expressing a law.

This approach to explanation, I would add, can be seen to cover traditional 'inference', such as argument by analogy, just as well as arguments by 'induction'. For, if we argue that this piece of brass will expand when heated because that piece has, the argument may be interpreted in the hypothetico-deductive system by inserting the suppressed premiss, "All brass expands when heated." Likewise with the criteria of causal determination to be discussed in Chapter XI, where it is maintained that the skeletons discussed do not provide *methods* of discovery but that they are schemas that could be adopted in practice, *i.e.*, schemas into which the *results* of scientific enquiry could be fitted. But that only means that the various criteria are equivalent to different modes of testing hypotheses—if you have a hypothesis it is sometimes appropriate to test it by a criterion of functional dependence, for instance, and at other times by one of counteracting causes. Thus there is no type of scientific inference that cannot be fitted into the hypothetico-deductive system.

We have next to point out one of the most important features of the system. This concerns the *additional undesigned scope* of a hypothesis.[1]

In Chapter IV it was pointed out that some statements have the specious appearance of expressing a law, when in fact they express no more than a certain set of observations. Thus "This axe belongs to the Bronze Age" is of this kind. Perhaps the best example is the following. The result of the Michelson-Morley experiment was that the speed of light is constant, and such that the relative speed of light is independent of the speed of the object to which it is relative. For example, though the speed of an aeroplane, whose ground speed is 200, is 140 relative to a train travelling in the same direction at 60, is 170 relative to it when travelling at 30, and is 230 relative to the train when travelling in the opposite direction at 30, yet the relative speed of light in all these situations is the same. To explain this it was suggested that the length of an object becomes foreshortened as the object moves in the direction of its length. This 'Lorentz-Fitzgerald contraction' made the numerical consequences of the constant speed of light self-consistent. But it was not an explanation, because no test of the contraction was even theoretically possible, and it merely described the known phenomena in quasi-scientific terms. Another example is the Ptolemaic account of planetary motion. It is possible to describe the motion of a planet, in the sense of obtaining a map of its course, by rolling on one circle another one,

[1] Popper, *Logik der Forschung*, S. 200.

called an "epicycle", with a point marked on the circumference
of the rolling circle; for the path traced out by this point gives
the map required. This procedure does indeed enable us to
predict the future course of a given planet; but it prescribes no
way of tracing the course of any planet merely from a knowledge
of its position, weight, and size, for we have first to find suitable
epicycles by observing the course of each planet; and if we know
the epicycle suitable for mapping one planet we have no means
of inferring a suitable epicycle for another. For the quasi explanation involved Popper has suggested the appropriate name
"*ad hoc* hypothesis". I think, however, it would be fair to say
that many '*ad hoc* hypotheses' are not absolutely unscientific but
only relatively so; the Ptolemaic hypothesis does provide for a
certain amount of interpolation and extrapolation. Again, "All
brass expands when heated" or any simple generalisation is not
wholly an *ad hoc* hypothesis, for the same reason; but it is not a
full scientific hypothesis in that there is a basic feature of the
scientific hypothesis that it does not contain. To this we now turn.

The basic feature of the genuine hypothesis, to which Popper
draws attention, is that it must cover facts of a different kind from
those the hypothesis was designed to explain. Thus the law of
gravitation was designed to explain the motion of the planets,
i.e. their motion could be deduced from the law, given certain
initial conditions; but the law in the same way was found to explain the motion of the tides. It is the capacity to cover unexpected fields that is striking. Strictly it is not the unexpectedness
that counts, for the application for instance of the law of gravitation to the tides might conceivably have been anticipated, but
the application to fields beyond those for which the hypothesis
was constructed. It is in this additional undesigned scope that
the explanatory power of a hypothesis lies.

Another basic point, perhaps the most basic, originated by
Popper, is that what the scientist tries to do is to *falsify* hypotheses,
not to confirm them.[1] It is never possible by way of confirmation
to do more than deduce predictions that are compatible with the
hypothesis; but they may be compatible with other hypotheses,
so that a hypothesis is not established by such confirmation.
Still more important, a confirmed prediction is perfectly compatible with and deducible from a false hypothesis. Moreover,
if we concentrate on seeking confirmation instead of refutation,

[1] *Id.*, S. 12–3.

we shall easily find ourselves satisfied with predictions that would be unlikely to tell against the hypothesis. Thus if we form the hypothesis that all gases explode and test it by putting a match to some coal gas, that is no confirmation at all; on the contrary we must take a specimen of gas, such as nitrogen, that is least likely, so far as we know, to explode—in other words we make it as difficult as possible for the test to be confirmatory. This is not to say we *wish* to refute a hypothesis; it only means that that is what we must try to do. It is akin to testing the reliability of a person's endurance or the strength of a bridge; the personnel selector or engineer does not wish to find the person or the bridge wanting, but he tries his hardest to make both fail. In short, the desire is that the strongest attack should fail; the testing of hypotheses is an endurance test.

Now as we have seen above Popper has also shown that advance of knowledge also comes about by refuting false hypotheses. I wish here to distinguish explicitly the two kinds of refutation, which are implied by his procedure.

The scientist may or may not have in mind the correct hypothesis at the beginning of his inquiry. Whether he has or not, particularly when he has not, he is concerned with some hypothesis or other. This is a rival—or rather, if he knew the correct one, would be a rival. In the course of his work he is concerned to refute many of these. For convenience this may be thought of as 'elimination'.[1] At some stage or other the correct hypothesis dawns upon him. This, he tries to refute.[2] But the attempt at refutation may become a process of refining the hypothesis and finding out new conditions in which it does and does not hold. This may be thought of, I suggest, as a process of 'tempering'.

Popper develops his theory of testability or falsifiability in further respects. He uses the idea of 'falsification possibilities':

A theory is falsifiable if there exists for it at least one . . . non-empty class of falsification possibilities.[3]

To present the idea graphically, let the field of all possible observations be represented by a circle, and suppose that the falsification possibilities for a hypothesis, *i.e.* those observations that would falsify it, are represented by a shaded sector. Then, if there were

[1] *Id.*, S. 63.
[2] *Id.*, S. 14.
[3] *Id.*, S. 67.

no shaded sector for a hypothesis, this would be a tautology, and, if the circle were completely shaded, the hypothesis would be self-contradictory. Various degrees exist in between. If we wish to compare two hypotheses, the one with the greater shaded sector will have more falsification possibilities than the other. And he goes on to discuss 'degrees of falsification':

The theory whose class of falsification possibilities is the 'greater' has more opportunity of being contradicted by possible experience than the other theory; it is 'falsifiable to a higher degree'.[1]

Naturally this does not mean that a hypothesis with large falsification possibilities is false or unreliable; it means only that the hypothesis takes greater risks—and the more important the hypothesis the greater the risks it takes—for it states more about the world. Thus that all matter gravitates according to the inverse square law is a hypothesis that takes greater risks than the hypothesis that heavy bodies when released fall to the ground. As Popper says, the best hypotheses are the most likely to conflict with reality:

The most certain system would surely be one with no hypotheses.[2]

He proceeds to replace these intuitive ideas by logical definitions[3], but details will not be required here.

These considerations lead him to point out the importance of *generality* and *definiteness* as characteristics of a good hypothesis. He gives the examples:[4]

> (i) All heavenly bodies have circular orbits.
> (ii) All planets have circular orbits.
> (iii) All heavenly bodies have elliptic orbits.
> (iv) All planets have elliptic orbits.

(i) has greater generality than (ii)—and (iii) than (iv). (i) has greater definiteness than (iii)—and (ii) than (iv). (i) has both more generality and more definiteness than (iv). (ii) and (iii) are not comparable, as (ii) is less general but more definite. It is assumed, of course, that a circle is a special form of ellipse.

[1] *Id.*, S. 67.
[2] *Id.*, S. 203.
[3] *Id.*, §§. 32–5, 38–40.
[4] *Id.*, S. 75.

Of two statements of which the generality and definiteness are comparable, the less general or less definite is derivable from the more general or more definite; except when the *one* is more general and the *other* more definite.[1]

Thus to greater generality and definiteness correspond greater content or degree of testability or falsifiability; the more general and definite a hypothesis is, the more possibilities it has of being falsified.

His treatment of falsifiability enables Popper to give an account of *confirmation*.

The mere fact that a theory is not falsified cannot alone be regarded as a positive confirmation. For at any time we can construct any number of theories which are compatible with a given system of accepted basic statements[2] [observation-statements].

We might suppose we have a positive degree of confirmation if part of the system of observations is derivable from it; but this is not sufficient, for it takes no account of degrees—we consider some hypotheses better confirmed than others. What Popper holds is that the higher the degree of falsification, the higher the degree of confirmation. But the latter depends on other factors as well. It depends in part on the number of instances of non-falsification—though we usually attach greater importance to the first of such instances than to later ones. It also depends upon obtaining non-falsification in diverse fields of enquiry, and upon generality and definiteness of the hypothesis.[3]

In general we regard an intersubjectively testable falsification . . . as final.[4]

The need for a positive account of confirmation lies of course in the asymmetry between confirmation or verification and falsification: for a hypothesis can be definitely falsified, but we never attain verification and can attain only degrees of confirmation.

Mention may be made of the relation between this approach and Operationalism on the one hand and metaphysics on the other.

[1] *Id.*, S. 76.
[2] *Id.*, S. 198.
[3] *Id.*, S. 200–1.
[4] *Id.*, S. 199.

Operationalism does not allow that a statement describes more than the set of observations that come under it—which in effect is a denial of the existence of universal statements so that the hypothetico-deductive system and deduction proper are not used. But Popper can and does use universal statements, thereby giving a sense to "explanation". His view may be said to be a description of explanatory power, or more fully a description of the explanatory power of universal statements in the hypothetico-deductive system.

It should be noted that Popper uses the criterion of falsifiability as a means of demarcation: to distinguish scientific statements from others, not as a means of attacking metaphysical statements; the approach in the *Logik der Forschung* is not that of a logical positivist.[1]

At this point we may take up the question of the relation between falsifiability as a criterion of a scientific statement and the criteria offered in Chapter IV. There it was asserted that a statement is scientific if it is confirmable or falsifiable, which requires that the statement should be relatable to an observation-statement just as Popper's criterion of falsifiability does. And further examination of the details of the criteria seems to reveal no difference: falsifiability, in his treatment, does not exclude confirmability, for this could happen only if the statement were self-contradictory. Nonetheless a difference of usage should be pointed out. When he speaks of a statement as "falsifiable", he means that there are possibilities of falsifying it or that it is the sort of statement that is capable of being falsified; in this sense it would be falsifiable even if it were never to be falsified, *i.e.* if it happened to be 'true' and therefore unfalsifiable in practice. In the usage of Chapter IV, however, "falsifiable" means that the statement would be capable of being falsified in practice; and the criterion of 'confirmability or falsifiability' is that a statement to be scientific has to be capable of being found in some instance either confirmed or falsified. Thus the criterion I have put forward seems to differ from Popper's only terminologically. His terminology, however, has the advantage of enabling him to develop certain other ideas, such as that of degrees of falsifiability.

The metascientific significance of the approach developed in this chapter is that it bears on the traditional problem of induction.

[1] *Id.*, §§. 4, 6.

Since methodology shows that science works according to the hypothetico-deductive method, and not according to an 'inductive method', the effect of this approach upon the traditional problem is considerable. Many presuppositions of 'inductive inference' vanish; we see that:

(i) Certainty is not guaranteed—or sought.

(ii) No postulate such as a Law of Uniformity of Nature is required.

(iii) Nor is any concept of absolute identity or essence.

(iv) The procedure is rational in the sense that it prescribes the use of the hypothetico-deductive system. The rationality of this lies in two features: it contains strict deduction and we retain a hypothesis only so long as it has not been falsified by tests.

(v) A meaning is assigned to "cause" and "effect" that does not involve 'necessity' or the 'inner nature' of things.

(vi) The treatment denies that the basic problem is one of inference from the past to the future either with or without probability.

It should be realised that Popper's treatment of confirmation is methodological: it describes what is discernible in scientific practice as 'confirmation'; and, so far as this description goes, it does not touch the 'inductive' question of whether there is any rational justification for accepting as confirmation what scientists in practice do regard as such. One may be tempted to raise a very similar question: what is the justification for expecting a hypothesis that has served us well in the past to continue to do so? And to this may be added the further question: why is it that some hypotheses are highly reliable?

CHAPTER VII

TWO TYPES OF SIMPLICITY

VARIOUS writers have drawn attention to the importance of simplicity in connexion with the laws of science. It has nothing to do, of course, with ease of understanding—some 'simple' laws are the most difficult to understand—though it bears on ease of calculation. At first it appears to be a feature of the form of a law. Thus the form of the classical law of gravitation, $F = m_1 m_2 / r^2$, is simpler than $F = m_1 m_2 / r^{2.000,000,016}$, which, Jeffreys remarks, would be discarded on sight.[1] In fact the whole machinery of interpolation and extrapolation is based upon assuming the simplest curve and simplest mathematical expression to represent it.

Jeffreys gives an interesting example,[2] which illustrates several points—that an infinity of hypotheses can be constructed to explain a given set of observations, that simplicity appears to be even an intrinsic characteristic of nature, and that Logical Positivist and Operationalism are too narrow as descriptions of the procedure of science—but here we are concerned only with simplicity. Suppose a sphere is rolling down an inclined plane and its distance noted every five seconds; the following pairs of values may be obtained, where t denotes the time in seconds and x the distance in centimetres:

$t =$ 0	5	10	15	20	25	30
$x =$ 0	5	20	45	80	125	180

The physicist will express this in the simplest hypothesis, namely,

$$5x = t^2;$$

but the observations would equally well fit the hypothesis

$$5x = t^2 - t(t-5)\,(t-10)\,(t-15)\,(t-20)\,(t-25)\,(t-30).f(t)$$

where $f(t)$ is any function that is not infinite at $t =$ 0, 5, 10, 15, 20, 25, 30. Now the physicist unhesitatingly adopts the former—and can confirm it. The latter, is is true, will not conform with fact

---

[1] Harold Jeffreys, *Scientific Inference*, Cambridge, 1931, p. 51.
[2] *Id.*, pp. 37–8.

for an interpolated value of t; but, as Jeffreys points out, if the former hypothesis was at variance with a subsequent experiment, the physicist would look for a mistake or a reason for the discrepancy. Thus the physicist in practice expects something of nature —expects it to conform with simple laws.

Again, consider another example. Suppose we have the following readings leading to Charles's Law for gases, where T is temperature in degrees absolute and v is volume:

$$v = 0 \qquad 10\cdot0 \qquad 21\cdot0$$
$$T = 0 \qquad 100 \qquad 200$$

We derive a law algebraically thus:— Let the law be

$$v = a + bT + cT^2$$

where a, b, c are numbers not yet known but determinable from the readings in the following way. Since $v = 0$ when $T = 0$,

$$0 = a + 0 + 0$$

so that $a = 0$. Again

$$10 = 100b + 100^2c$$
$$21 = 200b + 200^2c$$

Solving this pair of simultaneous equations we find that $b = \cdot095$, $c = \cdot00005$, so that the law is

$$v = \cdot095T + \cdot00005T^2.$$

Now the scientist would unhesitatingly take the simpler law, $v = \cdot095T$ or even $v = \cdot1T$, disregarding the term in T^2 as negligibly small, and this simple law is in fact the type that has held till lately. This process is equivalent to that of drawing the smoothest curve through the points of a graph. Incidentally this would have been done on the grounds that the term in T^2 was due to experimental error and that the absolute law was the simplest one; but nowadays the view would tend to be that the simplest one is chosen because it works best, without making any claim about the simplicity of nature itself.

But the reader will rightly object that corrections recently made in physics replace classical laws by others less simple. Thus the modern gas law is less simple in form than that due to Boyle, Mariotte, and Charles. Again, for Newton and Galileo the length of a moving rod remained the same for all observers. To make clear the interesting change in this situation, let an observer be stationed at one end of a rod and then let the rod move away from the observer in the direction to which the other end points; let it have a velocity v relative to him and move for a time t as recorded by his clocks, and let the far end of the rod be now at a distance s from the observer. For Galileo the length of the rod was given simply by $s - vt$, but for Einstein it is $(s - vt)/\sqrt{(1 - v^2/c^2)}$, where c is the velocity of light. Clearly the factor $\sqrt{(1 - v^2/c^2)}$ hardly differs from unity, because c is very large, so that there is only a minute error in the classical law. Where, then, is the simplicity in the newer version? The answer is that it is not here.

There is simplicity connected with the new expression, but it lies elsewhere than in the expression itself. The factor $\sqrt{(1 - v^2/c^2)}$ leads to an alteration in the fundamental expression for the distance between two points. We used to say that from Pythagoras' theorem, the distance s between the origin of a graph and a neighbouring point whose co-ordinates are x, y was given by

$$s^2 = x^2 + y^2;$$

now it is given by

$$s^2 = x^2 + y^2 - c^2t^2.$$

This shows that the 'shortest' distance between two points is curved if you take into account the time taken to go from one to the other at the speed of light. The strange simplicity involved here arises because we are enabled to see that matter is moving the shortest way when it moves in curves, so that the mysterious force of gravitation (or invisible pull) is no longer required. The simplicity that results consists therefore only in getting rid of a non-instantial concept for which no explanation has ever been given. It would seem that, in the final analysis, simplicity lies not, or not mainly, in the form of a law but in the reduction of the number of non-instantial concepts used in the basis of physics. Again, in classical physics energy and mass were absolutely different from one another. It was remarkable how different forms of energy were shown to be interchangeable—mechanical, electrical, and heat energy—at one time thought distinct; but we know now that mass even is a form of energy and can be converted into it. In fact the amount of energy into which a given mass can be converted is given by

$$E = mc^2$$

where c is the velocity of light measured in centimetres per second, m is the mass in grammes, and E is the energy in ergs. Thus, since c is 3×10^{10} cm. per sec., one gramme of matter can be transformed into 9×10^{20} ergs of energy, which would roughly be the output of a billion-horsepower engine per second. Here again there is a reduction in the number of fundamental concepts.

The apparent conflict between the scientist's insistence upon simplicity of form and the increase in complexity of some laws of recent times may now be explained: complexity in generalisations is clearly on the increase, but with non-instantial hypotheses this if it exists is less marked. So far as Jeffreys' contention is concerned, it remains true that, so far as existing data go, the scientist seeks the law that has the simplest form, but if the limits of experimental error are small enough to warrant introducing complex modifications of a law this is done without demur. In short, the scientist uses simple forms so long as he can, introduces complexity if he has to, but is perhaps more chary about doing this where non-instantial hypotheses are concerned than in the domain of generalisations. The real drive towards simplicity has little to do, however, with simplicity of form of law; it is in the direction away from non-instantial concepts, at the same time leaving room for these in approximate laws. It also is a feature not of isolated laws but of a system. Thus the increase of simplicity in physics leads us to suppose that there is a system, or at any rate a scientific unity about the universe. This may, however, be an attribute of knowledge, not of nature.

There is perhaps a certain resemblance between the view suggested here and that put forward by Popper[1] and Weyl.[2] Popper accepts Weyl's contention that simplicity depends on having the smallest possible number of parameters in equations; which is, I think, similar to the present idea, connecting simplicity with having the smallest possible number of non-instantial concepts. Popper further explains simplicity as a character of hypotheses that are in high degree falsifiable: only hypotheses of high degree of generality and definiteness are in high degree falsifiable, and these features perforce make a hypothesis simple.

---

[1] K. R. Popper, *Logik der Forschung*, Wien, 1935, § 43.
[2] Weyl, *Philosophie der Mathematik und Naturwissenschaft*, 1927, S. 116, quoted by Popper, *op. cit.*, §. 42.

CHAPTER VIII

DETERMINISM, ORDERLINESS, AND UNCERTAINTY

THE picture conveyed by Determinism may be described thus: Restart the universe at any moment of the past, and its subsequent history will be repeated detail for detail as the second performance shown by a cinematograph film repeats the first. Laplace's famous statement of the doctrine is this:

An intelligence knowing, at a given instant of time, all forces acting in nature, as well as the momentary positions of all things of which the universe consists, would be able to comprehend the motions of the largest bodies of the world and those of the smallest atoms in a simple formula, provided it were sufficiently powerful to subject all data to analysis; to it, nothing would be uncertain, both future and past would be present before its eyes.[1]

It is not easy to ascertain whether Determinism is exactly the same as the Law of Universal Causation or a wider form of it. They do not seem to play quite the same rôle: the Law is posited as a major premiss in induction; Determinism is more linked with universe-wide necessity. The main ideas that lie behind it seem to be the following. Laws of science have traditionally been supposed to give absolute truth or part of the essence of the universe. From this essence as a whole all changes would have been held to flow. Otherwise it would have seemed unintelligible why laws should be true or necessary or why changes should obey them. Thus Determinism may have been thought of as the explanation of the existence and truth of laws of science; or it might be described as giving the element of necessity to such law.

Whatever the background and purpose of Determinism may have been, it certainly included the concept of *necessity*. This is a concept that has no place in scientific practice; no statement about it is significant according to the criteria described in Chapter IV. Hence in order to bring Determinism within the orbit of metascientific discussion, we must split it into two components:

$$Determinism = Orderliness + Necessity,$$

[1] Quoted from Laplace, *Théorie analytique des probabilités*, Paris, 1820, by R. B. Lindsay and H. Margenau, *Foundations of Physics*, New York, 1936, p. 517.

where Orderliness is the claim that laws of science are true and that every event comes under some law, simply as a matter of fact without there being any necessity to ensure their continued truth. The claim is thus, as it were, one of *de facto* Orderliness. Meta-scientific discussion may fairly be limited to this. We wish to know whether even this is presupposed by science or postulated by scientific procedure.

It is difficult to state precisely what Orderliness involves—the comments to be made in Chapter XIV in connexion with the Law of Uniformity hold here. But the great source of scientific opposition comes from Heisenberg's Uncertainty Principle in quantum mechanics. This must now be explained.

It tells us first that it is impossible to have exact knowledge, both of the position of an electron and of its subsequent momentum.* Thus if you know its position you cannot predict its momentum, and *vice versa*. Heisenberg's principle asserts more than this however. If the position of an electron is observed with considerable exactitude, its momentum can be predicted only within a certain range, and no improvement of technique can enable us to reduce this range (and *vice versa*); moreover, all momenta in this range are equally probable. This comes from the discovery that if we take the range of error in estimating position (*i.e.* the range of values any one of which the position may take) and multiply it by the range of error in measuring momentum, the product cannot be less than a certain definable minimum. Thus the error in either position or momentum is subject to an important limitation. Suppose you estimate very carefully the momentum of a billiard ball, the analogy is not that the ball will be in a certain pocket if it is given a certain momentum, but that it will be somewhere within definable limits of the pocket; and this is more positive information than if we could tell only that the ball would be somewhere on the table—the principle is not one of complete uncertainty but of limited uncertainty.

Why is it impossible in principle to have exact knowledge of the behaviour of an electron? Because of specific physical facts: If you wish to observe the position exactly, you must first illuminate the electron. Now most forms of light are too coarse in

---

*"Momentum" means quantity of motion; everyone is familiar with the ordinary use of the word: one speaks of the 'momentum' of a car, and more than velocity is meant by this because a heavy car would have more momentum at the same velocity than would a light one. The classical mathematical measurement of momentum is simple and depends only on the weight and velocity of the moving body.

texture to reveal anything so small. The only form of light that is suitable consists of alpha rays, because their wave-length is short (the difficulty of illuminating small objects by means of coarse light of long wave-length is something like the difficulty of measuring a pinhole with a metre-rule marked in millimetres). Rays of short wave-length have high frequency and therefore great energy. The impact of these upon the electron disturbs it, and thus upsets one's calculation of its subsequent velocity or energy. Since there is no other way of tracing the behaviour of an electron, the nature of the light rays known to us precludes our doing accurate work—and even the discovery of new rays would not help because if they were fine enough to satisfy one requirement they would upset the other. Hence, exact knowledge of the behaviour of an electron is impossible; it is impossible in principle because no kind of light would show us exactly what was happening.

To some philosophers it would therefore seem that while the electron may have a perfectly definite behaviour there is no way of finding out what this is. The effort to know makes knowing impossible; the lunatic with his left thumb held projecting out of his right hand tries to catch the thumb with his left hand, but the trouble is that he is never quite quick enough. As Father Brown in one of Chesterton's stories says:

Gentlemen! A very terrible thing has happened: we have discovered the truth, and the truth does not make sense![1]

Or rather the scientist says we have discovered the truth and the philosopher replies that it does not make sense.

Parallel with the Uncertainty Principle it is important to mention the concept of *eigen-values*, which is just as significant as this principle for metascience though less often discussed. The principle applies to pairs of quantities such as momentum and position, but to other pairs such as momentum and energy it does not apply. Even then calculations and predictions are not exact. But instead of getting a range of possible values for the momentum, say, we get a set of precise values, called "*eigen-values*"; of these we cannot say which is the *correct* value, but we can assign to each the probability of its being correct. Consider, for example, the well-known amusement of putting a coin in a slot, releasing a ball which falls through a space studded with pins, and trying to catch

---

[1] A correspondent, Mr. Roger North, has put it to me in this way.

the ball in a cup as it emerges. When the game is repeated several times the ball comes out at different places, and it is impossible to calculate where to expect it. But there is a set of clearly defined places where it can emerge and no others; and, if the game is repeated often enough, we can get the proportions of games in which the ball comes to any one exit and therefore get the probability with which it will emerge at a given place. The exits illustrate the eigen-values. One of them must be obtained, but we can tell only the probability of each. This concept has the same sort of significance for us as the Uncertainty Principle, but the interesting difference between the two should not be over-looked—and it should not be thought that all calculations in quantum mechanics are imprecise as the principle suggests. As regards the hope that in some context a single precise value might be obtained, it suffices to say that the principle and the concept together cover most of the facts of quantum mechanics, and no alternative theory has been forthcoming.

It is impossible to explain the details of the Uncertainty Principle and of eigen-values without a good deal of mathematics, but an attempt can be made to describe what happens.

Certain facts about the behaviour of subatomic particles are discovered by physicists; a mathematical apparatus is set up which when transformed into various shapes accounts for the facts and when transformed into others enables facts to be predicted with some degree of accuracy. This procedure is the same in quantum mechanics as in classical mechanics, except that the symbols we begin with in the latter either stand for observables or very quickly lead to observables, while in quantum mechanics we begin with a symbol of so abstract a kind that we might despair of ever relating it to observation and it takes a long time before observation is reached. Nonetheless our symbol is said to describe the state of a system of particles (because eventually it leads to the right results). Now the mathematical apparatus that produces these results involves quantities known as operators. In order to calculate any dynamical quantity (momentum or energy) a corresponding operator has to be used (the momentum-operator or the energy-operator). And we always have to deal with at least *pairs* of operators (if we calculate momentum, it may be in connexion with some position; if the energy, it may be in connexion with some instant). What happens next depends on whether two given operators are *commutative* or not.

It is easy to explain what this means.

If p, q are two operators, such as doubling and squaring operators, let us apply them to our basic symbol: if we apply them in the order pq we get double the square of the symbol, but if we apply them in the order qp we get the square of twice the symbol; with this example, therefore, the result of operating with pq is different from the result of operating with qp. The operators p, q are then said to be '*non-commutative*'. (Hence the mysterious relation given in popular books that $pq \neq qp$. There is no difficulty in understanding the idea of a non-commutative algebra—invented by Hamilton—when we realise that the order in which operations are performed can be important.) Now if $\triangle p \cdot \triangle q$ are the ranges of error in estimating p, q respectively, it can be shown in the algebra of quantum mechanics that $\triangle p \cdot \triangle q$ is numerically greater than or equal to $h/4\pi$: that is to say $\triangle p \cdot \triangle q$ cannot be less than a fixed finite quantity. Hence the smaller one error is, the larger the other is; thus it is impossible to eliminate both errors, or to measure both p, q with absolute accuracy, where the operators are non-commutative. This is the Uncertainty Principle.

But, if p is a doubling operator and q a trebling operator, the result is the same no matter whether we proceed in the order pq or qp—we get a sixfold effect in either case. Then the operators are said to be '*commutative*'. The use of such operators leads not to vague values but to precise ones known as "eigen-values"—it is only with non-commutative operators that vague values and the Uncertainty Principle come in. There must be more than one eigen-value because no differential equation can have simply one solution.

Thus, in calculating dynamical quantities, where the operators are non-commutative we get a range of possible (in fact equiprobable) results, but where they are commutative we get a set of precise values (with various probabilities attached).

Since, in calculating a dynamical quantity, operators must either commute or not commute, the result must either lie in a range or be one of a set—no single unambiguous result is possible.

Concerning some corresponding experimental phenomena and their bearing on Determinism there is a good statement by Eddington:[1]

[1] Sir A. S. Eddington, "Indeterminacy and Indeterminism" (Symposium), *Proc. Arist. Soc.*, Sup. Vol. X, London, 1931, pp. 162–81.

The feature of the present situation is that, whether permanently or temporarily, determinism has disappeared altogether from the basis of modern physics. That is a statement of fact, not a prophecy; and so far as I am aware, there is no disagreement about the fact. The physicist may or may not believe in determinism, but in his own domain he has at present no evidence for it and, what is more, he has at present no use for it.

We may fairly claim to have demonstrated the possibility of a non-deterministic universe by having formulated one—an extraordinarily difficult achievement.

I must make it clear that the scientific doctrine of indeterminism is not that there exist occasional exceptions to deterministic law, but that every phenomenon is to a greater or lesser extent indeterminate.

The determinism formerly professed by the physicist was of a specialised kind, which I will call *predictability*.

Let us now compare two phenomena, one of which is supposed to be undetermined and the other (for practical purposes though not absolutely) determined. As an example of a presumably undetermined phenomenon I will take the breaking up of a radium atom; at the present moment t_0 it is undetermined whether the atom will break up at time t_1 or at some other time t_2 . . . Contrast this with an (almost) determined phenomenon, viz., the planet Pluto will reach a certain position in the sky at time t_1, not t_2. When we observe the radium atom to break up at time t_1 we can if we like 'infer' a retrospective property X_1 at time t_0; but in default of any other way of describing X_1 than by connecting it with the break-up at time t_1, we are merely stating the observed fact in different words. From the observation of Pluto we can likewise infer a property X_1 at time t_0; but in this case X_1 is a genuine inference, for it is not defined by reference to that which it is inferred from. Thus the property X_1 may be that Pluto was in a particular position in the sky at time t_0, or that it then exerted certain perturbing forces on Neptune. These properties are definable by reference to manifestations occurring earlier than t_1 . . .

I have contrasted the indeterminacy of the break-up of the radium atom with the determinacy of the position of Pluto; but I must make it clear that this is a difference of degree, not of kind. There is an indeterminacy in the position of Pluto, only it is too small to be of practical importance. . . . If we had chosen instead a lump of radium the size of Pluto, we could predict the amount broken up at any future date with about as much accuracy and certainty as we can predict the position of the planet . . .

We believe that Heisenberg's principle is one of the great fundamental principles of the physical universe (or of our mode of apprehending it) comparable with the principle of Relativity. . . . The indeterminism of modern physics is not merely a failure of deter-

6

minism such as we might postulate as an excuse for our failure to discover determining factors. If we are right, it is a positive discovery
about nature. It is a precise quantitative generalisation just as much
entitled to be called a law of nature as any of the generalisations which
constitute causal law . . .

The entrenchment of determinism in physics was due to the fact
that throughout the whole range of macroscopic phenomena the un-
predictability is negligibly small, so that for all practical purposes a
strictly causal scheme is the most obvious and simplest way of treating
them. It is only when we come to link on the microscopic phenomena
of the world that we realise that the present causal scheme is inexact
and cannot be fundamental.

Here there are several important ideas: (i) physicists do not
need Determinism; (ii) they have formulated the reverse; (iii)
they are concerned with predictability; (iv) Indeterminism per-
vades all nature, even large-scale phenomena; and (v) it is as
ultimate as any other great scientific principle. Eddington is
concerned to show that modern physics aims not at predicting an
exact result, which would be quite exact if physicists were more
careful or had better instruments, but at predicting results within
certain limits, small it is true, but irreducible, and that this irre-
ducibility is not due to imperfection of instruments. With this
one must agree. I would interpret Eddington as describing correctly the operations of modern physics, *i.e.* that physicists predict
upon a statistical basis, and that this procedure is simply one that
does not use the concept of Determinism.

In short, since predictions are often successful, Orderliness of
some sort must be supposed to exist; but, since prediction is
statistical, so is the Orderliness; thus the modern physicist is not
concerned with any kind of Perfect Orderliness. Eddington's
claim therefore comes to this: the universe is characterised by
Statistical Orderliness, both in the sphere of the macroscopic and
the subatomic. And this characterisation, he holds, is ultimate and
incompatible with Perfect Orderliness.

In order to deal with such questions as whether classical physics
did in fact presuppose Perfect Orderliness, and whether statistical
physics gives the *coup de grâce* to this postulate, it is necessary to
look more closely into the difference between the two kinds of
Orderliness.

Classical physics dealt with the macroscopic while modern physics has opened up the sphere of the subatomic. The latter is characterised by Statistical Orderliness; and Eddington holds that the macroscopic is also so characterised, but that this was not noticed in classical days. Hence for him all physics is statistical and the belief that part of it presupposes Perfect Orderliness is simply an error. Now this does less than justice to the classical view: for, even if macroscopic physics is statistical in practice, the claim would have been made that statistical aberrations could be accounted for in terms of Perfect Orderliness.

Consider the following analogue to the electron situation. Suppose you wish to observe the behaviour of a billiard ball. You must begin by illuminating it (we are not concerned with feeling it or smelling it). In classical physics you observe its position and you wish to know its momentum. To do this you have to observe it at two moments that are close together. You note its two positions and the time taken by the ball to travel from one to the other. From the distance and the time you easily get its velocity and hence its momentum. Now suppose that light is made of particles comparable in size with billiard balls (it makes the illustration easier to speak of particles instead of waves); and for convenience let the ball to be studied be red and let light consist of white balls. When you turn on the light a white ball will illuminate the red one, but only at the cost of giving it a knock, which will make calculation of its momentum difficult. The introduction of this fact about the nature of light does not, however, constitute the characteristic innovation of quantum mechanics; Newtonian mechanics would be equal to the occasion. You know the constitution of your light: you know its wave-length, frequency (therefore its velocity), and weight. Surely you will do a sum in ordinary dynamics, such as you find in the chapter headed "impact", from which you will calculate the subsequent velocity or energy of the ball? But it is not so simple as this. To do your sum you must know the initial conditions, *i.e.* the present position and momentum of the red ball. You must therefore observe the red ball in two positions in each of which it is deflected by a white one. Then our sum becomes more complicated, but surely not beyond the powers of a modest mathematician to solve: as a result of the two observations you know the distance, direction, and time of the red ball, from one position to the other; hence you know its velocity, and given its weight you know its momentum. Now at the second position, which you know, you have its momentum as it comes up to that position. When a white ball strikes it here, it is possible to calculate exactly the direction the red ball will take and what its future momentum will be. And in fact the prediction could be confirmed by calculating where the red ball would be and looking for it with a third white ball.

In the parallel situation in quantum mechanics, an electron is illuminated with photons; but an analogous calculation cannot be carried out. The details of the reason are very technical; but broadly speaking every move of the above kind that we make succeeds only in bringing in the Uncertainty Principle over again at a new point—to pursue the Newtonian line of reasoning is to beg the question at every turn.

It would therefore seem that classical physics aims at precision in a way that modern physics does not. But the modern physicist would hold that this difference was illusory, because in fact the precision of classical predictions was approximate or a statistical, average figure. Now the classical physicist would accept this, but point out that nonetheless there was a difference between the two approaches; for he would hold that aberrations could be accounted for, while the exponent of Statistical Orderliness would deny this. Otherwise expressed, the classical physicist thinks that there is a unique answer to be found, and that his prediction of it is the most likely to be the right one, though he admits the possibility of error within the range of error; but the modern physicist regards all predictions within the range of error as equiprobable. Put another way, in classical physics probability arises in relation to definite information but not enough of it; but for quantum physics there is an essential vagueness in the given information, which would make conclusions probable only, even if complete certainty reigned that there were no gaps in the data.

Clearly therefore Perfect Orderliness makes some additional claim or assertion over and above that made by Statistical Orderliness. While according to the latter there is no way of eliminating errors in prediction, according to the former improvement to an unlimited extent is possible by taking into account more and more facts.* The claim of Perfect Orderliness may now be expressed as follows:

* By analogy with Eddington's reasoning, an actuary might argue that Perfect Orderliness was otiose in insurance; he might even frame an 'uncertainty principle' on the grounds that his predictions were within certain limits elastic—which would

Aberration between prediction and subsequent observation down to the smallest detail of a situation can be accounted for by taking into account other ascertainable features of the situation and by allowing for small-order effects due to circumstances outside the situation.

Is this claim justified? The answer is simple: the field of enquiry studied by classical physics was true to it; but modern physics has opened up fields untrue to it—and, as Eddington points out, these fields are not restricted to the subatomic. If we ask whether classical physics needed the concept of Perfect Orderliness for any metascientific purpose, the strict answer is in the negative; but the concept is a very good spur to enquiry. Thus its value lay not in its being a postulate needed to justify classical procedure but in its being a maxim of research.*

Thus Universal Determinism is neither a concept required to justify scientific procedure nor a general truth about nature or the laws of science; and consequently there is no question of attempting the impossible task, so often tried in vain, of squaring the Uncertainty Principle with Determinism.

Apart from the foregoing scientific and metascientific opposition to Determinism, there is also metascientific opposition to it from many quarters typified by Operationalism. Whether or not this has anything to contribute to the characterisation of scientific statements we shall consider in the next chapter.

express that Perfect Orderliness was useless in a certain sphere. This habit of mind first arose towards physics when it became preferable in this field, as it is in insurance, to achieve large numbers of good but not perfect predictions instead of a few excellent ones. However, the upholder of Perfect Orderliness would look for causes of aberrations from statistical frequencies, and, in the field of insurance, it would be possible to find them. Thus, if the number of deaths before the age of 41 in a given year exceeded the range predicted by statistics, some reason could be found for this.

* Since this was written, Popper has published two fundamental papers to show that it is a tautology that an element of uncertainty is inherent in all prediction (K. R. Popper, "Indeterminism in Quantum Physics and in Classical Physics", *The British Journal for the Philosophy of Science*, Vol. I, Nos. 2 and 3, Edinburgh, 1950).

CHAPTER IX

OPERATIONALISM
AND THE DESCRIPTIVE INTERPRETATION

SCIENTIFIC laws are justified through the method of testing consequences, and in this method can be found the Principle of Testability by Deduction. It is characteristic that scientific laws that are not generalisations involve something unobservable; not all the concepts they contain denote something instantial. What, then, is their nature? They have been given an interpretation that may be called "descriptive" or "operational". This is to be found in Newton,[1] Berkeley,[2] Bentham,[3] Pearson,[4] Mach,[5] James,[6] Poincaré,[7] Wittgenstein,[8] Vaihinger,[9] Bridgman,[10] George,[11] and possibly others,* though it has not been explicitly formulated by any of them except Bridgman.

In a famous passage Newton wrote:

Hitherto we have explained the phenomena of the heavens and of our sea by the power of gravity, but have not yet assigned the cause of this power. This is certain, that it must proceed from a cause that penetrates to the very centres of the sun and planets . . . But hitherto I have not been able to discover the cause of those properties of gravity from phenomena, and I frame no hypotheses; for whatever is not deduced from the phenomena is to be called an hypothesis; and hypotheses, whether metaphysical or physical, whether of occult qualities or mechanical, have no place in experimental philosophy . . . And

---

[1] Isaac Newton, *Philosophiae Naturalis Principia Mathematica*, ed. by Cajori, Cambridge, 1934, Bk. III, General Scholium, pp. 546–7.

[2] George Berkeley, *Do Motu* (in Latin), *Works*, ed. by Fraser, Vol. I, Oxford, 1901; Eng. trans., *Works*, ed. by Sampson, Vol II, London, 1898.

[3] C. K. Ogden, *Bentham's Theory of Fictions*, London, 1932.

[4] Karl Pearson, *The Grammar of Science*, London, 1892.

[5] Ernst Mach, *The Science of Mechanics*, Chicago, 1907.

[6] William James, *Pragmatism*, New York, 1928.

[7] Henri Poincaré, *Science and Hypothesis*, London, 1905, esp. pp. 55–9.

[8] Ludwig Wittgenstein, *Tractatus Logico-Philosophicus*, London, 1922, 6.31–6.36.

[9] H. Vaihinger, *The Philosophy of 'As If,'* London, 1924.

[10] P. W. Bridgman, *The Logic of Modern Physics*, New York, 1927.

[11] W. H. George, *The Scientist in Action*, London, 1936.

* Some would include Hume, who held a view of this type in philosophy, but it is doubtful if he seriously considered its application to science, though this is implied by his treatment of causation. Kant may have held some such view in philosophy, but he certainly did not apply it to science.

to us it is enough that gravity does really exist, and act according to the laws which we have explained, and abundantly serves to account for all the motions of the celestial bodies, and of our sea.[1]

(Belief in the real existence of gravity is hardly compatible with the rejection of hypotheses.) According to Berkeley:

Force, gravity, attraction, and words of this sort, are serviceable for reasonings and computations concerning motion and bodies in motion, but not for understanding the simple nature of motion itself, or for denoting so many distinct qualities. Certainly, as far as regards attraction, it is clear that it is adopted by Newton, not as a real, physical quality, but merely as a mathematical hypothesis.[2]

Pearson's attitude is conveyed roughly by the question:

How far is the assumption necessary in order to obtain a model which will enable us to describe briefly the routine of perception?[3]

Mach and Poincaré held similar views. James's thesis of Pragmatism was that a concept was true if it could be successfully used, but he did not attribute to it truth in any other sense. According to Vaihinger:

We have repeatedly insisted above that the boundary between truth and error is not a rigid one, and we were able ultimately to demonstrate that what we generally call truth, namely a conceptual world coinciding with the external world, *is merely the most expedient error.*[4]

Bentham's thesis of fictions is much the same as those of James and Vaihinger. For George the process of forming a scientific hypothesis consists of pattern making; this is reminiscent of a striking passage given by Wittgenstein, according to which a scientific law is a network whose meshes correspond to elements in reality:

Newtonian mechanics, for example, brings the description of the universe to a unified form. Let us imagine a white surface with irregular black spots. We now say: Whatever kind of picture these make I can always get as near as I like to its description, if I cover the surface with a sufficiently fine square network and now say of every square that

---

[1] Newton, *Loc. cit.*
[2] Berkeley, *Loc. cit.*, § 17.
[3] Pearson, *Op. cit.*, Ch. VIII, The Laws of Motion, § 2, p. 340.
[4] Vaihinger, *Op. cit.*, p. 108.

it is white or black. In this way I shall have brought the description of the surface to a unified form. This form is arbitrary, because I could have applied with equal success a net with a triangular or hexagonal mesh. It can happen that the description would have been simpler with the aid of a triangular mesh; that is to say we might have described the surface more accurately with a triangular, and coarser, than with the finer square mesh, or *vice versa*, and so on. To the different networks correspond different systems of describing the world. Mechanics determine a form of description by saying: All propositions in the description of the world must be obtained in a given way from a number of given propositions—the mechanical axioms. It thus provides the bricks for building the edifice of science, and says: Whatever building thou wouldst erect, thou shalt construct it in some manner with these bricks and these alone.

Laws, like the law of causation, etc., treat of the network and not of what the network described.[1]

Bridgman's thesis of Operationalism maintains that scientific concepts must be definable in terms of operations rather than of properties:

the true meaning of a term is to be found by observing what a man does with it, not by what he says about it.[2]

The whole outlook is summed up in Newton's famous phrase, "*Hypotheses non fingo.*"

Thus a trend is visible; an attitude is adopted. This may be discerned in particular instances, *e.g.* with respect to absolute space and the like; but of general statement of principle there is little beyond an assertion of empiricism. Even George's admirable work, which is perhaps the closest examination of scientific practice, does not contribute to the present theme. There is no occasion, therefore, to elaborate the historical growth of the standpoint or of any divergencies there may have been between the opinions of the writers mentioned.

The most striking and obvious characteristic of the standpoint is its negativeness—it is opposed to absolutes and absolutism. Thus attacks have been levelled against absolute space, time, motion, matter, vital force, pure ego, and so on; but the standpoint has a positive side, and it is desirable to bring this out explicitly. Seeing that a non-instantial concept does not correspond

---

[1] Wittgenstein, *Op. cit.*, 6, 35.
[2] Bridgman, *Op. cit.*, p. 7.

to something in the natural world and a non-instantial hypothesis does not have observable instances, it is clearly incumbent upon us to enquire about their nature and how they can be of any service. The general answer to this from Newton and Berkeley onwards to the pragmatic one: a concept or a hypothesis is true if it works, *i.e.* if it leads to successful pattern making or assemblage of hitherto isolated phenomena and to prediction of events not yet observed.

Such a view may be called "descriptive" in the sense that according to it a law *describes* what happens in the world as opposed to *explaining why* things happen as they do.

It must be borne in mind that the statement of a law understood as a 'description' does not amount merely to a catalogue of all observations satisfying the law that have been made. On the contrary, it is taken to be *a shorthand expression with predictive power*. This view would be the same as the philosophical doctrine of Phenomenalism if this were applied outside its own philosophical field of perception to the field of science. The Principle of Testability by Deduction would be accepted as a test of significance, but the construction put upon this would be to the effect that a statement of a law means no more than the sum of the observations to which it gives rise. Thus, while the scientist of absolutist persuasion would regard gravitation as a property of matter, *i.e.* as instantial, so that to know this would be to know a piece of absolute truth, the descriptionist would (correctly) deny that it is a property of matter and would (questionably) hold that the assertion of its existence would mean only that it summarised the known facts.

I wish to suggest that the current doctrine of Operationalism, originated by Bridgman, is to be regarded, in one of its aspects, as the successor of the descriptive interpretation. The doctrine has much to recommend it, but the same cannot be said of its ancestor; on the other hand an operationalist would probably dispute the parentage. The appearance of paradox here arises because Operationalism is not a simple doctrine, but has three parts fused together which seem much the same. An important difference becomes visible, however, once they are differentiated. (*a*) Operationalism is sometimes used, I suggest, as the equivalent of the descriptive interpretation or Phenomenalism. (*b*) Bridgman's chief use of it is as a kind of inversion of the foregoing. He is concerned not so much, like the phenomenalist, with the operations leading to observations from a concept, as with the operations leading to a concept from observations. (*c*) It is sometimes used as a method of dealing with quasi-scientific statements, with the aim of showing that they are meaningless.

In (*c*), it is not being offered as an account of scientific inference. It is employed, rather, as a criterion of significance, and, like Logical Positivism, it can be used with advantage to deal with quasi-scientific statements. Part of the reason why the general doctrine attracts adherents is probably because of this feature—which doubtless seems less extreme than Logical Positivism.

It seems clear that sometimes Bridgman's use is not essentially different from the descriptive interpretation. In his stricter moments, such as when he asserts that two instances of measuring a length are different operations, he seems to be admitting that a concept can be no more than a condensation of a limited number of operations. Now it is this finitude that forms the link with the descriptive interpretation and constitutes the weakness of both.

We may now consider objections to the doctrine—the descriptive interpretation or Operationalism in the form (*b*), regarded as a method of giving the meaning of a word in terms of a finite number of operations (which create the meaning).

(i) The doctrine implies that a scientific law is in no sense an *explanation* of phenomena; yet it is impossible to doubt that scientists are imbued with a desire to find explanations. Thus

This renouncing of the macroscopic models would be the right way to follow, for the theory of microscopic phenomena, if the *only purpose* of science were to work out a convenient representation of quantitative relationships between the various sides of our experience, so as to enable us to foresee and to some extent control it . . . But the purpose of science is much wider: it is not only to enable us to foresee and control our experience, but also to *understand* it, which means to construct from it a wide picture of the universe around us which would satisfy our mind.[1]

What is demanded is that we shall not only know what to expect but also that we shall be able to understand.

(ii) If laws of science are taken to be successful results of pattern-making, it is difficult to understand how such success is more than mere good luck. Certainly the scientist has to be

[1] N. S. Japolsky, "A Theory of Elementary Particles", *London, Edinburgh, and Dublin Philosophical Magazine*, N.S. Vol. XX, London, 1935, p. 418.

able to form patterns and to predict; scientific prediction, however, must be based on neither guessing, magic, intuition, nor
lucky patterns—it signifies *prediction by rational means*, and this
alone. But, if laws consist of concepts that are determined by a
finite set of descriptions, where is their descriptive power?

This objection is illustrated particularly clearly in the use of
interpolation and extrapolation. A law is represented by the
simplest curve that can be drawn through the various points
representing the results of observation or experiment. The mere
points, unjoined by a graph, constitute a bare description of the
observed facts; the line joining them, however, makes a claim, for
it asserts that all the other points that make up the line correspond to observable facts. It is of some interest that the scientist
unhesitatingly trusts all points that lie inside the range of those
that are anchored in observation, *i.e.*, interpolations; points that
lie outside this range, *i.e.*, extrapolations, he is apt to treat with
reserve—in some circumstances he will accept them as readily as
interpolations while in others he will proceed with great caution.
However this may be, the scientist in practice is concerned only
with the *reliability* of extrapolation. Where he regards it as reliable
he is not troubled with further doubts—with the 'justification' of
extrapolation and interpolation he is concerned not at all. He will
wish to test a number of instances of the two and if these are confirmed he is satisfied; but he does not, and cannot, test all possible
instances even of interpolation; and there is, therefore, a limit to
the extent to which a law is related to observation, for the law
covers instances that have not and perhaps never will be observed.

Such is the daily practice of science. What is its significance for
the descriptive view and for a scientist who regards a law as in some
literal sense a law of nature? The scientist will expect future
confirmation of the law because he has established it; the descriptionist will equally well predict what will in fact be confirmed,
but he will have no good reason for expecting confirmation. The
scientist predicts from the points joined by a curve and the
descriptionist from the points alone—the former procedure is
possible, the latter not.

The present objection cannot be better illustrated than by an
example given by Jeffreys. This was cited in Chapter VII in
connexion with the simplicity of laws, but Jeffreys himself used
the illustration also against Phenomenalism. If we consider the
simple law he gives, $5x = t^2$, and the complex one, and if we try

experiments for interpolated and extrapolated values, we find
that the simple law holds and that the involved one does not. The
descriptionist would have no way of deciding which to adopt as a
basis for making predictions; for within his existing framework
he can make no attempt to grapple with the simplicity of laws.

I would put the case against the descriptive view further by
means of the following illustration. Suppose a water tank which is
full of water has a small hole in it at the bottom, so that it leaks
slowly. The experimenter watches the level gradually fall. He
now fills the tank and goes away, but returns at intervals to note
the different levels; he finds these have been reached after the
same lapses of time as when he was watching without interruption.
He judges that his presence and observation have made no difference to the flow of water, and holds that the flow has continued
steadily in his absence and has reached levels just as when he
watched. Now the descriptionist restricts himself to saying that *if*
he *had* gone to the tank at a specified time he *would have* found the
water at the predicted level; but he makes no statement—for he
holds it has no meaning—about the literal situation in the tank
when he is not observing it. He would be equally satisfied with his
tests if the water were drunk by birds and the tank filled again by
a temporary increase of flow for an appropriate time due to the
activities of workmen at the mains—or indeed if the water ceased
to exist when not perceived provided it reappeared at the correct
level when perception began again. We must remember that not
merely are the water levels found at their correct places on one
occasion, but that on various occasions they would be correct no
matter what levels were tested. Suppose the miracle could happen
of one set of levels being found correct, how much more unlikely
is it that this is true of all possible levels? Would not this be a
thoroughgoing pre-established harmony—or at any rate an
established harmony?

(iii) It is difficult to see how non-instantial concepts can be
interpreted operationally (or descriptively). Whatever may be
said for interpreting the concept of length by means of operations
of measuring, there is no clear way of doing this with the concept
of gravitation.

(iv) Operationalism obliterates the distinction between instantial and non-instantial concepts, and this leads to a curious
consequence.

Suppose you come into your flat and find a valuable ornament missing; you find a window forced and left open; you see foot-marks deep in the clay outside. You extrapolate from past experience and conclude that a burglar has been in your flat. If you are an ordinary scientist you will think of a man as being a burglar existing in the same sort of way you do yourself; but if you are an operationalist you may say that the concept of a burglar is sufficient to make a pattern of the experiences just described and that it is superfluous to claim the existence of anything instanced by the concept. Suppose the gardener comes in and tells you he heard a noise *as if* a man were running off though he did not see anything like this, the information will fit in with either point of view. If, moreover, a policeman came along with the ornament which he found lying not far off, as if discarded in a hurry, that too will fit either view. Only if the burglar is caught can the (shall we call it?) realist attitude be established against the operationalist interpretation. (Indeed even if the burglar is subsequently caught, this would not on the operationalist view establish his existence at the time he broke into your flat.)

The basis of your conclusion that you have been burgled, however, includes the existence of burglars, and it is a proper argument by analogy to argue in a new instance to an existent. On the other hand, where scientific concepts such as gravitation are concerned, the observational evidence *never* involves an instance of the existence of gravitation, and it would be improper to argue by analogy to an existent gravitation. But Operationalism treats an uncaught burglar and gravitation as on the same footing; it therefore fails to take account of an important distinction.

These objections concern the inadequate way in which Operationalism and the descriptive interpretation deal with explanation, rational prediction (including the serviceability of interpolation and extrapolation), and the distinction between instantial and non-instantial concepts. I wish now to put forward a more fundamental type of objection, concerning an inconsistency in their ways of treating scientific statements.

It is impossible to do science without formulating laws the generality of whose linguistic form refers beyond actual observations. This assertion, though it contains a tautology, is important. The non-tautological part is that we have in fact to use general modes of expression; the tautological part is that these refer beyond actual observations. The doctrines are trying to restrict the reference of general statements only to what is actually observed and thus are using general language while at the same time trying to eliminate the feature of generality—a self-contradictory procedure. To use Reichenbach's happy term, "interphenomenon",[1] for unobserved interpolations and extrapolations, scientific statements by their very nature refer to interphenomena. It is true, of course, that different alternative hypotheses refer to different interphenomena, and that it is always possible to construct rival hypotheses between which it is impossible to choose; hence we can never assert that any specific interphenomenon is necessary. But some interphenomenon or other is always necessary. For example, to cite Reichenbach, we may explain the shadow of a tree by the interphenomenon of light rays travelling in straight lines. But we could also explain it by the interphenomenon of rays travelling in a zig-zag (though there would have to be many compensating factors to make this complicated hypothesis square with experience). Jeffreys' example shows that the simplest hypothesis is the most likely to be correct—in his example the complex hypotheses are wrong—but it is certainly possible to construct more complex ones that would lead to correct predictions just as well as his simple hypothesis. Whatever choice the scientist makes, however, he has to posit *some* interphenomenon. Again, in the field of ordinary perception, all of us posit interphenomena to connect the gaps in our perceptual experience. On returning to my study I connect the desk-experience I then have with the desk-experience I had before leaving the room by the interphenomenon of an unobserved desk, or perhaps by the interphenomena of protons and electrons. This unavoidable feature of scientific practice, the descriptive interpretation and Operationalism treat in a self-contradictory way. They assert that the interphenomenon is a myth, instead of asserting that any particular interphenomenon is a myth and admitting that some interphenomena are required by the attempt to explain anything at all.

In brief it would seem that what is faulty in any form of descriptive interpretation lies not in what it denies, but in the narrowness of its claim. It is right to repudiate concepts that cannot be related in any way to observations by operations; but too narrow to correspond to the procedure of science, in depriving universal

---

[1] Hans Reichenbach, *Philosophic Foundations of Quantum Mechanics*, Berkeley and Los Angeles, 1944, p. 21.

statements of their universality. It thus fails to fit the hypothetico-deductive system. In practice, of course, Bridgman uses this framework; what I am suggesting is that Operationalism cannot be accepted as an account of this framework—it is not so much wrong as inadequate.

It would therefore seem that Operationalism, which set out with the rational purpose of opposing myth and concepts unrelated to what can be observed, is itself curiously irrational in expecting nature to conform to scientific-law patterns while deliberately excluding all possible basis for the belief.

What can be said in support of Operationalism? To place it in the most favourable light, we must regard a concept not as a summary of operations but as something indicated by them. Length is not the operation (or operations) of measuring, but something to which measuring refers. Also, what is relevant in explaining a concept is not a *particular* operation but a *kind* of operation. It is not the particular operation of laying a metre-rule against an object that is important, but this kind of operation.

Operationalism may then be used to explain a concept to those who are unfamiliar with it; but this amounts to no more than one of the well-known methods of definition. Thus length is what you get when you lay down a metre-rule against an object. But the function of such a definition of a word is to direct a person's attention to something he is familiar with, but has not yet associated with the word. Now, so far as Operationalism does this, it is useful but not new; and it is well-directed and in the spirit of Empiricism in that it focusses attention on an important type of definition. What is faulty is what is new: the twist given to such a process of defining, that the meaning is given, not merely revived, by the operation. Perhaps the most serious aspect of the doctrine is the implication that one important kind of definition provides the only way of using words correctly; and this leads some—*e.g.* classical behaviourists who are incompletely emancipated from metaphysics and therefore afraid of being found guilty of having a metaphysical attitude—to lose sight of the rôle of non-instantial concepts, which cannot be defined operationally.

Concluding Remarks on Part I

One of the chief aims of this Part is to stress the importance of distinguishing non-instantial hypotheses as a special type. This type, though not explicitly recognised, seems to have puzzled some metascientists and to be the *raison d'être* of the descriptive interpretation and Operationalism. But these approaches we found to be at variance with the hypothetico-deductive procedure of science and consequently they fail to provide a satisfactory account of non-instantial concepts. Positivists, too, have tended to overlook the type, but we have seen that its scientific significance can be readily defined. All these approaches overlook the diversity of testable consequences that is characteristic of the explanatory power of non-instantial hypotheses.

The interesting problem arises: how is it that there can be such things as non-instantial laws—that nature should work in accordance with concepts that have no instances? Perhaps our discussion of simplicity has a bearing on this. The goal of simplicity seems to be to reduce the number of non-instantial concepts. Thus the Newtonian theory of gravitation, which is an approximation to the Einstein theory, contains more non-instantial concepts than the theory that replaces it. There is therefore the possibility that non-instantial laws exist because of being approximations to laws containing fewer non-instantial concepts. But this interesting problem cannot be pursued further here.

We also discussed Determinism, but found no reason to suppose that it offers a general truth about nature or about scientific laws. Since it cannot, as used to be supposed, explain the necessity of law, it can throw no light on non-instantial hypotheses in particular.

Another aim of this Part is to bring out the bearing of non-instantial hypotheses on induction. Firstly we can see that hypotheses always precede observation in the sense that observations are made in the light of hypotheses. Hence there can be no such thing as an inductive *method*, which aims at producing hypotheses from observations. Secondly non-instantial concepts can be handled only in the hypothetico-deductive framework and thus a non-instantial hypothesis cannot be the conclusion in an inductive *inference*. Thus the field of induction is greatly reduced. This leaves open the question, to be discussed in the next Part, whether a generalisation, which contains only instantial concepts, can be the conclusion in an inductive inference.

PART II

CHAPTER X

THE TRADITIONAL APPROACH TO INDUCTION

In this part we shall be concerned with induction conceived as a form of inference. We shall not find any justification for this approach. Nonetheless it is still worth studying, because it contains contributions that are susceptible of being interpreted so as to fit the hypothetico-deductive system, because ingenious developments have taken place that may yet prove to be of some value, and because certain parts of the subject have an interest of their own. Thus the Law of Uniformity of Nature, so much decried, must receive attention, because, in spite of the difficulty of stating it and in spite of the overwhelming objections to it, it reflects something in which we all tend to believe. We must be capable of rejecting it, even if we feel that something must be put in its place and do not know what substitute to offer.

The traditional view was that scientific inference consisted, at least mainly, in induction. In presenting this view, remote historical material need not be brought forward. I open, not with Bacon, not even with a detailed statement of Mill's 'methods' but with a modernised version of them, which is intended simply to be more accurate than Mill's. Much discussion centres around the work of Keynes, which though of fairly recent origin is in the inductive tradition, however great an improvement it may be on the work of his predecessors. Even Positivism comes within the inductive approach.

I hope to show that the inductive approach leads to a complete *impasse*, and thus to give support to the contention that induction is the wrong concept to employ when studying scientific inference.

CHAPTER XI

CRITERIA FOR CAUSAL DETERMINATION AND FUNCTIONAL RELATIONSHIP

MILL's five Methods of Experimental Enquiry[1] are unsatisfactory in various ways and have been to a considerable extent honoured in the breach by scientists; Johnson gave Four Figures of Demonstrative Induction,[2] but, though they differ markedly from Mill's Methods, they are probably just as far removed from scientific inference; Stebbing improved on all these by enunciating four Special Principles of Causal Determination,[3] which, however, are not wholly satisfactory because they do not take sufficient account of the possible complexity of apparently simple factors or of the plurality of causes and effects or of the distinction between the necessary and the sufficient. Certain features of Johnson's Figures can yield matter that is relevant to scientific procedure, but it is simpler to treat the subject independently. What is required is to tabulate the criteria that are actually found in or implied by scientific procedure. What follows is, therefore, an attempt to give a new treatment from this point of view.

Tradition will be followed, however, in writing a conclusion after the statements of the relevant observations, as if it could be derived from them; for this leads on to the classical problem of induction. The alternative of writing the result first, as a hypothesis, with the statements of the relevant observations after it, ought to be obvious. It should be stressed, moreover, that the criteria here given are patterns of good scientific inference—not at all methods of discovery.

It will be convenient to use certain symbols as follows: Let X, X' be supposed causal factors; E, E' supposed effects; A, A', B, B' be supposedly non-causal factors; ξ the possible presence of a wholly unsuspected causal factor; let $\bar{X}$, $\bar{E}$ mean the absence, respectively, of X, E; let "$\|$" stand for "is found with", and "$\longrightarrow$" stand for "is a factor in producing", and "$-/\rightarrow$" for

---

[1] J. S. Mill, *System of Logic*, London, 1919, Bk. III, Ch. VIII.
[2] W. E. Johnson, *Logic*, Cambridge, 1922, Pt. II, Ch. 10.
[3] L. Susan Stebbing, *A Modern Introduction to Logic*, London, 1933, pp. 326–31.

"is not causally connected with"; and "+" or "—" before a letter will indicate that the factor denoted is respectively introduced to or withdrawn from a situation. The word "factor" will denote either a natural object, a change of state of an object, a property of an object, or an event. The word "situation" will have the somewhat vague use of a group of factors, such that when some of the factors of the group are changed we shall have simply a new form of the situation; in other words we shall have different determinate forms of a determinable situation.

Since scientific procedure is based upon *elimination*, the first essential is to have a criterion by which the irrelevant can be weeded out.

I. CRITERIA OF INDEPENDENCE

CRITERION OF INDEPENDENCE (1): *In a given situation, if a certain factor, E, is varied, while the other factors, including X, remain unaltered, then it is probable that X is not causally connected with E.*
This may be symbolised thus:

$$XAB\xi \| E$$
$$XAB\xi \| E' \text{ (or } \bar{E}),$$
therefore probably $X—/{\rightarrow}E$.

The strict conclusion is that probably X *is not sufficient* to cause E. X might nonetheless be *necessary*, and A and B might not contain the other necessary factors. The conclusion could be read: "There is no evidence that X is causally connected with E"; which amounts to saying that X is probably not connected with E.

The criterion may be illustrated by any superstition. X may be walking under a ladder, E subsequent misfortunes, and E' subsequent good luck; or E may be toothache and X Saturday afternoon. It may also be illustrated by a feature of Pasteur's experiments to disprove the spontaneous generation in putrescible liquids of the organisms known as infusoria: having boiled some liquid in a closed flask and admitted heated air containing dust into it, no infusoria developed, whereas previously he had found them develop in the presence of dust; hence, he concluded, dust (X) was not a cause of infusoria (E), since it was found without them (Ē).*

---

* Apart from the qualification to do with probability, the above criterion is equivalent to Stebbing's Special Principle No. 1, *id.*, p. 327.

CRITERION OF INDEPENDENCE (2): *In a given situation, if a certain factor, X, is varied, while the other factors, including E, remain unaltered, then it is probable that X is not causally connected with E.*

This may be symbolised thus:

$$XAB\xi\|E$$
$$X'AB\xi\|E,$$
therefore probably $X—/\rightarrow E.$

The strict conclusion is that probably X is not a *necessary* factor in causing E.

This criterion may be illustrated by one of Newton's experiments with the pendulum or by Galileo's alleged experiment of dropping weights from the Leaning Tower of Pisa or by features of Pasteur's experiment. Newton wished to know whether the effect of gravity upon a pendulum was influenced by its chemical constitution. He substituted pendula made of different substances (X, X', etc.), keeping other features the same, and found no change in the periodic time (E). Galileo is supposed to have dropped two different weights (X, X') from the Tower and observed that they took the same time (E) to reach the ground. Pasteur tried samples of air drawn from many different quarters (X, X', etc.) and always with the same results (E).*

Either of these criteria would usually be taken to be conclusive; but they sometimes lead to false conclusions. With (1) there is nothing to show that X is not a cause of both E and E'—there might be *a diversity of effects*. With (2) there is nothing to show that X and X' are not both causes of E—there might be *a plurality of causes*. So long as these possibilities are not tested, though there is some probability that X is independent of E, the probability is not so high as it would be if tests had been made and had proved negative. It is therefore necessary to examine the ways by which the relation of plurality of causes and diversity of effects could be established. This matter will be considered in Criteria III.

There is also the possibility of counteracting causes; this will be considered in Criteria IV.

---

* This criterion was not given by Stebbing; she used the experiment of the pendulum, but she did so to illustrate Criterion (1). Johnson's Figure of Agreement (and to a less extent Mill's Method of Agreement) is roughly equivalent to the present criterion, and he used the Galileo illustration.

II. Criteria of Probable Causal Laws.

The word "probable" is inserted to stress the absence of conclusiveness. It is not used here in the mathematical sense.

CRITERION OF PROBABLE CONNEXION (1): *In a given situation, if a certain factor, X, is always accompanied by a certain factor, E, no matter how the remaining factors and their combinations differ, then it is probable that X is or contains a necessary factor in causing E and rather less probable that X is a sufficient cause of E.*

This may be symbolised thus:

$$XAB\xi\|E$$
$$XA'B\xi\|E$$
$$XAB'\xi\|E$$
$$XA'B'\xi\|E,$$

therefore probably $X \longrightarrow E$ or $\|E$.

It should be remarked that, where the fundamental rule of experimental procedure is followed of varying the factors one at a time, there is no occasion for the fourth row containing the combination A'B'; but it may not always be possible to observe that rule and there is no harm in including this combination. Needless to say, the schema possesses more perfection and symmetry than should be expected in actuality. Further, there is no limit to the number of factors A, B; but for metascientific purposes it is sufficient to have two.

The present criterion is *pure induction*—or induction by simple enumeration as it used to be called. X does not *certainly* contain a necessary cause of E: because the conjunction might be a coincidence; because the various combinations of A, A', B, B' might contain a common element that was sufficient to cause E; because there is the possibility of ξ; because an A, a B, and ξ might be jointly sufficient; or because X and E might be concomitant effects of some other anterior cause. X need not be sufficient: because it might not contain a necessary factor at all; and if it did the various combinations of A, A', B, B' might contain the remaining factor necessary to produce E; or ξ might have this; or an A, a B, and ξ might jointly contain the remaining necessary factor; or X and E might both be due to an anterior cause. Clearly more has to be proved to show that X is sufficient than to show that it is necessary; hence it is rather less probable that X is sufficient than that it is necessary.

This criterion may be illustrated by the conjunction between

the positions of the moon (X) and the height of the tide (E)—
the moon being in a straight line with the two parts of the earth
that have simultaneous high tides. This conclusion asserts that X
is probably *found with* (and not *causes*) E, because in observation,
as opposed to experiment, X and E might be parallel effects of
some anterior cause.

Suppose we were to illustrate the criterion by the conjunction
always found between solidification (X) and crystalline structure
(E).* To do so would be to overlook the implied principle asserting a conjunction between X̄ and Ē, *i.e.* that more than the bare
criterion given was being used. This is true of nearly all examples.
Thus if we wish to base an inference on the observed conjunction
of swans with whiteness, we are also utilising the conjunction of
colours other than white with animals other than swans. It is
indeed very difficult to illustrate the present criterion, but it does
exist; in addition to the illustration given, there is also the conjunction between unconscious conflict and behaviour mistakes,
for which the negative aspect (requiring the absence of all mental
conflict) is probably always lacking. The present criterion concerns causes and effects that are irremovable or that exist permanently.

CRITERION OF PROBABLE CONNEXION (2): *In a given situation, if
a certain factor, X, is always accompanied by a factor, E, no matter how
the remaining factors and their combinations differ* [this repeats (1)]; *and
if, when one or more of these combinations is (a) conjoined with a factor
other than X or (b) without X, E does not occur; then it is probable that X
is a necessary cause of E and slightly less probable that X is a sufficient
cause of E.*

This may be symbolised thus:

$$\text{(i)} \quad \begin{array}{l} \text{XA B } \xi \| \text{E} \\ \text{XA'B } \xi \| \text{E} \\ \text{XA B'} \xi \| \text{E} \\ \text{XA'B'} \xi \| \text{E,} \end{array} \qquad \text{(ii}a\text{)} \quad \begin{array}{l} \text{X'A B } \xi \| \bar{\text{E}} \\ \text{X'A'B } \xi \| \bar{\text{E}} \\ \text{X'A B'} \xi \| \bar{\text{E}} \\ \text{X'A'B'} \xi \| \bar{\text{E}} \end{array} \qquad \text{or (ii}b\text{)} \quad \begin{array}{l} \bar{\text{X}}\text{A B } \xi \| \text{E} \\ \bar{\text{X}}\text{A'B } \xi \| \bar{\text{E}} \\ \bar{\text{X}}\text{A B'} \xi \| \bar{\text{E}} \\ \bar{\text{X}}\text{A'B'} \xi \| \bar{\text{E}}; \end{array}$$

therefore probably X⟶E, or ‖E

(the former conclusion referring to experiment, the latter to
observation or experiment).

This criterion is easy to illustrate. Pasteur found that putrescible

* Mill gave this to illustrate his Method of Agreement, which is something like the
present criterion, and he failed to notice the implied conjunction between X̄ and Ē
mentioned above. Johnson omits this criterion altogether. Stebbing does not give it
separately, but includes it as part of her Special Principle No. II, to which attention
will now be given.

liquids exposed to unsterilised air (X) developed infusoria (E) and that when exposed to sterilised air (X') they did not (Ē). This illustrates (i) and (iia). Again, fresh-vegetable deficiency (X) on polar explorations was associated with the growth of scurvy (E), which disappeared (Ē) when fresh vegetables were obtained (X̄). This illustrates (i) and (iib). Again, as Darwin found, earthworms (X) are responsible for vegetable mould (E) which does not occur (Ē) in their absence (X̄).

The same remarks about necessity and sufficiency as in (1) apply here; but the existence of (iia or b) increase the probability that X is or contains a necessary factor. Moreover, by ringing the changes among the factors, A, A', B, B', varying them one by one, the probability increases that X is sufficient. It is important to notice that this schema fits observation or experiment: X' and X may be observed or inserted deliberately by the experimenter. E can be observed only. There is clearly no great difference between (i) with (iia) and (i) with (iib).*

As a preliminary to the next criterion consider the following statement: In a given situation, if the introduction of a factor, E, is accompanied by the introduction of a factor, X; and conversely if the withdrawal of E is accompanied by the withdrawal of X; then E is effectually † connected with X.‡

It is important to stress that the two phases of the situation are not simply found together; they are created by the action of adding or withdrawing E. This would show both that E was or contained an *inevitable* effect of X and that E was or contained the *complete* effect of X; *i.e.* that X or part of X caused E or part of E

---

* Stebbing—apart from the probability requirement—gave (i) and (iia) as her Special Principle No. II (*id.*, p. 327). It was an improvement on Mill's Joint Method, which it closely resembles. Mill did not see the need for having one of the groups AB, A'B, AB', A'B' of (i) repeated in (ii), which makes his method valueless; he could have had A's and B's in (i) and P's and Q's in (ii). Thus if ordinary air (X) and water (A) left standing (B) produce infusoria (E), Mill's negative instance could have been that sterilised air (X') with acid (P) and alkali (Q) produce salt (Ē)—a truth that has no bearing on the relation between X and E. This was pointed out by Stebbing (*id.*, pp. 336–38) and previously by Broad, though he gave the credit to Johnson (C. D. Broad, "The Principles of Demonstrative Induction (I)", *Mind*, N. S., Vol. XXXIX, No. 155, London, 1930, pp. 316–17).

It is to be noticed that (i) and iib) roughly include Mill's Method of Difference, in that presence and absence are contrasted in different instances of a situation; the feature of Mill's Method that distinguishes it—and renders it weaker—is the lack of variation in the factors A, B. The present criterion asserts that X is probably necessary and probably though less probably sufficient; Mill's on the other hand asserts that X is probably necessary but tells us nothing one way or the other about its sufficiency.

† Using "effectual" as an adjective of "effect", in the same way as "causal" is used as an adjective of "cause".

‡ This is in fact Stebbing's Special Principle, No. III (Stebbing, *Op. cit.*, pp. 327–28).

and nothing else. But unfortunately the statement has no application, because it is impossible to withdraw an effect without
directly interfering with a cause.

There are two ways of making this into a serviceable criterion.
One is to alternate X and E in the statement. The other is to
delete the reference to *withdrawing* and *introducing* and to compare
two forms of the situation similar except for the presence of both
X and E in the one and their absence in the other.* Perhaps a
better way of expressing this is to distinguish between having two
similar but numerically different forms of a situation and having
one form at two different times; thus we are concerned with re-
duplication in space and identity through time. The latter has,
however, already been taken account of in the previous criterion,
or rather is a special case of it. Reversing X and E, then, we have
the next criterion.

CRITERION OF PROBABLE CONNEXION (3): *In a given situation, if
the introduction of a factor, X, is accompanied by the introduction of a
factor, E; and conversely if the withdrawal of X is accompanied by the
withdrawal of E; then it is probable that X is a necessary factor in the
production of E.*

This may be symbolised thus:

$$\text{(i)} \quad \frac{AB\xi\|\bar{E}}{+X} \qquad \text{and (ii)} \quad \frac{XAB\xi\|E}{-X}$$
$$\overline{XAB\xi\|E,} \qquad\qquad \overline{AB\xi\|\bar{E},}$$
$$\text{therefore probably } X \longrightarrow E.$$

Clearly the conclusion means that X probably is or contains a
necessary factor; there is no information that would indicate
whether or not X might be sufficient.

This criterion may be illustrated by the deflection of a magnetic
compass (E) when placed near a wire carrying an electric current
(X); or by the expansion of a metal (E) when heated (X), as
shown by a metal ball which just fits through a ring before being
warmed and sticks after this; or by the contraction of the pupil
(E) when a light is shone in the eye (X). Compass, ball, and pupil
revert to normal when the X's are removed.

Now there is no need to restrict "withdrawal" and "introduction" to action taken by human beings; they might have an
impersonal sense relevant to automatic natural changes. Thus
when the sun's zenith is high (X) the season is summer (E) and

* This is Mill's Method of Difference.

when the zenith ceases to be high (X), summer is gone (E). Here, however, it is not possible to infer that X is or contains a necessary causal factor, for there might be an anterior cause of both X and E.

The important distinction between this criterion and (2) is that the present one has to do with one form of the situation at two times (so far as the AB factors are concerned), *i.e.* with identity through time; whereas the other had to do with numerical diversity in space of the forms of the situation.* Whether there is or is not an essential difference in this, scientists undoubtedly place more reliance on whatever preserves its identity through time than on the supposed likeness between two numerically different natural objects—the feeling is that you can never be sure that two specimens of a substance have exactly the same properties but that you can be sure that a specimen retains its properties as time elapses. This may be true to some extent, but it should not be exaggerated: radium and organic substances do change when left alone. Nonetheless the difference between spatial and temporal unity seems to be great enough to warrant our having (2) and (3) as separate criteria.

Next it may be observed that part (i) of this criterion must be distinguished as a separate form:

CRITERION OF PROBABLE CONNEXION (4): *In a given situation, if the introduction of a factor, X, is accompanied by the introduction of a factor, E, then it is probable that X is a necessary factor in the production of E, even though the withdrawal of X is not accompanied by the withdrawal of E.*

This may be symbolised thus:

$$\text{(i)} \quad \frac{AB\xi\|\bar{E}}{+X} \qquad \text{and (ii)} \quad \frac{XAB\xi\|E}{-X}$$
$$\overline{XAB\xi\|E,} \qquad \qquad \overline{AB\xi\|E;}$$
$$\text{therefore probably } X \longrightarrow E.$$

This is needed for irreversible causal processes, *i.e.* for phenomena where effects persist even when their causes have ceased. Thus, if glass is crushed (E) by a weight (X), it does not recover—whereas a sponge would be restored to its original state. Again X prob-

---

* Mill's Method of Difference could perhaps be interpreted to refer to one form of a situation at two times, where the 'introduction' and 'withdrawal' were not due to human agency, illustrated above by the connexion between the high altitude of the sun and summer—previously I interpreted it under (2) as referring to diversity in space.

ably is or contains a necessary factor but it is not known to be sufficient.

III. Criteria of Explicitly Non-One-One Probable Causal Laws.

Criterion of Plurality of Causes: *In a given situation, if a certain factor, E, is always accompanied by X or X', no matter how the remaining factors differ, then, subject to a certain condition, C, it is probable that X and X' are connected with E as plural causes to single effect.*

This may be symbolised thus:

$$
\begin{array}{ll}
\text{(i)} \;\; X \, A \, B \, \xi \| E & \text{and (ii)} \;\; X' A \, B \, \xi \| E \\
X \, A'B \, \xi \| E & X' A'B \, \xi \| E \\
X \, A \, B'\xi \| E & X' A \, B'\xi \| E \\
X \, A'B'\xi \| E, & X' A'B'\xi \| E \, ;
\end{array}
$$

therefore, subject to C, probably X and X'——>E (or ‖E).

This situation may be illustrated by bomb blast (X) or earthquakes (X') breaking the windows of houses (E).

Criterion of Diversity of Effects: *In a given situation, if a certain factor, X, is always accompanied by E or E', no matter how the remaining factors differ, then, subject to a certain condition, C, it is probable that X is connected with E and E' as cause to diverse effects.*

This may be symbolised thus:

$$
\begin{array}{ll}
\text{(i)} \;\; X \, A \, B \, \xi \| E & \text{and (ii)} \;\; X \, A \, B \, \xi \| E' \\
X \, A'B \, \xi \| E & X \, A'B \, \xi \| E' \\
X \, A \, B'\xi \| E & X \, A \, B'\xi \| E' \\
X \, A'B'\xi \| E, & X \, A'B'\xi \| E' \, ;
\end{array}
$$

therefore, subject to C, probably X——>E and E' (or ‖E and E').

This may be illustrated by bomb blast blowing windows out (E) and blowing them in (E').

Criterion of Many-Many Connexion: *In a given situation, if a certain factor, X, is always accompanied by E or E', and if another factor, X', is also always accompanied by E or E', no matter how the remaining factors differ, then, subject to a certain condition, C, it is probable that X and X' are related to E and E' as disjunctive causes to disjunctive effects.*

This may be symbolised thus:

$$
\begin{array}{ll}
\text{(i)} \;\; X \, A \, B \, \xi \| E & \text{(ii)} \;\; X \, A \, B \, \xi \| E' \\
X \, A'B \, \xi \| E & X \, A'B \, \xi \| E' \\
X \, A \, B'\xi \| E & X \, A \, B'\xi \| E' \\
X \, A'B'\xi \| E, & X \, A'B'\xi \| E',
\end{array}
$$

$$\text{(iii) } X'A\,B\,\xi\|E \quad \text{and (iv)} \quad X'A\,B\,\xi\|E'$$
$$X'A'B\,\xi\|E \qquad\qquad X'A'B\,\xi\|E'$$
$$X'A\,B'\xi\|E \qquad\qquad X'A\,B'\xi\|E'$$
$$X'A'B'\xi\|E, \qquad\qquad X'A'B'\xi\|E';$$

therefore, subject to C, probably X, X'$\longrightarrow$E, E' (or $\|$E, E').

This may be illustrated by bombs (X) or earthquakes (X') blowing out windows (E) or blowing them in (E').

Are these criteria at all plausible? As they stand, they are not. We could equally well infer that A, A', E, E' were connected in the several instances in the way in which it is asserted that X, X', E, E' are connected. On what grounds, moreover, do we assert this connexion instead of inferring what is more probable, namely that neither X nor X' is causally connected with either E or E'? The grounds are the condition C, which consists of one or more of the following five forms:—

(α) It may be possible to find negative instances, which satisfy (ii*a* or *b*) of the Criterion of Probable Connexion (2), of the form

$$X''A\,B\,\xi\|\bar{E}\,\bar{E}'$$
$$X''A'B\,\xi\|\bar{E}\,\bar{E}'$$
$$X''A\,B'\xi\|\bar{E}\,\bar{E}'$$
$$X''A'B'\xi\|\bar{E}\,\bar{E}',$$

and others according to the criterion in question. This would show that X, for example, was probably a necessary factor in causing E and also E'.

If this is not possible, the connexion may be established:—

(β) By prediction. Thus the sun's altitude (X) is connected with organic growth (E) and the occurrence of summer (E') and upon this connexion predictions can be based. Usually, however, prediction is no more than guessing unless its basis is understood. Thus "I once met a Christadelphian who held on grounds derived from the Book of Revelation, that there would shortly be trouble in Egypt. There was. His belief was true, but not knowledge".[1]

(γ) By applying the supposed connexion successfully in a field wider than that from which it was inferred. Thus if the mutual attraction that holds between the moon and the earth is connected with the motion of the former and the phenomenon of the tides on the latter, and if this attraction can be used to describe the motion of an apple falling from a tree to the ground, there is reason to trust the supposed connexion. (An example dealing only

---

[1] Bertrand Russell, *An Inquiry into Meaning and Truth*, London, 1940, p. 227.

in instantial terms would be preferable—gravity being non-instantial.)

(δ) By showing that the supposed connexion covers an apparent exception—so that 'an apparent exception proves the rule'. Thus when Darwin found that vegetable mould was due to earthworms, which involved the sinking of objects on the surface, he noticed the exception that large boulders did not sink; this is seen to be an apparent exception, because the boulders keep the ground dry which discourages worms from loosening the soil there. (This is not an example dealing with plurality; but it illustrates the point required.)

(ε) By tracing the mechanism through which the supposed cause operates to produce the effect. Thus when polished glass or unpolished metal becomes bedewed (E and E' respectively) through being at a lower temperature (X) than the air, one mechanism can be traced by means of the discovery that vapour condenses when cooled; for the glass or metal cools the air which condenses and they thereupon become bedewed.

Clearly (β), (γ), and (δ) depend in general upon (ε). Unless we see reason to suppose that the mechanism can be traced, it is more probable than not that X is independent of E.

What exactly determines us to decide in favour of independence or of plural connexion in any given instance? Previous experience or intuition may suggest the likelihood of one or other of these. Whichever is accepted, it is entertained tentatively, and the possibility of subsequent revision is allowed for. There is in this nothing illogical, *so long as all inferences contain a reference to probability;* for, though it may be supposed, say, that X is probably independent of E, this probability statement is not invalidated by the subsequent discovery that X is more probably connected with E.

IV. CRITERION OF COUNTERACTING CAUSES

The criterion is as follows: *In a given situation, if a factor, E, is sometimes found with a factor, X, and if, when E does not occur, X does not occur or is replaced by some other factor; yet when X occurs E does not always occur; then, provided that there is some combination of an A and a B common to each form of the situation, it is probable that X is causally connected with E but that there exists a change in a factor that is not known to be present, K, which acts as a counteracting condition.*

This may be symbolised thus:

(i) $X(K)A B \xi \| E$ (ii) $X'(K)A B \xi [\bar{E}$ and (iii) $X(K)A B \xi \| \bar{E}$

     $X(K)A'B \xi \| E$ $X'(K)A'B \xi \| \bar{E}$ $X(K)A'B \xi \| \bar{E}$

     $X(K)A B' \xi \| E$ $X'(K)A B' \xi \| \bar{E}$ $X(K)A B' \xi \| \bar{E}$

     $X(K)A'B' \xi \| E,$ $X'(K)A'B' \xi \| \bar{E},$ $X(K)A'B' \xi \| \bar{E};$

therefore probably K exists and is not constant, such that both $X \longrightarrow E$ (or $\| E$) and $K \longrightarrow \bar{X}$ (or $\| \bar{X}$).

To clinch the matter requires that we examine the factors afresh, locating K, and showing after further experiment or observation that K is probably a causal condition by Criterion II.

As an illustration, there is the strongly based connexion between fresh vegetables (X) and health (E), unfresh vegetables (X') and scurvy ($\bar{E}$), but we might find scurvy developing in connexion with fresh vegetables, as in (iii) in the above schema. This would be due to excessive cooking or to the presence of sodium bicarbonate. Again, when the English priest, Needham, repeated Pasteur's experiments on spontaneous generation, he found that boiled liquid when kept in a stoppered bottle in the presence of heated air developed organisms, contrary to Pasteur; but instead of a glass stopper (K) for the bottle he used a cork (K varied) which was not wholly airtight. Similarly with the discovery of argon: atmospheric nitrogen was a half per cent. denser than chemically prepared nitrogen, and this disparity was found to be due to the presence of the much denser gas, argon, in atmospheric nitrogen.

With this last example it might be urged that the counteracting cause was not an obtruding factor, K, but a complexity within X—for the atmospheric so-called nitrogen was found to be a mixture of argon and pure nitrogen. That is true; but there is no important difference between finding the disturbance outside X or finding it inside, for on theoretical grounds we can always take it out of X and treat it as a K and on practical grounds the difference makes no significant difference to methodology. This last point is clear from the history of the discovery of argon. At one stage the false hypothesis was put forward that chemically prepared nitrogen was less dense because of dissociation of its atoms. Then the interference would have been due not to complexity in X but to change in a factor supposed to be constant. Evidently it was impossible to tell which form of interference was at work before the nature of the interference was known. It is impossible, therefore, to have separate criteria or schemata relevant to any intermediate stage of the discovery, and at the end it is unnecessary to have them.*

V. CRITERIA OF CO-VARIATION.

The general criterion is as follows: *In a given situation, if variation of a factor, X, is accompanied by some variation of a factor, E, then X is causally connected with E.*

This criterion has two forms, which logicians have not brought together under one species. Importance attaches chiefly to these forms and not to the general statement.†

CRITERION OF FUNCTIONAL DEPENDENCE: *In a given situation, if variation of X is accompanied by some variation of E, such that the series of corresponding values (X, E) fit a smooth curve within the limits of experimental error, then it is probable that E is a simple function of X*, i.e. $E = f(X)$.

This may be illustrated by Charles's law that changes in the volume of a fixed mass of gas at constant pressure are proportional to changes in temperature.

In practice it is taken that for interpolated values, *i.e.* within but not outside the range of experimentation, $E = f(X)$ is certainly and not merely probably a good approximation. In other words the lack of certainty attaches not to the existence of the law $E = f(X)$ but to its being absolutely exact. Thus nothing can upset the gas laws connecting pressure, volume, and temperature, but they are now to be regarded as good approximations—and they might come to be regarded as slightly less good approximations.

It might also happen that a new circumstantial limitation had to be imposed, thus narrowing the sphere of application of the law. For example, the early concept of psychical trauma derived from a study of hysteria was found not to be applicable to all mental illness.

X and E may be parallel effects of an anterior cause, or not, but

---

* The present criterion is not unlike Mill's Method of Residues; and something resembling it was given by Johnson under the heading of Figure of Composition. Johnson also gave a Figure of Resolution, the difference between them being that in the one there existed a K and in the other X was complex. He himself used the example of argon to illustrate Resolution (Johnson, *op. cit.*, p. 239), though its history shows that it might have illustrated either Figure. No matter which way one chooses to put the matter, there is a composition of causes and a resolution of factors previously not analysed.

† This criterion was given by Mill (Concomitant Variations), Johnson (Figure of Difference), and Stebbing (Special Principle No. IV).

in either event, X is necessary and sufficient to determine E (in the mathematical sense of "determine" according to which when the value of X is known that of E can be calculated), given the conditions in which the corresponding values of X and E are found.

It may be remarked that the present criterion covers periodic functions, such that, if X is increased by a certain fixed period, the same value of E recurs. It might be thought that, when sometimes E has the same value for different values of X, there was an interference factor at work. Such an inference, however, would be reasonable only if very few pairs of values of X and E were adduced, but would be impossible if sufficient pairs of values were forthcoming to give a curve. With periodicity, all that has to be done is to draw a graph in the usual way and the periodicity will be at once evident; no special steps have to be taken.

CRITERION OF CORRELATION AND INTERFERENCE: *In a given situation, if* (i) *variation of X is accompanied by some variation of E, where the series of corresponding values* (X, E) *do* not *fit a smooth curve within the limits of experimental error, but if* (ii) *it does fall within an approximately straight band, and if* (iii) *the value of r, given by* $r = \Sigma xe / N\sigma_x\sigma_y$ (*where these symbols have their obvious statistical meanings*), *is greater than at least twice the 'standard error', then r is 'significant', i.e. there exists a correlation between X and E* (*or it is probable that X and E are causally connected*), *and it is probable that there exists an interference factor which prevents the values of X and E from lying on a smooth curve.*

This is not the only criterion of statistical significance; but it is the simplest, and suffices for present purposes.

The criterion may be illustrated typically by the correlation between the tallness and weight of men.

Remarks upon the Foregoing Criteria

(i) It cannot be too strongly stressed that these criteria are used at a stage where scientific knowledge is rudimentary. Hence it cannot be held against them that the various factors involved are not known to be simple or analysed into their ultimate components (if any). The factors are avowedly likely to be capable of further analysis; and they are treated as units relatively to our knowledge at the time or to our expectation of what sort of entity is likely to occur in various circumstances without the need for decomposition. The latter point may be illustrated thus: when a compass is placed near a wire carrying a current, we do not split up the factor consisting of the wire with current into heavy, copper, polished, and so on—possible variation of this kind is present but judged without experimenting to be irrelevant.

(ii) It is no aspersion on science to express results in terms of plurality of cause and effect. Plurality is simply a fact of experience and must be included in a factual survey of scientific procedure. There is no suggestion above that plurality is ultimate— nor that it is not ultimate. This question is simply not relevant to forms of scientific inference.

(iii) It is traditional to deny any essential difference between observation and experiment. This is for the most part true, but slight exception to it was found. Thus, as a result of experiment we can infer that X is probably a causal factor producing E; but as a result of comparative observations we can infer only that X and E are causally connected, *i.e.* they might be concomitant effects of an anterior cause. Again, with all experiment, the negative instance can be investigated; while with some observation this is not so.

(iv) A judgment based seemingly on one criterion may well owe some of its force to other criteria—in other words, strength of inference may be due to coherence of conclusions derived from different criteria. Thus probable independence (Criteria I) is strengthened by our seeing no reason to suppose there is plurality (Criteria III) or counteracting cause (Criteria IV). This coherence or mutual dependence of inferences does not lead to circular reasoning: for, though it might seem that, if irrelevance depended upon denial of plural connexion and plural connexion depended upon denial of irrelevance, there was a circle; yet each inference is one of probability, it can have a degree of probability independent of the other, and this probability can be altered by the probability of the other. Thus Criteria I above will tell us there is a certain probability of independence; if we find that Criteria III and IV are satisfied, the probability of independence is diminished and *vice versa*.

(v) Mill has been criticised for including under the heading of "inductive methods" the Method of Residues, which is usually interpreted as deductive. I have included the Criterion of Counteracting Causes (IV) which is deductive. But I have aimed not merely at classifying inductive criteria but at classifying criteria of *any* kind relevant to the determination of causation; and there is no reason why all criteria of causation should be inductive.

(vi) It should not be supposed that any one of these criteria is *superior* to any other in the sense that it would be the most desirable one to apply. The criteria here offered relate to different scientific situations; each relates to its own type of situation and to no other. Further they relate to different *stages* of scientific procedure. Nonetheless, the highest probability attaches to Criteria I, Criterion II (3), and Criterion V (1). Criterion II (2) can attain a high probability, after a great deal of hard work has been put in on experiments.

(vii) According to Stebbing[1] and others, the nature of a cause gives us two principles: (*a*) "Nothing is the cause of an effect which is absent when the effect occurs"; and (*b*) "Nothing is the cause of a given effect which is present when the effect fails to occur". Put in plainer and corrected language, these should run: (*a*) "Nothing is a *necessary* cause of an event that occurs in its absence"; and (*b*) "Nothing is a *sufficient* cause of an event in whose absence it occurs" (where the relatives "that" and "whose" qualify the noun immediately preceding, and "it" and "its" refer to the subject of the sentence). These principles are obviously untrue; for they are falsified by plurality relations, and (*b*) is falsified by the possibility of counteracting causes.

Appendix to Chapter XI

Remarks upon Mill, Johnson, and Stebbing.

The following comments assume the point of view of the present treatment.

The utility of Mill's Methods is very small. Only three of the five can be used as they stand, and of these three two are seldom required: that of Agreement needs to be altered and broken up into Criteria of Independence and the Criterion of Probable Connexion (1); the Joint Method contains a mistake (perhaps it was a slip?) that prevents it from becoming the Criterion of Probable Connexion (2); of the rest, the Method of Residues becomes the Criterion of Counteracting Causes, which is hardly basic; the Method of Difference is an unimportant particular case of the criterion of Probable Connexion (2); and that of Concomitant Variations alone can be taken over more or less as it stands, though it suffers from being expressed in too general a way.

[1] Stebbing, *Op. cit.*, p. 319.

Though far from adequate as a catalogue of scientific principles of inference, Mill's Methods, if one is prepared to be sufficiently vague, give a picture of that inference. Granted such vagueness, one can understand that some scientists have thought they were using the Methods—though, in fact, there was only a small amount of truth in this.

Mill had a different kind of purpose from that of the present elaboration: he hoped to find ways of making some scientific inference certain. Some such intention, perhaps, underlay Johnson's work on Demonstrative Induction. Since this is foreign to the scientific outlook and irrelevant to it, there is no need to consider Mill or Johnson further from this angle. But Johnson's Four Figures do at first sight seem to give us principles of scientific inference, provided their apparently demonstrative character is removed. This is, however, largely delusive. The Principles of his Figures have been distilled very neatly by Mace, and the matter is most easily elucidated by reference to them.[1] The Principle of the Figure of Difference could be taken to be equivalent to the Criteria of Co-Variation (V), that of Agreement to those of Independence (I), and those of Composition and Resolution could be taken to be forms, with no important difference between them, of the Criterion of Counteracting Causes (IV). Hence, as with Mill, there is 'something in it'—perhaps more in his version than in Mill's. But the same criticism as that given of Mill's Method of Concomitant Variations applies to Johnson's Principle of the Figure of Difference—it is expressed in too general terms; those of Agreement and (between them) of Composition and Resolution are all right so far as they go, but they do not go very far; there is the serious omission of criteria of causal laws.

The most general feature of Johnson's Figures, which makes them unacceptable, is that they are given in terms of quantitative variation of factors. Now in the first place this is not true of scientific procedure in the field of natural and causal law, which introduces quantitative variation only in Criteria V; it is impossible to interpret other forms of scientific inference quantitatively—where *e.g.* a glass stopper is replaced by a cork. In the second place, having given them a quantitative form, Johnson seems to have been content with a contrast of a very small number of instances. This would be acceptable if the entities varied were objects and not degrees in which some property occurred; but, with his Figures of Composition and Resolution which aim to show that interference is at work, the result could follow on the quantitative plane only by collecting more instances and showing by statistical methods that a significant correlation existed between the two sets of properties involved. No doubt nowadays we can obtain significant correlations from samples containing very few members

[1] C. A. Mace, *The Principles of Logic*, London, 1933, pp. 331-39.

indeed; but this is rare, and indeed was not known when Johnson wrote. This defect places Johnson's Figures in a worse light than Mill's Methods.

Stebbing's four Principles are in a much better position. Her first (Irrelevance), second (Probable Connexion), and fourth (Co-Variation) from the present point of view seem to be correct; she fails here only in not giving a sufficient number of principles to cover the variety of scientific inference. Her third one (Difference) would be right if it did not contain the unfortunate mistake of supposing an experimenter could withdraw or restore an *effect*. Thus, according to the present standpoint, her treatment is right, apart from considerable omissions.

All three logicians fell short by failing to deal with questions of plurality.

CHAPTER XII

THE NATURE AND STRENGTH OF GENERALISATION, ANALOGY, AND INDUCTION

RESULTS that fit into the patterns given in the previous chapter may be of two types. The first consists of what is called "empirical generalisations" or simply "generalisations". When well tested they are often called "natural laws" or "causal laws". They are qualitative and refer to objects or to properties without regard to degree. The second type consists of what Mace calls "universalisations".* These are quantitative and refer to degrees of a property of an object. For most purposes in metascience there is no need to treat them separately, and "generalisation" may, in spite of ambiguity, be used to cover both.

In this Part, one feature of the traditional approach is retained for convenience. Generalisations or laws will be regarded as conclusions obtained from observational premisses, even though such 'conclusions' are in fact hypotheses in the light of which the premisses are selected.

In both generalisation and universalisation, the premisses express the material of a *finite* number of observations while the conclusion is a *universal* statement, standing for an *infinite* number of possible observations. It is therefore characteristic of this stage of scientific procedure to use a form of inference from *some* to *all*— from all *examined* instances of a situation to *all* instances *examined* and *unexamined*. No matter what criterion is used for determining a natural law, we are concerned broadly speaking with generalisation arrived at by this sort of inference. Such inference is called "inductive".

To make the most economical use of technical terms, induction may be taken to cover five different forms of inference: (i) generalisation from some to all of a species; (ii) generalisation from some species of a genus to all species of that genus; (iii) statistical generalisation from an observed proportion of examined cases to the same proportion of the unexamined; (iv) by analogy from one

---

* C. A. Mace, *The Principles of Logic*, London, 1933, pp. 261, 319 ff. The term was Johnson's but was not used by him in this sense—*Id.*, p. 342 n.

particular to another particular, which may be called "simple analogy"; and (v) by analogy from more than one particular to another single particular, which may be called "compound analogy". Though some writers have restricted "induction" to arguments with universal conclusions, it is here being made to cover those with particular conclusions, namely arguments by analogy. The latter usually refer to (iv) alone, where there is but one premiss; but it is easy to see from logic books that they sometimes, perhaps unwittingly, refer also to (v), where there is more than one premiss; and it seems desirable to distinguish them as simple arguments by analogy and compound arguments by analogy. The nature of these forms of inference must now be described and distinguished.

The first form of generalisation (i) is explained at once by an illustration: we may find that all examined lengths of brass expand when heated, and infer that *all brass* has this property. To illustrate (ii): we may find that all examined pieces of brass, iron, and copper expand when heated and infer that *all metals* have this property.* Here the examined metals may be regarded as different species of the genus metal. Clearly the second cannot hold good unless the first does, for the premisses about brass, iron, and copper are severally conclusions of the first type; but the form of the inference is the same with both—from some to all. It is also possible to distinguish between the first and the following: we may find that a piece of brass expands when heated *on several occasions* and infer that it will expand *on all occasions*. The first form deals with numerically different pieces *at different places in space* and the second with one and the same piece *on different occasions in time*— again the inference takes the same form. Accordingly there is no need to treat separately the various forms that induction may have—though we should, perhaps, bear in mind that scientists trust an induction about one thing at different times more firmly than an induction about several things at one time. (iii) is of special importance—a fact traditionally overlooked by students of inductive logic. Instead of saying that all the premisses of a generalisation agree about a certain property, the statistical argument merely makes this assertion about a certain proportion of them. Thus we may observe that $n\%$ of a certain lot of eggs are bad, and predict that $n\%$ of all eggs are bad. Here the argument is not precisely from some to all—it is not from some eggs to all

* This generalisation is in fact false, unless restricted to metals that are elements.

eggs, though it is from some lots to all lots—but it certainly is from examined to unexamined.

Apart from the statistical argument, a generalisation has several premisses and a universal conclusion. By contrast a simple argument by analogy (iv) has but one premiss and a particular conclusion. A typical example would be: "this piece of brass expands when heated, therefore that piece will". As regards (v), however, where we are given several premisses, we may at times not wish to establish a generalisation but be content to infer from a number of examined instances having a certain property that the *next instance to be examined* will also have that property— drawing a particular instead of a universal conclusion, a respect in which the argument resembles (iv). Since the only difference between this and (iv) is that there are here more than one premiss, and since the argument is very similar, it is designated "a compound argument by analogy". Thus, if we observe that all examined pieces of brass expand when heated, we infer that the next piece to be inspected will expand also. But, again, we argue from the examined to the unexamined; and, while it might be easier to establish the likelihood of the particular conclusion than that of the general one, no sharp distinction between the two forms of inference need be made.

From the traditional point of view universalisation should also be regarded as inductive. In the first place universalisation implies a prior generalisation; for degrees of expansion of brass, for instance, could not be connected with degrees of heat unless the generalisation were true that all brass expands when heated. In the second place universalisation is an argument from some to all: the relation that holds of some points on a graph is asserted to hold of all points on it. This is interpolation and extrapolation, which consist essentially in going beyond the data. Otherwise expressed, the argument is from some degrees of a property to all degrees of that property. After all, universalisation is no more than generalisation about degrees of a whole instead of about wholes.

Generalisation may, then, be regarded as argument from particular to general; analogy as argument from particular to particular; and induction simply as argument from particulars. Induction may be broadly characterised as an inference from the examined to the unexamined.

From the nature of the arguments it is time to turn to what determines their relative strength.

Compound argument by analogy rests upon simple argument by analogy: there is no difference of principle, but one contains the other; the one has several premisses, the other a single premiss. That is to say, a compound argument is made of a conjunction of several simple ones. For example, the compound argument that, because brass, iron, and copper expand when heated, therefore zinc does so, is a compound of the simple arguments that because brass expands when heated therefore zinc does so, that because iron expands therefore zinc does, and that because copper expands therefore zinc does.

Simple analogy is held to be often a weak mode of inference; it often is; but the strength of compound analogy is no more than the cumulative strength of the arguments by simple analogy it contains; hence, if a compound argument is to be strong, its conjoined simple arguments must severally contain some strength even if this is not very much; and so long as a simple analogy has some strength this can be increased by parallel arguments to form a reasonable compound analogy.

What similar sort of relation connects generalisation and analogy? Compound analogy asserts that because these pieces of brass expand when heated the next piece to be examined will do the same; generalisation from the same premisses asserts that all pieces to be examined will do this. We may therefore break up the generalisation into an infinite number of compound analogies of the same form. We may also break it up differently: we may say it consists of one compound analogy (that because all examined pieces expand therefore the next piece will) *i.e.* of an infinite number of simple analogies all of the same form. Thus generalisation rests upon analogy, compound and simple, and therefore ultimately upon simple.* Hence a generalisation with a general conclusion will not have strength unless an inference upon the same premisses that yields a particular conclusion has strength, *i.e.*, compound analogy, and, since this rests upon argument by simple analogy, all generalisation (apart from statistical) does so.

* It might be held that compound analogy was a particular case of generalisation, because it follows from generalisation as an immediate inference. The disadvantage of thinking of the relation in this way is that the degree of credibility attaching to the compound analogy would be no more than that attaching to the generalisation, whereas in general a compound analogy has a higher degree of credibility than a corresponding generalisation from which it could be deduced.

Universalisation, since it presupposes generalisation from the present point of view, therefore also presupposes simple analogy. Universalisation is often felt to be stronger, however, perhaps because it yields quantitative laws. This is often true in fact, but there is no reason to think it true in principle. So far as strong results depend upon the comparison of large numbers of instances or large numbers of premises, it is much easier to obtain these when operating in accordance with universalisation than generalisation once universalisation is a possibility at all. Hence there is no reason to look for anything stronger than analogy underlying it. What, then, is to be said about statistical generalisation? Suppose we have observed that $n\%$ of a certain range of eggs are bad, the generalisation that $n\%$ of all ranges are bad may be divided up into an infinite number of generalisations each of the form that $n\%$ of the next range to be tested are bad (we are not here concerned with the conditions that make a range a fair sample). Each such generalisation, then, comes to this, that an assertion about an observed range will hold of another range unobserved, an argument we might distinguish as statistical analogy. There seems no possibility of showing that statistical analogy depends fundamentally upon simple analogy.

Thus, within the traditional framework of induction, statistical considerations apart, argument by simple analogy is fundamental; whether some such arguments are bad or whether all such argument is of doubtful validity, it is the form of inference upon which induction rests.

To elucidate the factors that in practice determine whether an inductive argument is regarded as strong or weak, consider a compound argument by analogy.

The subjects of all the premises and the subject of the conclusion are alike in some respects. Keynes, to whom the approach of the present discussion is entirely due, has called the set of these respects the "positive analogy".[1] Similarly the subjects of all the premises—with the subject of the conclusion omitted—differ in certain respects. Keynes has called these respects the "negative analogy". Clearly, these must not be confused with argument by analogy. All such argument has a positive analogy so far as the subjects of the premises and conclusion are alike, and a negative analogy so far as the subjects of the premises differ. But a simple

[1] J. M. Keynes, *A Treatise on Probability*, London, 1921, p. 223.

argument by analogy has no negative analogy, for the existence of which two premisses at least are required. Further, it must be borne in mind that we may not know all the respects of likeness and unlikeness, and therefore must distinguish between the *known positive analogy* and the *total positive analogy*—and, of course, between the *known negative analogy* and the *total negative analogy*. Consider, for example, the following inference: This piece of brass expands when heated, this piece of iron does so, and so does this piece of copper, therefore this piece of zinc will do so. The known positive analogy includes being metal and being denser than water; the known negative analogy includes being of different density, and being of different colour; but obviously the total analogies, positive and negative, are much wider.

Keynes put his terminology to important use; it bears directly upon the strength of generalisations (not including universalisations) and arguments by analogy. Nearly all, and perhaps all, criteria for determining generalisations involve elimination of irrelevant factors or the rejection of supposed causes. The variation of such factors in the premisses, which reveals them as irrelevant, amounts to *increasing the known negative analogy*. It is obvious that the strength of a generalisation depends upon the degree to which these factors have been varied; hence its strength depends upon the amount of the known negative analogy. This statement does not, of course, provide new knowledge; it only gives old information in a new terminology—but a fruitful one. It may be added that these remarks apply to compound but not to simple argument by analogy. Now it is also true that to increase the positive analogy strengthens a generalisation. Supposing, for example, we have the premisses that iron, copper, and brass conduct electricity, consider inferring that zinc does so and that wood does so. The known positive analogy between the given metals and zinc is greater than that between them and wood. To take a crudely extreme example, if we know that cotton, linen, and silk shrink in hot water, what reliance will we place on the conclusion that stone shrinks? There is hardly any positive analogy, and we will not trust the inference. These remarks apply also to all argument by analogy, including simple. No reason is here offered to explain why the greater known positive analogy and the greater known negative analogy should lead to the stronger conclusion; but there is no doubt that any scientist would reason in this way. Here the new terminology expresses very well what has been intuitively recognised before but not made so explicit.

These conditions of strength can be intuitively apprehended, but they can be rendered clearer by some further analysis which at the same time brings to light the third factor that, according to Keynes, bears on strength.

Let us contrast four arguments, which may be called (A), (B), (C), (D) :—

(A)   (i) All observed mosquitoes cause malaria,
   therefore   (*a*) all mosquitoes cause malaria.   (s)

(B)   (ii) All observed anopheles mosquitoes cause malaria,
   therefore   (*b*) all anopheles mosquitoes cause malaria.   (s^+)

(C)   (iii) All observed mosquitoes cause disease,
   therefore   (*c*) all mosquitoes cause disease.   (s^+)

(D)   (iv) All observed anopheles mosquitoes cause disease,
   therefore   (*d*) all anopheles mosquitoes cause disease.   (s^{++})

We are not here concerned with the loose use of "cause"; nor with the truth or falsity of the statements so far as medical knowledge goes. All would be acknowledged to be fairly strong generalisations even if they should prove to be in fact false—hence the s written after them. Can we now determine their relative strength? If (B) is contrasted with (A) it is intuitively clear that (B) is the stronger—it is more likely that a specific kind of mosquito should have a certain effect than that all mosquitoes should have it— hence (B) is given the mark (s^+). Likewise it is clear that (C) is stronger than (A)—it is more likely that mosquitoes should cause some disease than that they should cause a specific form of complaint—hence (C) also is (s^+). There is nothing to choose between (B) and (C)—some arguments of the type (B) would be stronger than some of the type (C) but some would be weaker. Now (D) is stronger than (C) for one reason—the same reason that makes (B) stronger than (A)—and stronger than (B) for another reason—the same reason that makes (C) stronger than (A) —hence the mark (s^{++}).

From all this it is obvious that the more specific the subject, the stronger the argument; but this is only another way of saying that the stronger argument has the greater positive analogy. This mode of presentation throws no new light on negative analogy.

But a third factor emerges, which may be called the *scope of the predicate*.* Clearly the less specific the predicate, the stronger the argument, that is to say, the stronger argument has the predicate of wider scope.†

The question must now be raised whether there is any other factor, apart from positive and negative analogy and scope of predicate, that determines strength. It is common to find the notion that in a good argument there must be an inner or reasonable or important connexion between the subject group of properties and the predicate group.[1] From this point of view the following would be strong: The earth, which describes an elliptic orbit round the sun and which rotates on its axis, has its axis pointing towards the Northern Star; therefore Mars, which also has an elliptic orbit and rotates, has its axis pointing in the same direction. This (though false) would be strong because there could well be a connexion between the known positive analogy and the inferred property. The following, on the other hand, would be weak and some might even be inclined to hold it was not a valid analogy at all: The earth, which describes an ellipse round the sun and which rotates on its axis, has life; therefore Mars, which describes an ellipse and rotates, has life. This would be weak because there is no important known connexion (the argument would run) between the dynamic properties of the positive analogy and the conditions of life. Two comments are called for. (i) All such argument is probable, not certain; that is to say, the conclusion is a conclusion in relation to a premiss and has no strength in itself. It is proper, therefore, to distinguish arguments such as those just given as more probable or less probable, but not as reasonable analogues and pseudo analogues. To improve an argument one may increase the positive analogy or add more pre-

* *Id.*, pp. 220, 252. Keynes's exposition is obscured by poor terminology. There is no space to discuss this; I have simply introduced a different terminology by which his point can, I think, be clearly expressed in one sentence.

† One might be held up for a moment by the feeling that there is something strange in requiring the subject to be as specific as possible and the predicate to be as unspecific as possible, for, after all, if the group of properties constituting a mosquito is accompanied by the group constituting malaria, then the malaria group is accompanied by the mosquito group, so that the old predicate would be the new subject and would therefore have to change from being unspecific to specific. But this would be to overlook the order in which the arguments have their properties arranged: the arguments show that we are interested in finding out whether the mosquito group specifies the malaria group and not whether the malaria group specifies the mosquito group. Otherwise expressed, the arguments imply the expectation that the mosquito group will be found among the disease-producing group and not *vice versa*.

[1] L. S. Stebbing, *A Modern Introduction to Logic*, London, 1933, pp. 252–3.

misses. Suppose we either found a whole host of properties characterising both the earth and Mars or else found that several other planets had the same positive analogy and also had life, then the argument for life on Mars would have to be taken seriously. (ii) It is true that we intuitively attach more strength when there is an 'important' connexion as described than when there is not. This means we have an intuition of what constitutes being important. Now this can only be an intuitive deduction based upon past experience or an intuitive induction similarly based. That is to say, we assume a general principle about important connexions and use it deductively, or we adduce the result of a previous induction to the effect that all observed instances of good argument by analogy have been based upon discovered inner connexions and therefore all such instances will have the same basis. In either event, there is an infusion into the arguments about Mars of deduction based on previous knowledge. There is no objection, of course, to using previous knowledge; on the contrary it must be used. But if we are bringing it into an argument, then it becomes a premiss of that argument and should be explicitly stated. We should then be clear that we were really contrasting the two arguments about Mars in relation to further knowledge, which would be very likely to make one of them stronger than the other. *Per contra*, once previous knowledge is eliminated from the contrast, the two arguments stand on much the same level and the one about life becomes no more foolish than the other one. In short, the notion that strength of argument can depend upon inner or important connexions between subject and predicate is unjustified; it arises because we often have an intuitive apprehension of further relevant evidence or because we unwittingly introduce previous knowledge. The notion, therefore, does not provide a further criterion of strength for an inductive argument.

Now comes the interesting question of how far it strengthens an induction simply to increase the number of premisses. There used to be a tradition that induction by simple enumeration—by counting heads—was an important procedure. And there was a counter tradition that mere numbers proved nothing. Keynes's view was different: it was a modification of the latter tradition.

He held that the mere multiplication of premisses will be useless if they are exactly like existing premisses. But he also pointed out that such multiplication can *indirectly* strengthen an argument;

for mere multiplication, without the exercise of any control over the selection, is likely to introduce premises that are different in some respects from the existing ones. That is to say, the chances are that the negative analogy will be increased and thus the argument made more sure.[1] In short, it is not the mere multiplication of premises that helps, but the indirect effect this *may* have upon the negative analogy. Hence, to strengthen an argument, it is permissible to augment the number of premises blindly with this hope in mind.

The Keynesian view is, then, that the strength of an inductive argument depends upon the positive analogy, the negative analogy, and the scope of the predicate in the first place, but also, derivatively, upon the number of premises. It is now easy to see how to set about strengthening a generalisation: we may increase the positive or negative analogy, we may widen the scope of the predicate, and we may add to the number of the premises. For purposes of clarity there is one thing that needs to be stressed. This kind of phrasing may suggest that some alteration is carried out upon the elements of the argument, the terms, premises, or conclusion. But what it is essential to bear in mind is that questions of strength always involve a contrast between *different* arguments—if you like, the question is one of relative strength. Hence, what in fact takes place is that a given argument is *replaced* by another one in which the positive or negative analogy is increased, the scope of the predicate is widened, or the number of premises is greater: by means of these operations a new argument is built, the two are compared, the new one is considered the stronger, and it replaces the old one.

The method of adding to the number of the premises is a sign of weakness: it will be used only when it is difficult to increase the positive or negative analogy; and it is used simply in the expectation of increasing the negative analogy though it can fail to have this effect—and we cannot know whether it is succeeding or failing. Little importance is attached to the other factor—widening the scope of the predicate—for this would give us greater strength at the cost of losing information and precision.

In short, we try to increase our knowledge of the premises we have, and failing this we try to add new premises.

---

[1] Keynes, *Op. cit.*, pp. 219, 233.

CHAPTER XIII

INDUCTION BY REPETITION

ACCORDING to the interpretation of Keynes given in the previous chapter, the factors bearing on the strength of an induction are the positive and negative analogies and the scope of the predicate; to strengthen an argument the scientist tries to increase his knowlege of his premisses (or, more precisely, to obtain a new argument with similar but better premisses), thus increasing the positive and negative analogies, and, failing that, he has recourse in practice to repetition of his observations or experiments. In this, negative analogy is the basic factor. Against Keynes, however, it has been argued by Nicod* that the ultimate factor making induction possible is not negative analogy but repetition—repetition, moreover, that does not presuppose negative analogy (as it does in Keynes).

Nicod preferred to speak in terms of "elimination"; by this he meant a process by which some factors of a group that might be the cause of an occurrence E are found by experience to be irrelevant, so that the remaining factor or factors must be the cause of

---

* Jean Nicod, *The Logical Problem of Induction*, published in the English translation as part of *Foundations of Geometry and Induction*, London, 1930.

Nicod's ideas on induction are of some interest, though they must have seemed more important a quarter of a century ago than they do now. It is curious that his work in this field seems to have been neglected in Britain, where more than in most countries interest in induction has been traditional. Braithwaite wrote a critical notice, which contains important criticism, of the French edition of 1924 (R. B. Braithwaite, *"La problème logique de l'induction*. By Jean Nicod", *Mind*, N.S. Vol. XXXIV, No. 136, London, 1925, pp. 483–91); but since then, even though Nicod's work appeared in English in 1930, there has been no detailed treatment of his views, so far as I know, in subsequent books or papers in the English language. Textbooks when they refer to him usually merely mention a point or two. Eaton's textbook, which is American, is an exception; it gives a helpful account of some of Nicod's points but not all the important ones are mentioned, and no critical analysis is offered (R. M. Eaton, *General Logic*, New York, 1931, pp. 543–50, 569–70).

His work is written in lucid language and he liked simplicity of proof, but something in his arrangement of material or in his failure to stress significant points that seem at first to be of minor importance or in his lack of analysis in some places makes it difficult to extract his thesis from his blend of exposition and argument. Moreover, it comes as a surprise to find such clear writing expressing such obscure argument. Whether his conclusions are correct or not, most of his arguments seem to be faulty or confused, and some of them seem to be so thin as to make one wonder how they ever came to be offered as proofs—especially by a man of Nicod's calibre. Perhaps the reason lies in his bad state of health and the approach of death at the age of thirty.

E. Plainly 'elimination' is equivalent to 'increasing the negative analogy', so that the residual positive analogy must be the cause.

Elimination might be held not to be the ultimate basis of induction for the following reasons: (i) induction by elimination contradicts an important theorem in the mathematical calculus of probability, due to Bayes, according to which the probability of a generalisation is increased by repetition of instances, (ii) there would be no way of increasing the probability of a generalisation, such as that X causes E, to the extent of approximating to certainty, *i.e.* there would be no way of making a generalisation, as Nicod misleadingly puts it, *infinitely probable*; and (iii) induction by elimination either requires the support of a principle of causation asserting that events of one type are rigidly connected with events of another type by a causal relation, or else requires the support of induction by repetition.

Moreover Nicod uses the theorem referred to in order to show that repetition of instances is the ultimate basis of induction.

(i) Bayes's theorem asserts that, if a generalisation, that X causes E, has *some* initial probability, *i.e.*, probability in relation to the evidence for the generalisation, and if a new instance of E occurs (without its being certain on purely logical grounds that therefore an instance of X must occur), then if an instance of X is actually found the probability of the generalisation is increased. Now, if elimination is the basis of induction, then any new instance of the generalisation that merely repeated an old instance would eliminate nothing and could therefore add in no way to the probability of the generalisation; but this would contradict the theorem.

This would establish Nicod's point completely were it not for the condition to which the theorem is subject—that the generalisation should have some initial probability. This condition cannot be satisfied. This approach to the problem will be discussed in more detail in a later chapter.

In the absence of some justification for the condition required by the theorem, induction by elimination cannot be undermined nor induction by repetition justified by Bayes's theorem.

(ii) The objection that induction by elimination cannot make a generalisation infinitely probable is valid; but elimination is in this respect no worse off than other procedures. Nicod considers whether by means of induction by repetition the probability can be greatly increased. But the only known way of making a generalisation almost certain is by a development of the preceding theorem, and it is inapplicable. Apart from this, elimination might be the true basis of induction, but require the aid of some other procedure in order to give a high probability to a generalisation. Thus the objection carries no weight.

(iii) To consider whether induction by elimination presupposes a principle of causation, we may state the latter as follows. To say that E is caused is to say (a) that E has a sufficient condition, and (b) that other occurrences like E have sufficient conditions. We need not suppose that all the sufficient conditions are alike—there might be plurality of causes. Nor is it necessary that this principle of causation should be certain; less strain is imposed on induction by elimination if we require the principle to be probable only (as explained below in the appendix to Chapter XXII).

Why, then, may elimination presuppose the principle of causation? The process may eliminate all factors other than X from the list of possible causes of E; the position is thus one of 'perfect analogy'. Is the result, then, that X is the cause of E? No, says Nicod, all we may infer is that X *may* cause E.[1] What he meant may be expressed as follows. There are three and only three mutually exclusive possibilities concerning the occurrence of E: it may be due to a unique type of cause; it may arise from independent alternative causes, *i.e.*, there may be plurality of causes; or it may be uncaused or spontaneously generated. This last cannot be ruled out of court without a hearing, for after all it enters into a widespread interpretation of certain phenomena in quantum physics, and it might be held to apply to the occurrence of mutations in genetics. Elimination removes the irrelevant; but the possibility of spontaneous generation remains, for we could not be sure that X should not also have been eliminated as irrelevant. Clearly, therefore, something is needed to counter spontaneous generation. Now one way of countering this is to postulate a principle of causation, or rather the probability of one. Since this is not a happy choice on account of the difficulty, as will be seen in the next chapter, of finding grounds for such a principle, what alternative remains? After irrelevant factors have been eliminated, leaving only X as a candidate for the position of causing E, the only way of supporting the generalisation that X causes E is to gather repeated instances of E with X. Thus in-

[1] *Id.*, p. 260.

duction by elimination presupposes a principle of causation or induction by repetition.

Should Nicod be right in this contention, we are in no way debarred from using elimination in practice. The day-to-day work of the scientist demands it, and it is a much more powerful practical method than repetition. Nicod would probably not have denied this, but he was concerned with the fundamentals of induction. Again, so far as practice is concerned, the scientist feels little trust in mere repetition without variation—this is to demand, with Keynes, increased negative analogy. But let us not forget that, if a scientist obtains a strange experimental result, he *repeats* it, and he does feel some extra confidence if the same result recurs, though no doubt he will not feel satisfied until he has performed all manner of variations—this is to agree with Nicod that mere repetition is of some value.

How is the issue to be resolved? A clue comes from the last point, that a scientist must sometimes repeat an experiment. Why must he do so? He surely wishes to know that his result was not accidental. We thus realize a point that is seldom if ever mentioned, namely the aim of eliminating incidental factors. Moreover, there is the aim of eliminating the factors of position in space or date in time or both. These aims refute Nicod. Interestingly enough they also refute Keynes's contention that after the elimination of all factors save one there was no point in further incidental repetition; for we can never be certain that we have completely eliminated accidental and spatio-temporal influences.

Though we eliminate incidental and spatio-temporal factors when we repeat, nonetheless the converse is also true—when we eliminate we must at the same time repeat—for, if in the course of elimination we found ourselves without either X or E, we should have eliminated the baby with the bath water. Thus it would seem that the issue of induction by repetition *versus* induction by elimination is an unreal one: elimination and repetition are interwoven or inseparable features of testing.

CHAPTER XIV

THE LAW OF UNIFORMITY OF NATURE

In approaching metascience, there must be a preliminary investigation, which is here called "methodology". This study involves such questions as the practice of varying circumstances one at a time. Metascience then concerns itself with the patterns of inference underlying the method, which consist of the several criteria for determining natural laws. These may be regarded as special principles. In contrast with them is the general principle that may be found underlying them or providing their justification. Chapter XII aimed at showing that those principles are of a single type, which is called "inductive". This was preliminary to investigating any general principles there may be. To these the following chapters are devoted.

Tradition has regarded deductive inference as the ideal pattern; inference that did not conform to it was imperfect. Induction plainly suffered from this stigma; from *some* we make an inference about *all* or about *some other* or *others*; in other words induction *goes beyond the evidence* and thus violates the principles of deductive logic. Induction may be given the appearance of an invalid syllogism:

> Some S have p,
> This is an S;
> _____
> This has p.*

Or it may be represented as an immediate inference committing illicit process:

> Copper, brass, and zinc expand when heated;
> _____
> All metals expand when heated.

The general pattern of inductive inference may be simply expressed by means of symbols. At first sight an argument by analogy appears to be of the form: "S_1 has x; therefore S_2 has x", where x is some property. Thus we argue: "This piece of brass expands when heated; therefore this piece of zinc will", or "Life exists on the earth; therefore it exists on Mars". It is obvious

* Premises are written above the line and conclusion below.

at once, however, that we can argue thus only because zinc *resembles* brass or Mars *resembles* the earth. The argument is therefore of the form: "S_1 which has p is found to have x; therefore S_2 which has p will be found to have x". In general, an argument by analogy is of the form: "S_1 which has p, q, r is found to have x, y; therefore S_2 which has p, q, r will also be found to have x, y". In other words, we find one group of properties p, q, r associated with another group x, y and infer with regard to a new set of p, q, r that a new set of x, y will be associated with them. The only difference between this pattern of analogical inference and that of inductive inference in general is that in the latter we infer with regard to *every* new set of p, q, r that a new set of x, y will be associated with them. This pattern clearly contains illicit process.

The traditional way of dealing with the illicit process was by trying to remove it; and the traditional way of doing this was to add to the inductive premiss a new one consisting of some general principle. To arrive at such a principle we might begin by supposing that nature is *uniform*, for successful inductions seem to presuppose that some uniformities exist. But there is plainly much absence of uniformity also. There is a uniform connexion between rain and a certain season of the year in some places, but not in others. It might, of course, be suggested that there would be uniformity universally if we sought the right uniformities. It is natural, therefore, that the first attempt to make induction 'sound' should produce the *Law of Uniformity of Nature*, to be found in Locke, Berkeley, and Hume, but first made prominent by Mill. It is usual to phrase this in words to the effect that if two instances of a phenomenon agree in some respects they will agree in all other respects. It is desirable, however, to offer a more precise formulation, such as the following:—

In a given situation, if there is a uniform connexion between two occurrences A and B, then an occurrence exactly like A though numerically different from it will be accompanied or followed by an occurrence exactly like B though numerically different from it (and an occurrence exactly like B though numerically different from it will be accompanied or preceded by an occurrence exactly like A though numerically different from it).

This is sometimes supposed to need further support, something to guarantee the uniformity. The support then given is the principle that every event has a cause. The addition of this makes the uniform connexion between A and B consist of the relation of causation. We thus get the *Law of Universal Causation* :—

In a given situation, if one change C initiates another change E, then any change exactly like C though numerically different from it will initiate a change exactly like E though numerically different from it (and any change exactly like E though numerically different from it will be initiated by a change exactly like C though numerically different from it).

Roughly speaking, this asserts "same cause—same effect"; it asserts that every event has a cause, identical sorts of events have identical sorts of causes, and identical sorts of causes have identical sorts of effects.

Some thinkers hold that induction requires the Law of Uniformity; others that of Universal Causation. Some (including Mill and contemporary logical positivists) interpret the latter to mean no more than the former, on the grounds that causation *consists* of uniform connexion. This particular issue need not be discussed just now; it will be convenient for the moment to speak of the Law, referring indifferently to either—though it is not, of course, a law in the sense used elsewhere in this book, but a postulate or a principle.

The only plausible defence of this Law comes from the Aristotelian logician, Joseph,[1] who sought to prove the Law by means of pure reason alone. For him, the Law is not to be established inductively but is to be deduced from the law of identity of traditional formal logic, hitherto expressed as "A is A". From this law it follows, according to Joseph, that if one property of a thing were changed the thing would not be itself. Hence if a thing has certain properties it must always have them so long as it remains itself; and, if an occurrence is found to possess a certain set of properties, all other occurrences exactly like it will have the same set of properties. In particular, a cause will have one and only one effect and will always have the same effect. In this way the Laws of Uniformity of Nature and Universal Causation and the validity of induction follow from pure logic. In spite of Joseph's repetitions it is worth quoting his argument fully because he puts with great cogency what many people feel :—

[1] H. W. B. Joseph, *An Introduction to Logic*, Oxford, 1925, pp. 405–10.

If one thing the same in nature at different times, or two things the same in nature, are to act in situations the same in their nature, they must act on both occasions in the same way. This is not a generalisation from experience: it follows from the sameness of thing and of situation, and whether there exist many things of one kind, we must learn from experience.

If a thing *a* under conditions *c* produces a change *x* in a subject *s* . . . the way in which it acts must be regarded as a partial expression of what it is. It could only act differently, if it *were* different. As long therefore as it is *a*, and stands related under conditions *c* to a subject that is *s*, no other effect than *x* can be produced; and to say that the same thing acting on the same thing under the same conditions may yet produce a different effect, is to say that a thing need not be what it is. But this is in flat conflict with the Law of Identity. A thing, to be at all, must be something, and can only be what it is. To assert a causal connexion between *a* and *x* implies that *a* acts as it does because it is what it is; because, in fact, it is *a*. . . . To deny this is to deny the possibility of reasoning altogether.

He admits it may be rare or impossible to find things that are exactly alike but denies that this has relevance—he assumes there is qualitative sameness:

all that is maintained is, that so far as things are qualitatively the same they have the same attributes, and so far as conditions precisely the same recur, they must, if there is such a relation as cause and effect at all, have the same effect . . . For the causal relation which connects *a* with *x* connects a cause of the *nature a* with an effect of the *nature x*. The connexion is between them *as a* and *x*, and therefore must hold between any *a* and any *x*, if they really are *a* and *x* respectively; in other words, it must be uniform. The denial of this is just the denial of universals.

Before proceeding to more fundamental discussion we may briefly consider traditional arguments or modern arguments of traditional type against the truth of this Law.

(1) Traditional criticism has focussed on the impossibility of proving the Law, for any attempt to demonstrate it must be circular: the Law has been found to hold good in the past, but to infer that it will continue to do so in the future is to make an inductive jump. This is the easy way of criticism—not that it should by any means be disregarded but it sometimes seems to have a damping effect on new investigation. Keynes's ingenious attempt to circumvent this attack will be considered in a later chapter.

Meanwhile the Law ought to be given its strongest form. Its traditional expression amounts to this:

> In all observed situations, the Law has held;
> Therefore in future situations it will hold.

But our knowledge of the past tells us not merely that the Law has held (assuming for the moment that the Law is the required one) but that inductions based upon it have held. The form should therefore be:

> The induction that,
>   In all observed situations, the Law has held,
>   Therefore in future situations it will hold,
> has itself held of future observations now past;
> Therefore this induction will hold of observations now future.

This is not, of course, free from the circularity of the inductive jump. The contrast is analogous to that between

> All observed brass has expanded when heated
> Therefore all brass will

and

> The induction that,
>   All observed brass has expanded when heated
>   Therefore all brass will,
> has itself held of future observations now past;
> Therefore this induction will hold of observations now future.

(2) Most inductive logicians, including Mill, have held that the Law, if it could be satisfactorily stated, would overcome the illicit process that renders induction suspect. The modern answer to this is that if the Law had this effect it would be doing too much—it would be rendering induction deductive with conclusions that would be certain. This would conflict with the obvious fact that any inductive conclusion may in the future turn out to be false—no matter how much evidence you may have that brass expands when heated it is quite conceivable or it is logically possible that the next piece of brass to be tested will contract.

Traditional reverence for deduction had the effect of making logicians seek some way of transforming induction into it. The change of approach to the subject that has come about of recent years may be described as a recognition that induction is not simply deductive and therefore not a debased form of deduction. Accordingly, the fundamental notion came to be that induction is a form of *probable argument*: a conclusion is probable in relation to its premisses—perhaps overwhelmingly probable but nonetheless not absolutely certain—which leaves open the possibility—however faint—for the next instance to be tested to go against the conclusion. This change was mainly due to Broad[1] and Keynes.[2]

From this point of view, then, the problem of induction reduces to finding a premiss that shall render conclusions probable and not certain. But in this connexion there seems to me to be a point that has been overlooked.* If the required inductive premiss were found, and if, for one reason or another, conclusions were no more than probable, the pattern of inductive argument could still be deductive. Consider the probable argument:

> All men are probably mortal,
> Socrates is a man
> _____
> Socrates is probably mortal.

This is every whit as deductive as its more famous forebear. Again, we know that the probability of throwing an ace with a true die is one-sixth and that this is also true of a second die; from these premisses we can *deduce* that the probability of throwing a double ace is one in thirty-six. The widespread view that induction has been shown to be something different from deduction should therefore be entertained with caution.

(3) Reverting to the traditional attempt to overcome illicit process, we should do well to note an important point made by Broad. Supposing that the Law can be known, can be used as a premiss in an induction, and is a universal statement, even then the minor premiss is *particular*, and hence the conclusion is particular, so that a generalisation *must* contain illicit process.[3] From this it follows that no premiss whatsoever can lead to a universal conclusion that is certain.

(4) If the Law were successful it would be useless, for it would not enable us to distinguish between true uniformities and acci-

---

[1] C. D. Broad, "On the Relation between Induction and Probability (I)", *Mind*, N.S. Vol. XXVII, No. 108, London, 1918, pp. 389–92.
[2] J. M. Keynes, *A Treatise on Probability*, London, 1921.
* Quite recently this point has been emphasised by Williams; his treatment will be discussed in a later chapter.
[3] Broad, *Op. cit.*, p. 390.

dental ones or those that are really subject to some limitation. Thus, even with a fairly large number of premisses, it would be possible by coincidence to obtain an inductive conclusion that further investigation would show to be false or to be true only if severely qualified. Thus an inhabitant of Cairo might conclude that it never rains in summer. But if the Law worked at all it would make such a conclusion just as good as those that have stood the test of time.

New criticisms of a slightly different kind may be added.

(5) If we inspect the Law itself more closely, we find a vagueness in the scope of the concept of identity, which is clearly from Joseph's account the pivotal concept. His argument includes a premiss of the form that, if anything that has p, q, r is found to have x, y, then anything the same in nature which has p, q, r must be accompanied by x, y. When he speaks of two things, the same in nature, he must mean either that they have the p, q, r in common or else that they share all their properties—p, q, r, x, y. Clearly he means the former (if he meant the latter he would beg the question by assuming the Law).* Then observation might tell us that identical things exist, but the law of identity could no longer lead from this to the required Law—for no application of purely formal principles could transform statements about actual observations into a Law that went beyond observation. The fallacy may therefore be given the form of a dilemma: the conclusion is either subtly assumed, or it is deduced by a form of logic that cannot bear the strain.†

(6) 'Identity' was clearly intended by Joseph to refer to the nature or essence of things. Now if things are found by experience to be the same, this is a judgment based upon the outer form of things, not their inner nature. How, then, do we pass from one to the other? Only by means of his form of the Law according to which things with their inner nature the same will have other properties, including the outer ones, the same. At this point, therefore, the Law is assumed. An interesting corollary is that if we were able to argue from outer to inner and thence to other outer properties, where lies the need of the inner at all, is it not an

---

* If he meant the latter, he could not know that identical things exist without inspecting x, y. In fact he postulates only that identical things *might conceivably* exist; but clearly this amounts to no more than the assumption that the Law might conceivably be true.

† According to Braithwaite, Joseph's view is due to a confusion between causal necessity and logical necessity: R. B. Braithwaite, "The Idea of Necessary Connexion", *Mind*, N.S. Vol. XXXVII, No. 145, London, 1928, pp. 65–6.

unnecessary hypothesis, and could we not pass straightaway from outer properties to outer? The possibility of this must be admitted on Joseph's principles, and yet it does away with the inner nature of things on which his argument depends.

We may turn now to other new arguments of a more fundamental kind, which do not, like those just given, focus on logical considerations, but which are metascientific in character.

(A) Keynes[1] interprets the Law as equivalent to the assertion that considerations of space and time are irrelevant to uniform connexion. The equivalence is obvious from a formulation of the Law such as that given above; for uniformity depends upon identity of occurrences apart from numerical difference, that is, apart from spatio-temporal difference. The Law is thus a Law of Spatio-Temporal Irrelevance. This is a striking way of putting the matter, but it does not add to our knowledge or make the Law more sure. The new form would require just as much justification as the old, and be open to the same criticisms.

Nonetheless the strong impression of 'self-evidence' produced by the interpretation demands sympathetic consideration. Upon what grounds is the irrelevance of space and time to be held? It clearly does not follow from the essence of thing, space, and time. But every day and in different places we find objects displaying the same sorts of properties. Can it then be regarded as a generalisation from experience?

Some evidence can be found against its generality, though to gather it we have to resort to unfamiliar facts such as those connected with Einstein's special theory of relativity. Suppose a railway train is standing in a station and another train passes through with uniform velocity, and suppose an observer on the platform notices that the two trains are of equal length when they are abreast. Some time after the second train has passed, the observer measures its length by measuring the difference in time it takes for two light signals to come to him from the front and rear of the moving train. He discovers the extraordinary fact that the train is now shorter than the one in the station. From this it follows that the modification of the spatial and temporal properties of the train changes something apparently intrinsic to the train—its length. Now the reader may ask what the theory of relativity has to do with the result, which was found by simple observation and calculation. The apparently trivial answer is that the phenomenon

---

[1] Keynes, *Op. cit.*, p. 226.

of alteration in length could not be discovered from observations carried out on railway trains; it was in fact found from observations on the astronomical scale (which led to the theory of relativity). That is to say, the change of length is extremely small—a minute fraction of a millimetre. For most practical purposes the change is and must be ignored because it is so small. When ignored, the error involved, in relation to the original length may be conveniently described as being of 'small order'. Thus Keynes's interpretation of spatio-temporal irrelevance may be accepted, provided it is taken to be a statement about approximations and not absolutes. But then it will not serve the purpose for which the Law of Uniformity was constructed; this will become plainer from the discussion immediately following.

(B) Should the Law be expressed in terms of occurrences that are *exactly alike* (apart from numerical difference) or in terms of *similar* occurrences (apart from spatio-temporal difference)? The former was given above, because on the whole it seems that this was what Mill and others had in mind. Now it is certain that the Law stated in terms of identity will not serve the needs of science, for scientists in fact make generalisations about occurrences that resemble one another only. Even if in the form of exact likeness the Law could serve induction, it would provide a type of argument that no scientist ever uses.

Even more serious is the *absence of any test for identity*. Suppose that one occurrence has p, q, r and also has x, y and suppose that another occurrence is observed to have what seems to be exactly p, q, r; how can we tell that the second occurrence really has p, q, r instead of simply having properties closely resembling them? No amount of inspection will make this certain beyond all question. The only way to find out is *to see whether the occurrence also has* x, y. But—even if the efficacy of this is not doubted—we should then be taking the trouble to find out experientially that the second occurrence actually had x, y, which would render the inductive argument to its possession of x, y useless; the whole point of successful induction is to obviate the need for carrying out actual investigations, to forestall them so to speak.

A parenthetic word should perhaps be inserted at this stage. When two occurrences were spoken of above as being "identical", this meant that their properties were identical; when spoken of as being "similar", this meant that their properties were similar. And to speak of two properties as being "similar" or as "resembling" each other should convey that they resemble each other closely. Thus if a scientist wishes to base an induction upon premisses involving blades of grass, he is content provided the shape, size, colour, texture, and so on are more or less alike—they need not be identical. This, of course, makes sense only if "property" is equivalent to "determinate property" (denoting, for example, some quite specific shade of green). The several properties of the two blades of grass, more or less alike, would be *identical* if "property" were equivalent to "determinable property" (denoting, for example, some *sort* of green). If we chose, we could adhere to the above formulation of the Law, provided we inserted that the occurrences were exactly alike with respect to determinable properties; but this would amount to the same thing as reformulating in terms of similarity with respect to determinates—it would differ only in being more cumbrous.

The result of this discussion is, then, that the Law ought to be expressed in terms of similarity. It would read :—

In a given situation, if there is a uniform connexion between two occurrences A and B, then an occurrence more or less like A apart from spatio-temporal difference will be accompanied, preceded, or followed by an occurrence more or less like B apart from spatio-temporal difference.

Mutatis mutandis, the form in terms of causation can also be given.

Can this form of the Law serve as the inductive premiss required? It does not specify the degree of resemblance needed, and without this no conclusion could be derived. Further, the Law merely states in general terms what is stated in particular terms in the observational premisses of an inductive argument; thus it fails to be a postulate or a principle. Moreover, we should wish to know why the Law should continue to hold in the future, assuming that it has held in the past.*

(C) There is a further defect in the foregoing attempt to formulate the Law, in that there is no reference to *conditions*. Joseph, indeed, does make such a reference. But the same difficulties as

---

* Connected with the themes of the last two discussions is the philosophical doctrine of internal relations (Bradley) and that of the identity of indiscernibles (Leibniz), a form of which Keynes adopted in his treatment of 'perfect analogy'. These doctrines need not be examined here; they all run counter to facts of the type just described, in that they depend upon a concept of absolute identity in time or in space.

were found in his conception of identical causes mar his conception of identical causes operating *in identical conditions*. Conditions may be similar, not identical.

But an additional difficulty arises. Joseph would not maintain that the whole universe repeats itself or at any rate repeats itself often enough to cover even such good inductions as we make; he would therefore have to draw a hard line of distinction between the conditions that must recur for induction to be possible and the remaining features of the universe that could vary without interfering with induction. There would thus be a strange hard and fast dichotomy in the universe between conditions absolutely relevant and conditions absolutely irrelevant. How, then, are the relevant conditions to be ascertained? Presumably they would be the residue after the rest were eliminated by experience. Thus there is no reason to suppose that conditions in Sirius have any bearing on ordinary laboratory experiments, such as those concerned with the Boyle-Mariotte law. But this procedure would mean that an inductive argument could not be constructed without *full* knowledge of its circumstances—that is to say, we should need to have an enormous amount of knowledge before science could begin.

Thus the Law makes insatiable demands upon our prior knowledge of our environment or else posits an arbitrary dichotomy between relevant and irrelevant conditions.

These criticisms arise, not as the first group did from discussing pros and cons of a Law without regard to what it means, but from considering how the Law can be stated, whether the statement has a meaning, and whether it can be used. Joseph and others have been misled into supposing they have innate concepts, such as thing, space, and time, from which a truth about the universe would follow: he puts forward the essence of a thing as being what has the same properties for all changes in space and time, not realising that this is not an absolute essence but an approximation, slightly faulty, to what we learn from experience, namely that a thing is more or less independent of spatio-temporal changes; he has over-simplified what he has learnt from experience and thus supposed that what he has learnt was taught him not by experience but by Reason.*

* It is interesting to note that Joseph did not follow out consistently his belief in the existence of the essence of a thing: if a thing must have the same properties so long as

This chapter should not be ended without stressing the cogency of the Law, which lies in its apparently obvious character: it is difficult to avoid feeling that if you have identical causes in identical conditions they must produce identical effects; but we now see that such a statement has no application in the world of experience.

Space has been devoted to this Law, because for all the hostility it meets with I know of no adequate discussion of it. Again, although rejected by scientific thought, its superficial cogency makes examination of it desirable. And further, criticism of it is the simplest way of bringing out the features that would be required in a more satisfactory inductive major premiss.

it remains itself, as he claims, then change would be impossible and the world would be static.

As regards his remark that to deny his view is to deny the existence of universals, it suffices to mention that a treatment of induction in terms of resemblance instead of identity obviates the need for universals (determinates).

It is worth stressing Joseph's lack of concern whether or not identical things actually exist; he was content to produce an academic law *in vacuo*, even if it was never used as a premiss in any actual inductive argument. Again, supposing there are *some* identical things, it seems not to have occurred to him that even then there are many things that merely resemble each other about which we commonly make scientific inferences. I submit that methodology and metascience cannot be satisfactorily investigated on such lines.

CHAPTER XV

REQUIREMENTS FOR AN INDUCTIVE PRINCIPLE

IF we are to seek a satisfactory inductive principle, it is advisable to have before us a complete set of the requirements that such a principle must satisfy.

A

(1) It must be such that no inductive conclusion can be certain but that all inductions are probable in various degrees.

(2) The possibility must be allowed for that inductive arguments can be deductive, in the sense in which a probable conclusion can follow by formal logic from probable premisses.

(3) Accidental uniformities must not be treated as if they were just as good as true uniformities.

(4) Nor are they to be treated as different in kind; they are simply to have a lower probability or perhaps a non-significant probability.

B

(5) The inductive principle must be such that the basic form of induction is argument by analogy.

(6) And it must be such that the strength of this kind of argument lies fundamentally in the positive analogy and the number of instances entering into the premisses.

(7) But in general where a good analogy can be obtained by repetition, the method of increasing the negative analogy can be used to improve it, *i.e.* to remove from a sufficient condition factors that are not necessary.

(8) And inductions vary in strength according to the scope of the predicate.

(9) Exact likeness in properties about which we have inductive arguments must not be sought; similarity or resemblance must suffice.

(10) Spatio-temporal differences among the instances that enter into inductive premisses must be more or less irrelevant, *i.e.* capable of being neglected without appreciable error.

C

(11) With properties that are similar, some measure must be sought of the amount of departure from identity that is permissible.

(12) In neglecting spatio-temporal differences the existence of an error of small order must be admitted as possible.

(13) For its existence there ought to be some criterion and some means of measuring it.

D

(14) The probability of an induction must be capable of approaching indefinitely close to certainty.

(15) If an inductive principle is to function as a premiss in an inductive argument, it must have some degree of probability.

E

(16) The inductive principle must not be a tautology.

(17) If it is to be a premiss in induction, it cannot be established empirically, *i.e.* by induction.

The probability approach takes care of group A. The principle must be formed out of B and C; it must satisfy D; and there remains the epistemological problem expressed in E.

CHAPTER XVI

FOUR PRINCIPLES OF INDUCTION

SEEING that the Law of Uniformity of Nature was wholly inadequate to justify induction, Keynes and Broad, independently, made a bold attempt to find a substitute. This interesting attempt is much more important than its predecessor and part of it at least should be developed in detail. It consists of two closely connected principles; but it will transpire on examination that four principles are involved.

(I) *The Principle of Limitation of Independent Variety.*

When an inductive argument turns out to be a good one, the properties involved have evidently recurred together in *groups* or formed what may be called a *natural kind* (let us be content with this modest statement and refrain from the more tendentious substitute that for such argument to be *possible* properties *must* recur in groups or kinds). Keynes begins with the notion of groups and Broad with that of natural kinds; they both present very much the same general idea though in wholly different forms. Broad has clearly elaborated his idea and it may be conveniently taken first.[1]

He observes that in successful inductions we are dealing with *substances*, and, moreover, with *natural kinds* of substances (he actually says we presuppose these, but, as before, let us be content with the milder statement); the emphasis is on natural kinds. Thus most reliable inductions are about crows or swans, silver or salt, and the like; individual crows or pieces of silver are substances (in the ordinary non-philosophical sense of the word), and crows and silver are natural kinds of substances.*

[1] C. D. Broad, "The Relation between Induction and Probability (II)", *Mind*, N.S. Vol. XXIX, No. 113, London, 1920.
   * A good sign of a natural kind is the existence of a general name; for, if there were no natural kinds, whether existing objectively or man-made, we should have to have a separate name for every individual substance. The existence of such a name is not, of course, an absolute criterion that a kind exists objectively; it is an inductive criterion: the existence of a general name implies that an induction has already, even though not with conscious deliberation, been made; for, after observing a number of similar substances, we take for granted the induction that other substances like these in some respects will resemble them in further respects, *i.e.* we take for granted the existence of a kind, and to this we give a general name. In drawing attention to this, Broad makes an important though subsidiary point.

132

A substance is something that persists if only for a short time. Rightly or wrongly it is our practice to regard a substance as being the same at different times. We do this even though the *states* of the substance vary from time to time—thus the state of a well-groomed crow may change to that of being bedraggled after it has been out in the rain and the state of polished silver may become one of being tarnished. If the properties of states are called "first-order properties", the substance persists throughout change of its first-order properties. The property that substance persists—and all the more or less permanent properties—is a property of the substance itself, not of its states, and it may be called a "second-order property". Superficial observation may lead to the notion of natural kinds simply because first-order properties sometimes remain for a long time the same; but it is clear that such properties may and usually do change continually; hence natural kinds must relate to second-order properties.

First-order properties are the same as determinates. Second-order properties include determinables but also, as will be seen when the third principle is dealt with, inductive properties. Now the interesting feature of kinds is that, however many are the determinates of their states, these states come under comparatively few determinables—we do not have crows that are swan-shaped as well as crows that are crow-shaped—or, if this way of expressing the matter is not acceptable because a swan-shaped 'crow' would be relegated to a different kind, the variety of ways in which determinables are grouped is comparatively restricted. Prior to experience we might expect to find determinables scattered all over the universe in a random manner: thus we might find one substance with the properties p, q, r, s, another substance with the properties q, r, s, t, another with r, s, t, u, and another with s, t, u, v. Such continuous variation would preclude the existence of kinds and induction would be almost impossible—there would be an enormous diversity of effects. But our actual experience is very different:

What we have found is not a regular distribution of all the states at a moment among all the possible sorts of states, but a 'bunching together' of instances in the neighbourhood of certain sorts of states. Intermediate possible sorts are scarcely represented in nature, so far as our experience has gone, at all.[1]

[1] Broad, *Op. cit.*, p. 25.

Our actual experience is graphically described by Broad somewhat as follows. Suppose that different sorts of states are represented by dots on a sheet of paper and suppose that the dots have varying degrees of blackness according to the number of states situated at the dot. Then, prior to experience when we should expect states to be uniformly scattered, we should expect the paper to be uniformly shaded. But instead we should find a number of blobs of heavy black, dark near the centre and shading off very sharply towards white; and in between blobs there would be no dots or only very faint ones. Thus, instead of finding matter evenly distributed throughout the universe, we find the stars and empty space between them. This is the sort of distribution that would correspond to our experience and to the peculiar groupings that constitute natural kinds. This is a way of saying that, where there are natural kinds, properties are sharply gathered together into groups.*

This exposition of Broad's ideas is condensed and omits much of his valuable discussion of allied points and much of the precision of his own presentation; but it is sufficient, I hope, to convey his conception of the pattern of induction. The further development that he gives is relevant to a later section of this chapter.

The Principle with which this section is chiefly concerned is due to Keynes. Oddly enough it has never, so far as I know, been expounded in full by anyone, not even himself. He devotes merely ten lines to its contents.[1] One can see the sort of thing he has in

---

* A difficulty raised by Broad should be noted (*Id.*, p. 23). We have spoken as if the notion of substance was primary, because presupposed by that of natural kind; but equally it would be difficult to develop the notion of substance unless we found various instances of the same natural kind. If this really is impossible, there is no alternative to supposing that the two notions are inseparable aspects of experience that must be abstracted together; but there is another way out of the difficulty. Why does substance presuppose natural kind? According to Broad this is because we regard a substance as persisting when unobserved and therefore as being of the same natural kind as observed ones. But we may begin with a less sophisticated notion of substance, simply as what persists throughout changes of state while under observation; we form this notion about several substances while all are under observation; we thus develop the notion of kinds; and from that we can extend our original notion of substance to include persistence in the absence of observation.

A similar difficulty arises if it is true that we cannot perform an induction without natural kinds and therefore without the notion of substance, for the notion of unobserved substance cannot be obtained without induction. Here again, we can begin with observed instances, thus originating a pattern of induction which we can later extend to the unobserved.

[1] J. M. Keynes, *A Treatise on Probability*, London, 1921, p. 258. A short and clear account, however, is given by Russell (Bertrand Russell, *Human Knowledge: Its Scope and Limits*, London, 1948, Pt. VI, Ch. 3).

mind, but it is puzzling and obscure unless one takes the trouble to analyse it in detail.

Though Keynes speaks of groups of properties, his Principle constitutes an analysis of the notion of natural kinds. Thus the two approaches, though much the same in essence, contain supplementary features. An attempt must now be made, therefore, to expound and analyse Keynes's Principle.

In accordance with requirements (5) and (6) of A, stated in the previous chapter, we find that phenomena with the properties p, q, r also have the properties x, y, and we infer that the next phenomenon to have the positive analogy p, q, r will also have x, y. Thus p, q, r and x, y form a group or natural kind which possibly includes other properties as well—call this an "inductive group". If the analogy is good, then p, q, r *specify* x, y—we have found a subject-set that specifies a predicate-set. In this there is no new information; it is merely a statement of what happens when an inductive argument is successful. We must now analyse its implications.

Suppose there was an unlimited number of properties within a group. Then p, q, r would specify an unlimited number of other properties. This does not mean that *all* properties would be included—we can have an unlimited number of ordinary whole numbers even if those from 1 to 10, say, are omitted, or even if all the odd numbers are left out. Thus a streptococcus might cause fine weather, a treatise on methodology, blue crows, and so on. Now there is nothing, so far as we know, inherently impossible about such a state of affairs; the universe might very well be like that. However, we can and do use requirement (7), *i.e.*, we use negative analogy as a means of paring down sufficient conditions so as to approach conditions that are strictly necessary. Now this fact is incompatible with the unlimited diversity of effects just described: for, in that situation, since p, q, r would in all instances specify the same infinity of properties, we should have in conjunction with p, q, r other properties, which could not be eliminated by negative analogy, and we could not tell which were necessary or how many sufficient; indeed the distinction between necessary and sufficient conditions would cease to have any application. It follows that, whenever the negative analogy can be increased, whenever the concept of negative analogy can be applied, there is a limitation on diverse effects. In general, with good inductions it is possible to increase the negative analogy.

Hence by requirement (7), where there is good induction, there is a limited diversity of effects, *i.e.* the number of properties in an inductive group is not unlimited. Moreover, the scope of the predicate varies from induction to induction; but, if an inductive group contained unlimited properties, the scope of all inductions could be made the same. Hence requirement (8) also shows that a successful induction cannot involve a group with an unlimited number of properties.

Suppose next that, instead of having inductive groups containing an unlimited number of properties, we have an unlimited number of groups each containing a limited number of properties. Suppose further that there is overlapping, *i.e.*, that properties can occur in more than one group and even in all of them. Once again we should have the phenomenon of unlimited diversity of effects: thus, in one group a streptococcus would cause fine weather, in another blue crows, and so on. This would conflict with the practice of induction because of requirement (8), though not for precisely the same reason as before. Inductions would not all have predicates of the same scope; but many more would than is the case with actual generalisations. The phenomenon would conflict with requirement (7): for we might find some groups in which an elephant caused fine weather, blue crows, and so on, possibilities that are often ruled out by negative analogy. Thus unlimited plurality of causes would conflict with scientific practice.

Now it is important to be clear about what this establishes. Some part of the initial supposition must be denied. But the possibility of an unlimited number of groups may and must be admitted; for, in fact, there do exist properties in an unlimited number of groups—colour, shape, and size, for example. These properties can specify a table, a daffodil, a blue crow, and so on without limit. This only means, however, that it is impossible to construct an inductive argument where the subject properties are colour, shape, and size. It follows, then, that, though the number of groups may be unlimited, the amount of overlapping is limited. It is not limited to the extent that a given set of subject properties can occur only in one group; this might be true of nature, but it would be too stringent a condition in the light of present knowledge. All that may be said is that properties about which we have inductions cannot enter into an unlimited number of groups. This amounts to saying that no one set of properties specifies every other set, which would be chaos, though it is not claimed that any one set specifies one and only one other set, which would be rigidly deterministic; so far as our inspection of induction has gone, a certain amount of plurality and diversity is not denied, *i.e.* the universe is taken to be "loosely jointed", to use Mace's happy phrase.[1]

The result is that we may not have an unlimited number of properties in any one group, or a limited number of properties entering into an unlimited number of groups; this does not, however, prevent the total number of properties or the total number of groups from being unlimited.*

These restrictions must be relaxed in two ways. The first relaxation is this. It is not necessary that the limitation should apply to all properties without exception; for some properties may be logically dependent upon some others (being coloured follows logically from being blue), and in fact there might conceivably be an unlimited number of logically dependent properties resulting from a limited number of independent ones; but that would be of no consequence; all that is needed, therefore, is to impose the limitation on independent properties and independent groups. The second relaxation is this. In an inductive argument it is rare to find the subject consisting of only one property. Now if a subject consists of more than one, it is of no consequence to the induction if the constituent properties occur in an unlimited number of groups; all that matters is that the subject-set should be restricted to a limited number of groups—and likewise with the predicate-set.

An important point must now be made. In general the word "property" refers throughout to *determinable* property, but deter-

[1] C. A. Mace, *The Principles of Logic*, London, 1933, p. 371.

* The words "finite" and "infinite" have been deliberately avoided and "limited" and "unlimited" used instead because less ambiguous. The number of properties, for instance, is not to be infinite (unlimited); if it were infinite (unlimited), it would nonetheless be finite, in the sense that however many are known they are finite in number, though they are also infinite in number in the sense that no limit to the number can be set. If the word "finite" were used above, as it often is in such contexts, it would have to be defined to mean a number that cannot be increased indefinitely: that is to say, there must be a point beyond which it does not go, or there must exist a number that always exceeds it. This is very simply expressed mathematically (for brevity only positive numbers need be dealt with): n is a finite number if there exists a number N such that n is less than N. We meet the same thing at the other end of the scale. If n is to be finite in the sense of not becoming indefinitely small, then again there has to be a point beyond which it does not recede, *i.e.*, a number always exceeded by it. Mathematically this is: n is a finite number if there exists a number ε different from zero such that n is greater than ε. The point is simple, but the non-mathematical reader is likely to be puzzled when he comes across what is to him the surprising condition that some finite number or other is described not as being greater than zero but as being greater than a fixed number greater than zero.

minates are not excluded. Some discussion of this is needed. Suppose we have a determinate property *equilateral* in a context of triangles. This comes under the determinable *triangular*. But this in its turn is determinate relative to the determinable *rectilinear*. And this is determinate under the determinable *bounded by lines* (curved or straight) or *having shape*. Which, then, of these determinables could enter into an induction? Fortunately there is a stop to the process, and it might seem that the final determinable was the one required. But there are many inductions that a final determinable would not fit. Nonetheless there is no difficulty. In practice an induction names one or other of the possible grades; with a grade other than the final determinable this is done by adding qualifying adjectives. Thus we may have the premiss: "all triangular figures have been found to have the sum of their angles equal to two right angles"; or the premiss: "all polygons have been found to have the sum of their interior angles equal to twice as many right angles as they have sides minus four". These properties, triangular and polygonal, are determinables *in their contexts*, and the induction involving them *holds of their determinates* of any grade. The form of the induction would be:

Some determinates of a certain determinable have been found to have x, y; so all determinates of that determinable will have x, y.

In general the predicate x, y forms a determinable also. Now we can also have generalisations about equilateral triangles, *i.e.* about an absolutely determinate property. When this is so, the induction holds of its particular instances. This is not to deny that the other inductions hold of particular instances, for after all it is always instances of triangles or polygons that have been found to have their angles of a certain total. Hence fundamentally the determinable property mentioned in an induction covers particular instances, which in fact may be instances of the determinable itself or of any grade of determinate under it.* Seeing that while most

* An infinity of instances can be denoted either by a determinate or by a determinable; it matters little whether we put all of a class of instances directly under one determinable, *e.g.*, putting all instances of colour under the determinable colour, or split them up and put subclasses under several determinates which come under the one determinable, *e.g.*, putting instances of all kinds of blue under the determinate blue, instances of all kinds of red under the determinate red, and so on, where the determinables blue, red, and so on become new determinates under the determinable colour.

Further, the multiplicity of instances here involved should not be confused with the number of combinations of properties previously discussed: the multiplicity is simply

inductions are about determinable properties some are about determinate ones, it is desirable to take account of this explicitly in expressing the limitation imposed on properties. We saw that any property capable of entering into an induction must occur in only a limited number of groups. No modification is needed here, for the statement holds of both determinable and determinate properties; in fact, if a determinable property occurred only in a limited number of groups the same would hold of all its determinates, and if a determinate property was thus limited in its occurrence the same would hold of its determinable. But we also saw that a group cannot contain an unlimited number of independent properties. Now obviously if a group has a limited number of determinables it cannot avoid having an unlimited number of determinates, because any determinable must have an unlimited number of determinates. Hence this limitation must refer only to determinables. It is therefore not possible to express the necessary limitations upon properties by putting determinables and determinates indiscriminately into one class.*

With regard to inductions about determinables, the very way in which an unlimited multiplicity of instances is contained under one determinable, no matter how much they may differ from one another within certain limits, shows that endless multiplicity within one property is not excluded by our restrictions—on the contrary it forms the subject matter of inductions about determinables. Hence our restrictions do not require that the determinates or the instances of properties covered by a determinable should be identical; it is enough that they respectively resemble one another sufficiently to come under the determinable. Thus requirement (9) is satisfied. With regard to inductions about determinates, a word must be said about resemblance. Such inductions deal with an unlimited number of instances of a determinate property. Now it might seem that these instances would have to be *identical* in order to be denoted by one determinate. Then such induction would be unreal because we can never know

the different instances that are denoted by one determinate or that resemble one another sufficiently to be instances of one determinable; the number of combinations is the amount of grouping of determinable properties.

* It may be noted that the treatment takes account not only of the number of ways in which properties are grouped but also of the *amounts* in which properties occur, or, if we prefer, their degrees. Thus, if density enters into an induction, what is important is not simply density but the amount or degree of density. It is easy to see that this is covered by determinate properties : every degree of density is a determinate property, and it is not just density whose occurrence is limited but the determinate values of density.

that two instances are exactly alike. Need we, then, have spent time over inductions about determinates? We must, for instances about them can occur. In these, however, it is not assumed that instances are identical; it is assumed only that they resemble one another enough for practical (= inductive) purposes. This is equivalent to the assumption that small divergencies, if any, may be neglected. This is not an unwarranted assumption, however, because it is based upon experience—the generalisation that small differences do not count. We have here an important rider to our restrictions on properties and groups, when taking account of requirement (9).

It is clear, moreover, that the whole treatment implicitly takes spatio-temporal differences among the instances to be relevant. On the one hand, it is implied that an assertion about any instance of a property would hold at one time as well as at another, for otherwise the inductive form would not exist. On the other hand, this fact, which is not self-evident, depends upon the experiential conclusion that space and time are irrelevant: that is to say, we observe the same conjunctions of properties at different times in different places and make the generalisation that time and place will continue to be irrelevant. Requirement (10) is satisfied, then, by this addendum to our restrictions.

This concludes the analysis of the number of ways in which properties can occur in groups, which may be spoken of as the "*variety*" that is found in the domain of induction. The result expresses a limitation imposed on the variety, or rather the variety that is independent, and constitutes in part at least a description of what the universe is like wherever generalisations actually hold. It is based on requirements B, (5) to (10); part of it amounts to a restatement of the Law of Uniformity given in Chapter XIV; that restatement, however, took account only of (9) and (10), but did not deal with the limitations that must be imposed to satisfy requirements (5) to (8). The result constitutes an interpretation of Keynes's *Principle of Limitation of Independent Variety*, which may be formulated as follows:

When induction has any success, (i) independent sets of determinable and determinate properties (whether subject or predicate) are distributed in groups, (ii) which are in practice independent of spatio-temporal position; and, though there may be an unlimited number of independent determinable properties and sets of determinable properties and an unlimited number of independent groups, (iii) each group contains a limited number of inde-

pendent determinable properties or determinates and (iv) each independent set of determinable properties or determinates occurs only in a limited number of independent groups, where (v) instances that do not differ discernibly may be classed as one determinate since the differences between them (if any) are in practice irrelevant.

The assertion of natural kinds expresses, and does so crisply, the sort of limitation upon the groupings of properties that must occur if induction is to take place successfully.* It does not explicitly bring to light precisely the limitations that were found above to be part and parcel of the Principle of Limitation of Independent Variety; but it is clear that analysis of the notion of natural kinds must lead to those limitations. Moreover, the notion takes explicit notice of resemblance. I think, too, that the concept permits of inductions involving properties that are determinate, though this may necessitate extending the meaning of "kind". The exposition in terms of natural kinds, however, has at least one advantage over the Principle of Limitation: this principle denies unlimited diversity of effects, but the principle of natural kinds denies that this diversity can be large if induction is to be practicable. The Principle of Limitation permits of far too great a diversity of effects and this is difficult to remedy. To prevent this diversity from rendering induction impracticable, we must restrict the number of ways in which properties can occur in groups: it is not enough that this number should be limited, as the Principle asserts; it must not be much greater than the number of properties. It is hard to see how a more precise restriction could be found.

(II) *The Principle of Spatio-Temporal Proximity*
The concept of natural kinds reveals another weakness in the Principle of Limitation: for a kind to exist and for conformity with a great deal of experience, properties must not be scattered at random in space-time but must be bunched in islands, and this is not taken account of in the Principle.

* The Principle of Limitation, though less graphic, also draws attention to a striking feature of the universe. The principle imposes a limitation upon the behaviour of determinables. But if we make any observation of nature we find an instance in all respects determinate. Loosely speaking, there are no such things as determinables. Thus we find specifically red things and specifically round things but never things that are just coloured and shaped—though of course a thing cannot be red and round without being coloured and shaped. In other words, the fundamental observables are determinates. But if nature possesses only determinates, is it not striking that it operates according to a principle involving determinables?

When we perform an induction, we try to make an approximately closed system. That is to say, we try to remove anything that might influence our experiments in an undesirable way; we close the door of the laboratory and shut off the rest of the world from our inductive premisses. Naturally we never succeed in having all surrounding conditions exactly the same when an experiment is repeated. We simply treat variations in such conditions as irrelevant—itself a general conclusion based on past experience. Here, then, there may be great changes, yet they do not influence the result—outside the laboratory there may be quiet or a students' rag. Hence, *in order to be members of an inductive group, properties must be either in 'close' spatio-temporal proximity, where 'close' is intuitively apprehended in relation to the scale of the facts embodied in the premisses, or such that a chain of inductive connexions can be found between them, where each pair in the chain is in 'close' spatio-temporal proximity with the next.* This *Principle of Spatio-Temporal Proximity* deals not with inductive groups at different points of space-time, where space and time are external properties of the groups, but with spatio-temporal changes within a group.

Without some such Principle the Principle of Limitation would be too wide to describe natural kinds; with this auxiliary, however, it is more satisfactory than the principle of natural kinds, which is too narrow to cover inductions about properties not belonging to one kind.

In the main, the relation between the two is that the concept of natural kinds affords an extraordinarily graphic description of what underlies induction and that the Principle of Limitation (plus auxiliary) constitutes the analysis of the concept.

(III) *The Principle of Uniform Generation of Properties*
Once again we have parallel and independent developments by Keynes and Broad; we begin with the latter.[1]

Inductive conclusions, including causal laws, are laws about changes of states of substances; thus induction presupposes substance. How, then, is a substance to be identified? There are two possibilities: first-order properties and second-order properties. We might, for instance, try to identify the substance salt through its first-order property of taste or through its second-order property of solubility in water. The objection to the latter course, however, is that we should be using an inductive conclu-

[1] Broad, *Op. cit.*, pp. 33–42.

sion; and, since induction presupposes substance, it would be circular to define a substance in terms of its inductive properties. On the other hand there is reason for defining a substance in terms of its first-order properties: thus, though solubility is part of the nature of salt, it is not part of the meaning of the word "salt", because we should have to know the meaning of the word and should have to be able to identify the substance denoted by it before we could speak of its solubility. Against this, it is true, there is the marked instability of first-order properties. Nonetheless for long periods salt, for instance, remains unchanged. Its solubility, however, might lead us to say that the substance disappeared along with its characteristic first-order properties, whiteness and powderiness. But the process of dissolving is reversible, for the salt would reappear when its solvent evaporated, and the first-order properties would be restored. Still, to justify the notion of substance, we should have to give an account of it when it had to all appearances disappeared. The taste of the water in which the salt was dissolved would tempt us to suppose that the salt continued in the water even though invisible. This would be supported by the discovery that the weight of the mixture was equal to the sum of the weights of the water and the dry salt; and similarly with chemical compounds, as when silver disappears into silver chloride and reappears, the total weight always remaining the same. In this way the notion of substance, as persisting throughout change, even when there is superficial disappearance, can be preserved, while a substance can be described in terms of its superficial properties.*

We may therefore assert that natural kinds of substances persist and are identifiable by their first-order properties. But this is obviously not true of all natural kinds. Thus chemical mixtures and compounds and biological structures built upon them begin to exist and come to an end; salt water ceases to exist when the water is distilled off the salt, silver chloride when it is separated into its component elements, and crows when their bodies disintegrate. Such kinds may be the first to catch the eye because they are relatively stable over long periods, whereas many of the

---

* An objection of a different kind might be levelled against describing a substance in terms of its first-order properties, on the grounds that they are essentially relational properties and therefore involve inductive conclusions. Thus the taste of salt would be connected by an inductive law with salt and the percipient. Should this be granted, however, we should have to distinguish a substance as what gave rise, in relation to a percipient, to a first-order relational property, and avoid describing a substance by its relation to objects other than percipients.

chemical elements which persist in the sense described are much less stable; in spite of this, however, it is only the elements and not the other kinds that can be said to persist. Let us distinguish the elements, mixtures and compounds, and biological structures as respectively kinds of the first-order, second-order, and third-order. Then the assertion under discussion is true of first-order kinds but not of kinds of higher orders; thus the second-order kind, silver chloride, cannot be said to persist when broken down into silver and chlorine.

Thus first-order kinds persist and are identifiable by their first-order properties; and they form the elements out of which higher-order kinds are constructed. Now the variety and complexity of higher-order kinds is very great compared with that of first-order kinds. In fact, until lately chemists would have said that the number of first-order kinds was ninety-two—ninety-six if the new elements such as Plutonium of atomic bomb fame are included—and not so long ago these elements would have been held to be simple substances; and the number of higher-order kinds built out of these is of course enormous. To-day, however, we should revise the above classification of orders of kinds, because every chemical element is constituted by a small number of subatomic entities—chiefly the proton, electron, and neutron; if we do not wish to alter the denotation of the above orders of kinds we may regard these last as ground-floor kinds. Since by altering the arrangement of these entities it is now possible to transmute one element into another, first-order kinds can no longer be regarded as permanent substances. Nonetheless it is hard to escape the supposition that there are entities in the sense here required, though this may be at the ground-floor level instead of among first-order kinds. Thus we

seem to have hit on the ground-plan of the material world, however inadequate may be our knowledge of the details.

The world as it presents itself to superficial observation fulfils to a highly surprising extent the condition of consisting of permanent substances of a few marked kinds.[1]

Let us turn from this interesting conclusion of Broad's to Keynes's more or less parallel development,[2] which will eventually carry us a little further.

[1] *Id.*, pp. 37, 39.
[2] Keynes, *Op. cit.*, pp. 249–50, and Ch. XXII, esp. pp. 251, 253–4.

Let us call the ground-floor entities "generator elements" or simply "generators" (Keynes calls them "legal atoms"). They are

such that each of them exercises its own separate, independent, and invariable effect, a change of the total state being compounded of a number of separate changes each of which is solely due to a separate portion of the preceding state.[1]

Then every inductive group or natural kind would be produced by some combination of generators. This amounts to saying that the universe constitutes a *system*. The notion of a system is that of a collection of members, a few of which form the ultimate elements and the rest of which depend upon these ultimate elements. Thus in a system of propositions in logic the majority can be deduced from a small number known as axioms. This is as far as Keynes takes us.

The Keynes-Broad proposal answers to the structure of the advanced and fundamental sciences—logic, (including mathematics), physics (including chemistry), biology (evolutionary and genetic), and psychodynamics. Huge numbers of inductions will depend upon a much smaller number of inductions between ground-floor entities or generators and the properties to which they give rise. A chemist may say, "Give me the ninety-six elements and I will construct the material universe." A physicist may go further and say, "Out of a handful of subatomic entities I can construct the elements". An evolutionary biologist may say, "Given the principle of natural selection and fact of mutation I can produce all the variety of the animal kingdom and plant life". A genetic biologist may add, "From a small number of changes among the genes I can construct the variety of heredity." And a psycho-analyst may say, "With the six components of the Œdipus situation and the pleasure-unpleasure principle I can construct all personality types". The similar claim in the field of mathematics, familiar to everyone in the form of Euclid, and in formal logic need hardly be stressed.

A striking tendency of scientific thought is the constant endeavour to go back to more and more ultimate entities and to reduce their number to a minimum. Russell threw all mathe-

[1] *Id.*, p. 249.

matics and logic into a form in which the whole body of these sciences followed from a few primitive ideas and a few primitive propositions—about a handful of each. It was the achievement of Scheffer and Nicod respectively to reduce them to one primitive idea and one primitive proposition, and of Popper to dispense with the latter. The same process was at work in chemistry when the molecule ceased to be the fundamental unit and became replaced by the atom (though this is rather an over-simplification of the story). The process certainly occurred in physics, when the attempt was made to get behind the atoms—even though by 'definition' they were the smallest particles of matter. The biologist who studies large-scale changes accounts for them by means of the concepts of a few kinds; his claim is therefore of the same sort, though he should stipulate that he be granted a fair amount of time and the power to create the required conditions if he is to carry out his construction; and the process remains at work to-day, for the genetic biologist tries to analyse large-scale kinds into a few genetic structures. Similarly the psycho-analyst may—and does—begin by ascertaining the Œdipus structure of mental phenomena; but once again, not content with that, he seeks to go behind this to the pre-Œdipus factors upon which the Œdipus situation is built.

The Keynes-Broad proposal is clearly a result of scientific discovery. What is most remarkable about it is that it constitutes a *quasi* explanation, if only partial, of the existence of natural kinds of all orders except those on the ground floor, for the generators can be put together in a sufficient number of ways to produce all inductive relations that do not explicitly concern generators. Moreover, we can see, if only dimly, that the resulting kinds would differ sharply from one another as a rule, which, as the first section of this chapter showed, is characteristic of the universe as we experience it. But as yet we know nothing of why the generators form kinds and give rise to the same superstructures on different occasions—is it that there is a law of uniformity of nature or a law of universal causation holding between kinds of different levels of order?

In the further analysis of generators we depart from the Keynes-Broad conception. Here the aim is to be descriptive or to express the result of certain inductions in terms of generators.

The evidence that leads us to speak of generators consists of a pattern to be found in chemistry, physics, biology, and psychology. The examples given suggest that we should think of single generators as being responsible for single elements (more strictly, for the first-order properties of single elements) and combinations of generators as being responsible for compounds. If now we think of generators as analogous to protons, electrons, and neutrons, we find that the number of these is far too small to account for the chemical elements if the generators are taken merely singly and in combination. In fact, the elements are produced by ringing the changes upon the number of one generator that is put with another one, *i.e.* upon the *proportions* that are combined — and to some extent upon their spatial arrangement. In genetics we seem to be dealing with combinations pure and simple as with some chemical compounds; to get the parallel required we should have to investigate the structure of the gene. In psychodynamics we have a proper parallel, for variety of personality seems due to a small number of fundamental components integrated together in different amounts, just as the enormous variety of colours can be derived from different proportions of three primary colours.

Have we, then, allowed some law of uniformity or universal causation, holding between kinds of different levels of order, creep in through the back door? Something of the sort has crept in. It should be noticed, however, that in contrast with ordinary causation which is horizontal, what has crept in here is a vertical causation. This may be illustrated as follows. When a man pulls the pin out of a grenade, that is commonly called the "cause" of the explosion that ensues. Now suppose we watch a film of this projected on a screen, the image of the man pulling out the pin is not the cause of the image of the explosion. The cause of both images lies in their respective generator-elements, the pieces of film and the source of light. Now if we think of the real action as being like a sequence of images, we may think of it as horizontal causation and think of the effect produced by the pieces of film as being due to vertical causation. A graphic illustration like this may be misleading, but it is easy to supply an exact one. We ordinarily say that hydrogen plus oxygen causes water; this is horizontal causation. In terms of subatomic entities, however, we have one electron and one proton causing hydrogen; this is vertical causation. And we have eight electrons which revolve round a nucleus of eight protons and eight neutrons causing oxygen; this again is vertical causation. When all these subatomic entities are put together in the right conditions, with of course two hydrogen groups to one oxygen group, we get water; this is a compound effect of vertical causation. Thus the ordinary horizontal causation is replaced, or analysed into, three relations of vertical causation. The ordinary relation is in itself no more than a uniformity; there is, as it were, no power in the hydrogen and oxygen to produce water. If the notion of power as an ingredient of causation is significant at all, it must lie not in horizontal causation but in the vertical kind. But, without entering just now into the vexed question of agency, the vertical relation, whatever its ultimate nature, is fundamental; horizontal causation is secondary.

Thus a principle of uniform vertical causation has thrust itself upon us. But it is a conclusion, not a presupposition of induction. We may express the result as the *Principle of Uniform Generation of Properties*:

Natural kinds are vertically caused by distributions of a small number of generators.

This is further analysed in the following principle.

(IV) *The Principle of Small and Great Changes.*

Since differences between natural kinds are due to the proportions in which generators are mixed, there must be some limitation upon these proportions, *i.e.* there could not be an unlimited number of proportions shading into one another—if indeed there could be any at all—else we should not have sharply marked natural kinds but a series of things differing from one another only in small degrees. Our principles have therefore to be supplemented by yet another one.

If properties are produced by combining generators in various proportions, it is tempting to suppose that small variations from one determinate to another will correspond and be due to small variations in the proportions in which the generators are mixed. But, as it stands, this does not agree with the actual results of science; for, if we are thinking of subatomic entities as generators, small changes of their proportions produce startling changes in properties.

It is therefore necessary to distinguish between primary and secondary generators, where those that are primary are subatomic and those that are secondary are derived from them and are in fact any observable entities that occupy a fundamental place in any science. Thus the chemical elements are secondary generators in chemistry, for they generate the properties of chemical compounds.* Again, the genes are generators which produce the hereditary properties of organisms. And the six components of the Œdipus situation are generators which produce the properties of personality types. In all these examples there is no difficulty in saying that secondary generators when mixed in various proportions give rise to natural kinds, in such a way that to a small change in the proportions of the generators there corresponds a small change in the properties produced. Thus the induction that alcohol intoxicates holds because small changes in the proportions of the secondary generators of alcohol produce only small changes in its properties, *i.e.* in the degree or kind of intoxication that ensues. It should be stressed that this sort of assertion is fundamentally a result of experience.

Broad took note of resemblance,[1] though he did not pursue the matter. Keynes seems to have had something similar in mind when he referred to what mathematicians call the superposition of small effects:

there might well be quite different laws for wholes of different degrees of complexity, and laws of connection between complexes which could not be stated in terms of laws connecting individual parts. In this case natural law would be organic and not, as it is generally supposed, atomic. If every configuration of the Universe were subject to a separate and independent law, or if very small differences between bodies—in their shape or size, for instance—led to their obeying quite different laws, prediction would be impossible and the inductive method useless. Yet nature might still be uniform, causation sovereign, and laws timeless and absolute.[2]

Again:

If the fundamental laws of connection changed altogether with variations, for instance, in the shape or size of bodies, or if the laws governing the behaviour of a complex had no relation whatever to the laws governing the behaviour of its parts when belonging to other complexes, there could hardly be a limitation of independent variety in the sense in which this has been defined. And, on the other hand, a

---

* If the generators are properties it would sound queer to say that the property of being oxygen generated the properties of oxygen; but if the generators are substances we could say that oxygen generated its properties. It is not important to decide on the correct way of speaking and I propose to leave the matter open.

[1] Broad, *Op. cit.*, pp. 33, 38, 41.

[2] Keynes, *Op. cit.*, p. 249.

limitation of independent variety seems necessarily to carry with it some degree of atomic uniformity. The underlying conception as to the character of the System of Nature is in each case the same.[3]

Nonetheless Keynes did not make his point explicit in his principles. Incidentally, he used an unhappy metaphor in speaking of the possibility of 'organic' wholes in contrast with atomic ones, for he had certainly no wish to exclude our knowledge of the organic world from the sphere of induction, and in fact the existence of organic wholes is in no way incompatible with the several principles under discussion. With regard to the underlying idea of the quotations, it is altogether too restricted; there are two facts Keynes failed to take into account, and these bring in the notion of primary generators.

The first fact is this. Although there is enormous variety within a kind, there is on the whole a fairly sharp boundary between one kind and another, as witnessed by the existence of general names and as graphically described by Broad. It is true that this distinctiveness of kinds is not absolute and at times somewhat arbitrary. Thus to a western eye a camel may have one hump or two, while to an Egyptian there are two types designated by different names. One might imagine that biologists would be in trouble if the law of natural selection had not deprived them of nearly all the kinds of living things that have ever existed. If all the varieties of ape-man were to exist now side by side with all the varieties of ape and all the varieties of man, one might imagine that there would be a continuous shading of one variety into another. This is probably true as a matter of degree: that is to say, lines of demarcation of kinds would have been more arbitrary and classification would have been more difficult. Nonetheless it would always be possible in general to distinguish kinds, even if it were difficult to know what to do with border-line cases. But, even if there were such a continuous shading, it is certainly true that the chemical elements do not shade into one another. This leads to the second fact. In the subatomic sphere, a small change in the proportion of generators produces a great change in the properties produced. Thus, if from the eight electrons, eight protons, and eight neutrons that form oxygen we take away one of each, the result is nitrogen. Now we cannot alter the number of electrons in oxygen by a hundredth of an electron; we can alter the propor-

[3] *Id.*, p. 261.

tions only in whole numbers. It might therefore be urged that the change made in the numbers of subatomic entities was not a small one; but, while this might reasonably be maintained where oxygen is concerned, it could hardly be claimed with uranium.

These two facts can be described by means of the concept of primary generators: although there is great variety within a kind and the change from one kind to another is sometimes due to a large change among the generators, it is sometimes, as with the chemical elements, due to a small change in the generators, which are here distinguished as primary. Thus the concept of secondary generator is being used in the context of small changes producing small changes, and that of primary generator in the context of small changes producing great changes.* The importance of the distinction is that it affords a way of describing the general fact that in the universe there is a great deal of continuous shading of one thing into another and yet that there is also a certain amount of non-continuous change. It is important not to stress one at the expense of the other. It would not do to be over zealous to introduce the notion of resemblance into induction or continuous change, and forget that subatomic physics is concerned fundamentally with the discontinuous.

The preceding discussion may be summed up as the *Principle of Small and Great Changes*:

Certain entities, known as secondary generators, are found, which are such that small variations in the proportions in which they are mixed produce small changes in the properties they vertically generate. And certain other entities, known as primary generators, are found, which are such that small variations in the proportions in which they are mixed produce great changes in the properties or in the secondary generators they vertically cause.

What light is thrown on the requirements previously laid down for induction? It is evident that (9) and (10), already satisfied by the Principle of Limitation of Independent Variety, are again satisfied and even explained. Thus the Principle of Small Changes

---

* The distinction may not be absolutely precise, because it is possible to find examples in which small changes in secondary generators do produce great changes in the resulting properties. Thus small changes in the heat of water do not appreciably affect its properties; but there comes a time when another small change produces the properties of steam. And the same sort of phenomenon can happen with shall changes among genes. It might be possible and for some purposes desirable to make further distinctions within the concept of secondary generator; but for the purpose in hand there is no need to do so, for we are concerned with the broad distinction between generating small changes and generating great changes.

justifies the requirement of resemblance (9). With regard to C(11), how much departure from identity is permissible? No general formula can be given for this, but it is easy to describe the practical method for deciding it. Things that are classed together as similar are so classed on intuitive grounds: it is intuitively clear that they are much closer to one another than to other things. Thus, in general, it is easy to class various shades of red together and not be tempted to include a blue one or to omit a red one; and similarly with the alcohols. No doubt intuition is not a magical capacity; it must arise out of experience. In practice it is probably a rapid operation based partly upon the existence of general words and partly upon previous experience. Thus if a certain perceptual degree of departure from identity is allowed to enter into an induction, this is because this sort of departure has been found inductively not to lead to wrong results. The intuition involved is a perceptual intuition. The possibility of introducing small errors through neglecting spatio-temporal differences (12) is admitted, but there is no general formula for estimating the error; in practice the scientist neglects any possible error until it becomes persistently noticeable, and in a given domain of inquiry he may then be able to find a way of estimating it. Thus in astronomical physics it was assumed since Newton that a train travelling at uniform velocity with respect to an observer at a station always remained the same in length; but with the advent of the theory of relativity it was realised that for this observer the train became foreshortened, and a formula can be provided that shows precisely the size of this minute change. Similarly in Newtonian mechanics the calculated rotation of the perihelion of Mercury during a century is wrong by as little as three-quarters of a minute, which necessitates a small change in the law of gravitation, and a formula for this could be shown in detail. In particular cases, therefore, requirement (13) is covered, and so far as secondary generators are concerned requirements C do not give rise to any difficulty.

The Principle of Small and Great Changes would apply to the spatio-temporal proximity of generators: while small changes in the spatio-temporal position of secondary generators would in general have only a small-order effect, small changes in that of primary generators might well be expected to have large-scale effects. Thus the presence of a neutron in an atomic nucleus on the one hand or on the other just outside the nucleus though within the atom might cause an explosion or merely the properties of an element.

Discussion of the Principles.

Keynes's attitude towards the Principle of Limitation of Independent Variety and his treatment of it are in an important respect different from that presented in this chapter. He hoped that it would provide a basis for induction, *i.e.* a premiss that would make inductive reasoning probable; he therefore took steps to establish it. He made no attempt to prove it certain—it would serve his purpose as a prop for induction if it could be shown to be probable; subsequent experience would then increase its probability.* Broad, working on similar lines, mentions the difficulty of proof and also thinks of his concept of natural kinds as providing a premiss.[1] Thus the Keynes-Broad view invests the Principle of Limitation with an epistemic status, *i.e.* the principle must be independently known if inductive inference is to be valid. But, if we adhere to the scientific outlook and eschew the transcendental conception of *a priori* synthetic propositions, then the principle can be known only as a tautology, which it certainly is not, or as a result of experience.

According to the present treatment it is at best a result of experience— and abstracted from certain very general scientific conclusions. It therefore presupposes scientific inference and cannot without circular reasoning be an epistemic ground of such inference. I conclude, therefore, that the Principle of Limitation of Independent Variety is not an inductive premiss at all. Its status, though not epistemic, may be constitutive, *i.e.* without it induction could hardly be successful; but we cannot prove it constitutive without induction, and it remains without a logical basis so long as induction remains without one. *The principle as here presented is no more than a description of the structure of the universe as depicted by plausible inductions or rather by accepted hypotheses. I em-*

---

* Keynes, *Op. cit.*, pp. 259–60; explained below, Appendix to Ch. XXII. He seems to add an argument to show that the Principle of Limitation has some probability: *i.e.* he seems to argue that there is a probability of a limited number of groups, because otherwise it would be improbable that a given set of properties p, q, r would specify another set x, y (Keynes, *Op. cit.*, pp. 252–3). This is not valid because there might be some means other than the principle of making it probable that p, q, r would specify x, y. But there is a further difficulty: at most the principle would make it probable that p, q, r would in the past have specified x, y; we should continue to lack grounds for thinking it probable either that p, q, r would specify x, y in the future or that the principle itself would hold in the future.

[1] C. D. Broad, "The Relation between Induction and Probability (I)", *Mind*, N.S. Vol. XXVII, No. 108, London, 1918.

phasise that it is a description. It is not asserted to hold of the universe in general but simply to describe the parts of the universe where scientific inference works.* Alternatively it may be interpreted as a formal hypothesis we entertain about experience, i.e. *as an expression of the formal structure of our expectations.*

The same remarks apply to the other three principles.

The two principles, Limitation of Independent Variety and Uniform Generation of Properties, constitute the Keynes-Broad 'inductive hypothesis'—at least Keynes used the phrase.[1]

Keynes took the two principles to amount to more or less the same thing; but close analysis shows that they are very different. He probably supposed they were the same because he insensibly lumped together two different applications of the Principle of Limitation: he arrived at it from considering properties, but he thought of it in application to generators. It does apply in so far as there cannot be an unlimited number of generators in a group each producing a property; and it would apply completely if generators were determinable and determinate each producing a property; but all this is foreign to the present conception. It does not apply to the number of groups in which a generator can occur, because there is simply no limit to this; for, according to the present treatment, differences between natural kinds are due not to limitations upon groups of generators but to the proportions in which generators are mixed.

The conception of generators in one-one correspondence with properties, or a conception approaching this, is in fact the interpretation put upon Keynes, probably correctly, by Broad in his further development of the subject; many problems then arise, whether there can be a plurality of generators, whether there can be generators producing no property, and so on, which are obviated by the treatment adopted here.

From this point of view induction remains without a logical foundation; to base it on the four principles would be wrong. But this is not to say they are useless. On the contrary they give, or rather express, some real knowledge about the universe: they

---

* Keynes indeed places some such limitation upon it, and Broad is at some pains to show how unlikely it is that other parts of the universe should be different in this respect. Keynes would seem to be right in restricting it to that part of the universe that we are acquainted with; we should perhaps allow that, so far as present knowledge goes, there might be 'other worlds than ours' in which induction could not take place. The alternative would be to hold that such 'worlds' had no meaning. The truth of the matter is hardly fundamental.

[1] Keynes, *Op. cit.*, p. 260.

select the kinds of generalisation that are fundamental in giving a picture of the universe, though in this they do no more than give a forceful picture of what a scientist knows.

The Principle of Small and Great Changes, which really contains that of Uniform Generation, serves to explain the Principle of Limitation; in other words, the more fundamental generalisations serve to explain the more superficial ones; or horizontal causation, in terms of which many laws are expressed, is analysed into relations of vertical causation. Our troubles arise mainly with this relation and the concept of primary generator. Are we to say, for example, that there exist identical primary generators, which are numerically distinct, and that they produce secondary generators that are identical apart from spatio-temporal differences? Or are we to say that the generators are only similar? We met this point in connexion with the Law of Uniformity of Nature, and found that there was no criterion for identity. For the same reasons as were given in that connexion, it is equally meaningless to seek identity here, either for the generators or for their surroundings. There is no alternative to interpreting the Principle of Great Changes in terms of similarity of primary and of secondary generators. I do not think that this is objectionable. The result may remove a pleasant air of self-evidence or *a priori* guarantee from the most fundamental of our principles—but if they were self-evident or *a priori* there would be something wrong with them. What, then, is to be the test of sufficient similarity? There is no precise test; there is only an intuitive apprehension, reinforced by previous experience, that some generators are sufficiently alike to be put into one class and sufficiently unlike others that are put into another class.

Very recently principles similar to the preceding ones have been elaborated by Russell,[1] because he considers that Keynes's 'inductive hypothesis' is arbitrary and not sufficiently fundamental.[2] He puts forward five postulates: (i) quasi-permanence; (ii) causal lines; (iii) spatio-temporal continuity; (iv) common origin of similar structures; and (v) analogy.

These are easily explained. (i) We have no evidence that an object, such as a chair, is absolutely identical at different moments

---

[1] Bertrand Russell, *Human Knowledge: Its Scope and Limits*, London, 1948, Pt. VI, Chs. V–IX, pp. 471–515.
[2] *Id.*, p. 462.

or in different positions. But we have evidence of relative per-manence in that a chair at one moment in one place is *very similar* to what we identify as the 'same' chair at another moment when we have moved it; great changes do not take place. This 'quasi-permanence' is postulated by Russell as characterising most objects in the universe. (ii) If we consider the chair during a stretch of time, we may for convenience speak of it at any instant as a 'momentary chair'. Then the time sequence of 'momentary chairs' constitutes a 'line' through time, and Russell regards it as a 'causal line' because he holds that a 'momentary chair' is causally dependent on the preceding 'momentary chair'. (iii) The sequence of 'momentary chairs' is continuous—we do not find two suc-cessive 'momentary chairs' widely separated in space. Thus the postulate asserts that one 'momentary chair' is in the neighbour-hood of its predecessor. (iv) 'Momentary-chair' experiences by different people at one time are to be referred to one 'momentary chair' as their cause. (v) If there is reason to believe that X causes E, then when we observe X it is probable that E is present also. This is the postulate of analogy.

It will be noticed that Russell's postulates of continuity and of quasi-permanence are very like those of proximity and of small changes, which I have added to Keynes's. His postulate of com-mon origin of structures is not the same as the Principle of Uni-form Generation of Properties but closely connected with it. Those of causal lines and of analogy seem to me to be implied by the Principle of Limitation of Independent Variety, *i.e.* to amount to being descriptions of some of the ways in which independent variety is limited.

Thus Russell's contribution here seems to me to consist of an explication of Keynes's 'inductive hypothesis' together with some additions; consequently the same comments I have made on Keynes apply to Russell—the postulates cannot be established even as probable, cannot be part of the structure of induction, and can only be the result of experience or, alternatively, formal features of our expectations about experience.

There is, however, one general feature of Russell's presentation that may be mentioned: his postulates relate more closely than those of Keynes to the unity in space and time of the ordinary objects of perception, as exemplified in our repeated experience of sugar melting in tea or of lead being heavy; and this might give them additional importance in the philosophy of sense-perception.

CHAPTER XVII

INDUCTION AS A SUCCESSFUL HABIT

THE Keynes-Broad treatment of induction is in the line of descent from Mill: it is largely, though not wholly, empirical; it seeks a basis that shall justify induction. There is, however, one great difference: Mill sought for a certain postulate leading to inferences that were certain; the Keynes-Broad view is content with a probable postulate leading to probable inferences. The chief rival of this tradition comes from Logical Positivism, which is uncompromisingly empirical.

Induction is regarded by positivists as a pseudo-problem: that is to say, it is held to be a mistake to seek a basis for induction in some postulate; nothing is really required to guarantee the validity of inductive inference. Causation may be regarded as a special case of the inductive relation; hence with it, too, no ground is to be sought. Causation must therefore consist only of regularity of conjunction, without the backing of any necessity. This interpretation of causation is very like the Law of Uniformity of Nature, so far as this asserts mere concomitance, but in the positivist view it is not a law or a general truth used as a premiss in induction. Thus it differs from the Keynes-Broad view in being more radically empirical and in not being a postulate.

It will be convenient to speak of the inductive or causal relation, according to the positivist interpretation, as consisting of *de facto* uniformity. The germ of it is to be found in Occasionalism and in Berkeley. According to both, there was no necessary connexion between phenomena, no active agency in the perceptual world by which a cause necessitated an effect. They went beyond Positivism, however, in seeking a ground for uniformities: these were due to the agency of a non-empirical power, namely God. This was thus a fundamental cause, and what are ordinarily called "causes" were causes only by courtesy. It is interesting, incidentally, that the kind of causation admitted was of a vertical kind and not horizontal.

To be clear, it would be well at this point to dispose of a verbal point. It is open to the positivist to hold that there are horizontal causes but that the relation is merely one of *de facto* uniformity; or to hold that there is no such thing as a causal relation, because of the assumption that the word "cause" signifies, in addition to *de facto* uniformity, a relation of necessity or some mystical relation underlying the uniformity. The latter way of speaking means that causation is a myth; the former means that a technical meta-scientific use is recommended for the word. Either way will serve provided we do not allow ourselves to be misled. On the whole it is simpler to retain the word "cause", giving it a purely empirical sense.

Hume took over the Berkeleian doctrine of *de facto* uniformity without, however, basing it upon a non-empirical ground[1]; he was undoubtedly, therefore, the first real positivist. Though Mill, so far as he was an empiricist followed Hume, the unadulterated form of the doctrine lay dormant till it was revived in the present century. It has been adopted by Wittgenstein,[2] Ramsey,[3] Carnap,[4] Ayer,[5] and others.

Hume's account is well known. If you put a piece of paper in the fire, you do not *observe* any causal activity in the fire, burning the paper; all you see is the paper first in the fire and then the paper on fire. For the occurrence of the consequent after the antecedent there is no agent, and there is no justifiable reason to expect similar consequents in the future following similar antecedents. Nevertheless human beings have an expectation to this effect, and this belief is founded upon custom. Hume's full account would therefore not be that causation consisted in *de facto* uniformity but that it consisted in *de facto* uniformity customarily expected.

The fullest and most original modern account is given by Ramsey. Though causation consists of *de facto* uniformity,

we make sentences called causal laws from which . . . we proceed to actions and propositions connected with them in a certain way, and say that a fact asserted in a proposition which is an instance of causal law is a case of causal necessity. This is a regular feature of our conduct, a part of the general regularity of things.[6]

[1] David Hume, *A Treatise of Human Nature*, Bk. I, Pt. iii, Sect. 14; *An Enquiry concerning Human Nature*, Sect. 7.
[2] Ludwig Wittgenstein, *Tractatus Logico-Philosophicus*, London, 1922, 6.3–6.3611.
[3] F. P. Ramsey, *The Foundations of Mathematics*, London, 1931, "General Propositions and Causality"; also pp. 197–8.
[4] Rudolf Carnap, *The Logical Syntax of Language*, London, 1937, esp. p. 323.
[5] A. J. Ayer, *Language, Truth and Logic*, London, 1936, pp. 46–8, 56–8, 242–4; *The Foundations of Empirical Knowledge*, London, 1940, pp. 183–220.
[6] Ramsey, *Op. cit.*, p. 252.

Thus our conduct, too, displays regularity and we may speak of this as causation. He calls this not a "descriptive theory" but a "forecasting" one:

to regard a law as a summary of certain facts seems to me inadequate; it is also an attitude of expectation for the future.[1]

Ramsey is analysing causation into *de facto* uniformity plus a mental habit; the habit consists of basing our beliefs about the uniformities of the future upon those of the past.

We should all agree that inductive beliefs were *reasonable*; but, since the approach appears to make them unreasonable, it is necessary to see if they can be called "reasonable" in a satisfactory sense. According to Ramsey, they are reasonable in the sense that they are useful or successful—the habit of relying on such beliefs works, *i.e.* the beliefs turn out on the whole to be true, for the future usually supports them.

This position has been examined with care by Ewing.[2] He points out that, though we may agree that the habit *has been* reasonable in the past in the sense that it *has been* useful, *i.e.* that the habit of using induction in the past *has* worked, yet this does not show that the habit *will continue* to be useful or *continue* to work in the future; and Ramsey undoubtedly wished to hold that a habit that has been useful in the past will also be useful in the future. What, then, is the ground of the inference from past utility to future utility? If the inference is reasonable, continues Ewing, it must be reasonable in a sense different from that employed in the argument, and Ramsey has made no attempt to give an account of this new sense of "reasonable". Ewing might have added a criticism of another point: Ramsey asserted that the habit in question was itself a regular feature of experience and could be spoken of as a causal law; then it, too, would have to be analysed into regularity plus a habit; hence the analysis of the inductive habit involves what we might call a second-order habit which itself would involve a third-order habit and so on *ad infinitum*. This would seem to be unsatisfactory but Ramsey might have accepted it.

Ewing's objection to the Hume-Ramsey view seems to be insuperable. I add another objection that also seems insuperable. The view entails that a cause has nothing to do with its effect

---

[1] *Id.*, p. 255.
[2] A. C. Ewing, *Idealism*, London, 1934, pp. 157–8.

beyond being present in a certain corner of space-time; since causation is objectively no more than *de facto* uniformity, apart from the psychological addendum about habit, there is nothing about the cause other than its mere *presence* that *produces* the effect. A metaphor will explain the point involved. Positivists seem to regard a cause as a kind of *catalyst*, *i.e.* something that, as chemists once believed, brought about an effect by its *presence* alone without undergoing any changes. In chemistry manganese dioxide is a well-known catalyst: when heated with potassium chlorate, oxygen is produced; but the manganese dioxide remains practically intact as if it had not entered into the chemical action. It is, of course, now known that catalytic agents do in fact enter into a chemical process: for instance, the manganese dioxide first forms another compound with oxygen which it derives from the potassium chlorate, and then it gives off this oxygen, thus resuming more or less its original state. It seems to me that, just as chemists felt the need to look deeper into the nature of catalytic action, so positivists should ask whether there is not something more than catalytic causation (as "catalytic" was once understood), *i.e.* whether causes are not catalysts (in the modern sense), which deeper investigation will show really enter into the production of an effect, instead of merely enabling the effect to take place in an aristocratic way by their presence alone.

I would add another criticism, one that accuses the Hume-Ramsey position not of being false, but of failing to mention and discuss an integral part of the subject—the theory of probability. The position must satisfy requirements (4) and (14), to the effect that one inductive argument can be more probable than another and that it is possible for an inductive argument to become extremely probable. If the Hume-Ramsey view is to be justified, it ought not to overlook the need to investigate the theory of probability; in fact the view is almost certain to go with the frequency theory, and writers on this subject are very much alive to the bearing their work has upon induction. Discussion of the theory of probability, however, must await another chapter.

A word should be added about a treatment of induction that is either positivist or nearly so. Lewy[1] takes the unusual course of making induction deductive, but not of course in the way that

[1] Casimir Lewy, "On the 'Justification' of Induction", *Analysis*, Vol. VI, Nos. 5 and 6, Oxford, 1939, pp. 87–90.

would now be almost universally rejected. We have a good reason to believe an inductive conclusion and we have a good reason solely because of the evidence for it contained in the premisses. On account of the usage of the phrase "good reason to believe" involved here, our having a good reason to believe the conclusion of an induction follows logically or deductively from the premisses, for the denial of this assertion would contradict the premisses.[1] It should be noted carefully that it is not the denial of the conclusion that would contradict the premisses, but the denial of the final assertion, *i.e.* that we have a good reason to believe the conclusion. This way of treating the matter does not differ essentially from Ramsey's, for it amounts to saying that it is reasonable to believe inductive conclusions. No attempt is made to investigate 'a good reason for a belief'. As it happens, there exists an attempt to define "a good reason for a belief", made earlier by Moore:[2] a good reason is a statement which is true, but which would prob-ably not be true unless the belief were true. Here the good reason consists of the premisses of the induction, and it is supposed to be true if the belief is true. Unfortunately the old difficulty about induction breaks out again. This definition may provide that the premisses follow from the conclusion of an inductive argument; but that does not help us to justify the converse, that the premisses yield the conclusion, which in fact constitutes the formal fallacy of affirming the antecedent. We know very well that in induction we do commit this fallacy with monotonous regularity; but why is it successful? Another difficulty is this. We have a good reason to believe an inductive conclusion, asserts the argument. Pre-sumably this means the conclusions not of all inductions but only of good ones; if so, how do we tell the good from the bad? The answer would presumably be in terms of positive analogy and the like; but why would inductions with high positive analogy be better than those where this was low? The striking feature of Lewy's argument is the deductive form he gives it. But it is evident that the argument is also one of probability. Hence he is regarding an inductive conclusion as one that is deductively probable, a contention that was made in Chapter VI; unfor-tunately his stress on deduction suggests deduction that is certain. I do not think, however, that he was aiming at expounding the

---

[1] *Id.*, pp. 89–90.
[2] G. E. Moore, *Philosophical Studies*, "The Nature and Reality of Objects of Per-ception" (1905–6), London, 1922, esp. p. 35.

notion of deductive probability; his aim seems to have been to deny the need to justify induction by *persuading* us that induction can be trusted.

This last point is of some importance. It is no doubt of value to remind philosophers with pathological doubts about generalisation that the method is a very good one; but to remind them or to persuade them of this is not to furnish them with the essential nature of inductive inference. Positivists, who try to show that induction is a pseudo-problem or that there is no need to 'justify' induction, display a blind spot for an obvious fact: it may be perfectly true that induction is reliable and that it is a different kind of inference from formal logic, but these points help in no way to make us understand the reasonableness of a process that actually violates the principles of formal logic. Why do we say that it is a different kind of inference from ordinary logic? The only reason is that it violates the principles of the latter! In other words we can find out that an argument *need not* obey formal inference only by noticing that it *does not* in fact obey. Those who are primarily interested in the frequency theory of probability but also hold the positivist belief in *de facto* uniformity do not make the mistake here discussed; they are willing to speak of justifying induction and they hold that the frequency theory can do it.

On the different approaches to induction some comment may be made. The positivist view is commonly regarded as in opposition to the Keynes-Broad hypothesis. They are in opposition, because the hypothesis is designed to justify induction, which the positivist holds needs no justification. But, according to the present approach, the Keynes-Broad account, or rather the four principles I have substituted for it, those of Limitation of Independent Variety, Spatio-Temporal Proximity, Uniform Generation of Properties, and Great and Small Changes, can be seen to be without opposition to the Hume-Ramsey view; for the four inductive principles constitute no more than a description of the universe where scientific conclusions have in fact held good; and, if no more is claimed for them there would be no need for the positivist to deny them (except in so far as they are inaccurate or incomplete).

But, if the Keynes-Broad attempt to justify induction does not succeed, this does not mean that Positivism is correct. We may hope that some other approach will prove more fruitful—such as

that of the hypothetico-deductive system. And in this connexion
we may mention one more—perhaps the strongest—objection to
the positivist approach to induction: the explanatory power of
hypotheses, by which they explain facts lying outside the field of
facts they were originally constructed to explain, remains un-
accounted for.

CHAPTER XVIII

THE VERTICAL CAUSAL NEXUS

ASSUMING that the objections to interpreting causation as *de facto* uniformity are valid, what is the alternative? Following the historical lead of the Leibniz-Wolff approach we might ask if the causal relation was essentially a logical one, such that a cause *entails* its effect in the same sort of way that the premisses of a syllogism entail the conclusion. This has in fact been advocated by Ewing,[1] who holds that no inference would be possible from cause to effect unless there were a logical relation between them. His case consists not so much of a positive argument for his view as of an attempt to dispel the difficulties that may be ascribed to it. Thus we find it hard to see an *a priori* connexion between any given cause and its effect; but he thinks that there may for all that be such a connexion, which is as difficult for us now to see as it was for mathematicians some three thousand years ago to see the necessary relations that hold between properties of triangles. And he holds that there may be some *a priori* intuition enabling us to see such relations, though not in the physical sphere, at least in the realm of the mind:

It seems to me that we can see and to some extent really understand why an insult should tend to give rise to anger, why love should lead to grief if the object of one's love die or prove untrustworthy, why a success should give pleasure, why the anticipation of physical pain should arouse fear.[2]

Undoubtedly we do intuit the psychological relations described by Ewing; but it is not clear that they are logical in character; unfortunately to settle the point in this way would require a detailed psychological analysis. It is not difficult, however, to criticise Ewing's view in another way. It is hard to see any analogy between the causal relation and that between premisses and conclusions of a deduction, and it is likely to be more profitable to seek another view. This of course is not a refutation; but refuta-

[1] A. C. Ewing, *Idealism*, London, 1934, pp. 167–77.
[2] *Id.*, p. 176.

tion can be given by pointing out that if Ewing were right, it would be self-contradictory that the effect should fail to occur, given the cause; and this is generally held not to be self-contradictory, no matter how unlikely it may be. We may go further and say that, even if the effect always in fact occurs when the cause does, and even if it always in fact will occur, yet it is not self-contradictory to suppose that the effect might not take place, given the cause.

What is the alternative? Arguments have been given in the previous chapter against regarding causation as *de facto* uniformity, and now the only alternative apparently is rejected.

Part of the difficulty disappears if we make use of the distinction between horizontal and vertical causation, for which inductive justification has already been found.

The argument that there is nothing self-contradictory about failure of the effect when the cause occurs shows that *horizontal* causation at least is not a logical relation; to this extent positivists are right. But the arguments against Positivism, given in the previous chapter, show that laws involving horizontal causation, if this consists of *de facto* uniformity alone, would be fortuitous and untrustworthy. Thus horizontal causation has no logical foundation and is not strong enough to stand on its own. The difficulty is overcome if the strength required in the causal nexus is placed in causation of the vertical kind. Now we have seen that the Principle of Uniform Generation of Properties appears to throw some light on the way in which inductive groups of properties occur. Let us develop this a little further.

Suppose for the moment that this principle contains a relation such that, given the generators, the things they produce *must* occur. Then the demand made by Ewing is satisfied, because in fact sets of properties found together in an inductive group *must* occur in such a group seeing that both sets would emanate from a given arrangement of generators. Thus hydrogen and oxygen when sparked must form water, because the pattern of hydrogen plus oxygen plus spark is produced by the same arrangement of generators that produces water. But we can see that, apart from this principle, *i.e.* if we limit ourselves to the Principle of Limitation of Independent Variety, there is nothing but *de facto* uniformity, and the reason why it would not be contradictory to suppose that water would not result from the sparking of hydrogen and oxygen is simply that we should be overlooking the generators.

12

This amounts to saying with Ewing that there may be a necessary relation that we have overlooked (though we may not commit ourselves to holding that it is a logical relation).

The foregoing paragraph was written upon the supposition that the Principle of Uniform Generation of Properties contained a necessary relation, and here our difficulties crop up again. But it will at least have been useful to focus the controversy in the proper place; for it seems to me that the rationalist *versus* empiricist dispute about causation has expended its energies wastefully by concentrating upon horizontal causation when it should turn on the nature of the vertical relation.

I have written for simplicity as if the Principle of Uniform Generation were the principle that involved a necessary relation, but clearly it is the more detailed analysis of that principle that is important in this connexion, namely the Principle of Great and Small Changes. There is not much doubt that, if the Principle of Great Changes were found to contain some necessary relation, then there would be little or nothing to settle with regard to the Principle of Small Changes.

The problem therefore comes to this. What is the nature of the relation, is it a necessary one, involved in the vertical causation of properties by subatomic entities? Is it necessary, for instance, that hydrogen should result from one proton and one electron? Is it necessary that when two pairs of protons and electrons (*i.e.* two units of hydrogen) are brought into contact with eight of each (oxygen) in the right conditions these entities should arrange themselves in the configuration of a molecule (of water)?

Consider the arguments from contemporary philosophy already mentioned; when applied to vertical causation they are just as cogent or just as weak as in their original setting. With Hume and Ramsey we must agree that no necessary relation can be *observed*. In accordance with Ewing's argument there is no meaning in saying that it is reasonable to expect the effect, given the cause, if there is no necessary relation. I have added that without a necessary nexus a cause would be a kind of catalyst. In seeking a necessary relation, we might interpret causation as a *dynamic* relation—as opposed to catalytic; we might seek something analogous to the power in a wound-up spring to release itself. The positivist would agree that there is in a sense such power, *i.e.* if you hold the spring you will feel pressure and if you release your hold the spring will in fact unwind—at least you may confidently expect this to happen—but there is no necessity about it. What, then, is the evidence for necessity? It would be fatally easy to fall back on worn-out arguments, such as that a proton and an electron would not be what they are if they did not always have the properties we have come to expect of them, or that from the law of identity they must have these properties so long as their surrounding conditions remain the same. But all such arguments are just as defective here as in their original sphere. No necessity can be found.

CHAPTER XIX

IMPASSE IN THE INDUCTIVE APPROACH

We have seen in Part I that the hypothetico-deductive system is the characteristic framework of scientific inference. This means that there cannot be a *method* of induction. We have also seen that there are non-instantial concepts, and that a non-instantial hypothesis, which embodies them, cannot be the conclusion in an inductive *inference*. In Part II we have considered the claim of induction to be a type of scientific inference concerned with generalisations which are instantial. To justify it, one or other of the major premisses discussed has to be introduced: the Law of Uniformity of Nature or of Universal Causation, the Principle of Limitation of Independent Variety or some principle of uniform connexion between generators and inductive properties. But none of these is successful. On the other hand, the positivist approach, which corresponds to the operationalist handling of hypotheses, leaves the problem unsolved. Thus neither approach to induction solves the problem.

It is worth bringing out this *impasse* in a particular form. Discussion of induction has led to concentration on the nature of the causal relation; the problem of induction is epitomised in the problem of interpreting this relation.

Let X be a factor afterwards identified as a cause and E be a factor afterwards identified as an effect. Let us perform some experiments and apply the criteria for causal determination given in Chapter XI. Suppose we select those experiments to which the only relevant criteria are the four 'criteria of probable causal laws' forming group II of that chapter. Of these three the last four give the basic usage of "cause" (the first one constitutes the first half of the second and yields a causal conclusion because it affords some evidence that the second half would not be falsified if tested). Considerations of plurality and diversity being omitted for simplicity, we obtain the conclusion "X is probably a necessary condition for the occurrence of E" or "X is probably a sufficient condition for the occurrence of E"; and, as we prefer to use the word "cause", this is written "X is probably a necessary cause of

E" or "X is probably a sufficient cause of E". The reference to more than one state of affairs (X, E present and then X, E absent) shows that we cannot define "X causes E" by saying that if a factor like X occurs then one like E will occur, because we should have to hedge the definition around with conditions which would make it as long as the causal criteria.

It is important to stress that the conclusion, "X is probably a cause (necessary or sufficient) of E", depends upon more than one experiment; we cannot in general base a causal connexion upon a single instance (in the rare cases where this is possible a great deal of previous experience comes into play). We are therefore dealing with a class of experiments in which X occurs, a class in which X does not occur, and similarly for E. Hence the conclusion is a statement about classes of experiments. Moreover in these experiments the X's must be taken to be resembling and not to be identical in character, and also the E's. We thus arrive at the following definitions: "X is probably a necessary cause of E" means *If a member of a class of resembling E's occurs then a member of a class of resembling X's has occurred, and if an X does not occur then an E does not occur.* "X is probably a sufficient cause of E" means *If a member of a class of resembling X's occurs then a member of a class of resembling E's occurs, and if an E does not occur then an X has not occurred.*

This approach to a definition is in keeping with Empiricism. It shows the difficulty of a conception such as *causal essence*: we are always dealing with classes of resembling factors; to interpret these in terms of *causal essence* would be to give an untestable speculation about resembling factors. It would be difficult to persist with such a conception if we bore in mind the importance of classes and of the relation of resemblance.

This conclusion, which is equivalent to saying that "X causes E" is not a statement about a causal essence, is fatal to the attempt to justify induction. It is no doubt difficult to accept, for most of us—perhaps all—think of "cause" as standing for a particular thing and not as referring to a class of things. On the other hand, if we interpret "X causes E" as a shorthand way of speaking about classes, we have no principle that can make the slightest pretence of justifying induction. Induction is not a method. Interpreted as a type of inference it leads to an *impasse*. The hypothetico-deductive system offers the only alternative approach known to us. It is the pattern of all scientific inference, whether this is concerned overtly with hypotheses or apparently with 'inductive' generalisations. It is therefore satisfactory methodologically; whether it is an adequate basis for dealing with the fundamental metascientific questions is another matter.

PART III

CHAPTER XX

SOME THEOREMS IN PROBABILITY

RENEWED interest in the problem of induction has developed during this century as a result of progress in the theory of probability; great expectations have been aroused that the problem could be solved by this theory. After all, if inductive conclusions are no longer required to be certain, may we not hope to prove them probable? Whether or not this approach leads up a blind alley remains to be seen.

The study of probability may be divided into three parts: (i) the mathematical theory, which contains theorems used in the solution of theoretical and practical problems; (ii) the logical theory, which is the mathematical treatment of the foundations of the ordinary superstructure of mathematical theorems; and (iii) the metascientific problems of the meaning of "probability" and the relation of probability to induction. It would be foreign to the purpose of this book to give any detailed treatment of the mathematical theory, which can be found in various textbooks. The logical theory, initiated by Keynes,[1] is a branch of mathematical logic; a knowledge of it is essential in order to understand some of the metascientific arguments that have been put forward in connexion with induction. It will be omitted for reasons of space, apart from a sketch given in the appendix to Chapter XXII, because it is possible to explain what are the issues involved without recourse to the basic theory, and because Jeffreys[2] has given a short and simple treatment of it.

This chapter aims mainly at describing the contents of some celebrated theorems, the names of which unfortunately vary widely in different books, and to sift out the very small number of theorems that are referred to in discussions of probability and induction. It will be assumed that the reader knows how to carry

---

[1] J. M. Keynes, *A Treatise on Probability*, London, 1921.
[2] Harold Jeffreys, *Scientific Inference*, Cambridge, 1931, Ch. II.

out the simplest of probability calculations, as explained in an elementary algebra book.

If you are throwing a die and are betting on turning up an ace, it will be convenient to call this result a "positive alternative" and any other result a "negative alternative". It will be convenient to refer to the result of a set of trials as "the field". As usual, 'certainty' will be denoted by 1, 'impossibility' by 0, and probability by a fraction between 0 and 1 inclusive.

It is easy to see that simple calculations are carried out with the aid of two basic rules: the *multiplication* rule and the *addition* rule. Thus if the probability of a certain horse winning one race and that of another horse winning another race are given, the probability of 'a double', *i.e.* of both horses winning, is obtained by *multiplying* the two given probabilities. The multiplication rule concerns combined events. Again, given the probabilities of each of two horses in a race winning, then the probability of *one or other* winning is the *sum* of the two given probabilities. The addition rule concerns disjunctive events. We note that, if p is the probability that a certain horse will win (positive alternative), and q that it will lose (negative alternative), $p + q = 1$, and also that the probability of the negative alternative is $1 - p$.

We shall have occasion to discuss the average value of the spots shown by a throw of a group of dice; that is, with the 'mean' of the set. If the dice are thrown many times, we can find the average of the means of the sets (or mean of means). This can be calculated otherwise thus: take the average of the spots of the first die for all its throws, the average for the second, and so on, and then of these means take the average. Thus, it is all one whether we take the average of the means of the sets of throws or the average of the means of all the throws with each die. We shall then be concerned with the probability of getting a certain average of means, especially when the number of throws is increased indefinitely and/or the number of dice in a set.

Now all such illustrations with dice over-simplify the situation involved in general theorems, because the probabilities of getting all spots with a die are equal—provided the die is 'true', and if we introduce examples to do with loaded dice, where the probabilities of each face are unequal, the complexity defeats the point of the examples. But unequal probabilities must be taken account of in general theorems, and this leads to the notion of the *weighting* of probabilities. Suppose a coin is loaded so that the probability of getting a head is 2/3 and of a tail is 1/3; and let the head be marked 18 and the tail 12. If we throw a set of six such coins several times we should not expect to get an average of means equal to $\frac{1}{2}(18 + 12)$ or 15, because of the loading in favour of 18's and against 12's. What has to be done is to *weight* the proportion of 18's that would be expected if probabilities were equal by multiplying by the probability of an 18, and *weight* the proportion of 12's similarly with the probability of a 12. You would normally expect three 18's and three 12's; but here you would expect four 18's and two 12's. The average expected number would be obtained by calculating $18 \times 2/3 + 12 \times 1/3$, *i.e.* 16. Thus the weighted average is the sum of the results of multiplying each alternative by its probability. When, therefore, we come to questions of averages, weighted averages will be meant where demanded by the context.

We shall be concerned with two classes of theorems: (I) those that tell us what may be expected to happen, given a probability; and (II) those that tell us, given that something has happened, what some unknown probability was.

I. Direct Theorems

Tchebysheff's Theorem

Consider n quantities $x, y, z, \ldots$ which severally vary and which have probabilities $p, q, r, \ldots$ that vary with them. Take their weighted mean and their mean: that is to say, first take the weighted mean of x, then of y, and so on, by allowing each quantity to vary, and then take the average of these means; and second take their mean as a group. We now have an average of weighted means and a mean. Consider the difference between these two results, bearing in mind that both depend on n. Tchebysheff asserts that the statement, "this difference is less than a quantity that diminishes (towards zero) as n increases (indefinitely)", has a probability less than unity by an amount that diminishes (towards zero) as n increases (indefinitely). An immediate consequence is that it is practically certain that the difference in question is less than any assigned quantity or approaches zero, as n approaches infinity. Or we may express it thus: the statement, "the average value of single quantities $x, y, \ldots$, as the number of them increases indefinitely, approaches indefinitely close to the average value of their weighted means obtained by letting each vary separately", has a probability that approaches indefinitely close to unity.

To illustrate this, let a set of several dice be thrown several times. The spots of the first die are values of x, those of the second are values of y, and so on. Take (i) the mean of spots for each die for all its throws (not a weighted mean if for simplicity we consider only the case where the probabilities of all spots are equal) and then the average of these means; and take (ii) the average value of spots arising from a single throw of the set. Then it is increasingly probable that (i) approaches (ii) as the number of dice increases.

This theorem provides one of the best ways of leading up to others that are generally regarded as of greater metascientific interest.

Poisson's Theorem

If we are interested only in throwing aces, which will therefore be positive alternatives, and call them 1 and negative alternatives 0, then the values of x, y, . . will always be 1 or 0. Hence the average of the weighted means taken for each die for all possible different throws will be the expected proportion of 1's; and the average of the spots of a single throw will be the 'frequency' of aces in that throw. From Tchebysheff's theorem we infer that the statement, "the frequency of aces in a single set approaches indefinitely close to the expected proportion of aces, *i.e.* to the probability of an ace, as the number of dice increases to infinity", has a probability that approaches unity as the number of dice approaches infinity.

This illustrates Poisson's theorem or the Law of Great Numbers. The example is perhaps misleading because unloaded dice do not provide an opportunity for weighting the means. But we could replace the set of dice by a set of urns containing black and white balls in different known proportions, where a positive alternative consists of drawing a white ball. In this way we reach a truer picture of the theorem: the statement, "the frequency of white balls, for one draw from each urn, as the number of urns approaches infinity, approaches the weighted probability of a white one", has a probability that approaches unity as the number of urns approaches infinity.

If we were giving a full account of the theorem we should also state it in a form referring not to the frequency of the positive alternative but to the actual number of positive alternatives; but this form will not be useful to us. Moreover, a mathematical treatment would introduce the theorem in a form involving only finite terms and then proceed to the form described; again this is not useful to us.

The general statement of Poisson's theorem may be put as follows: If we have n quantities $x, y, . .$ such that the probability of the occurrence of the positive alternative in x is p, that of its occurrence in y is q, and so on, then the statement, "the frequency of the positive alternative in $x, y, . .$ in a single set of these quantities, approaches indefinitely close, an n becomes indefinitely great, to the expected proportion of positive alternatives in the quantities $x, y, . .$, i.e. to the weighted probability of the positive alternative", has a probability that approaches indefinitely close to certainty as n approaches infinity.

Bernoulli's Theorem

Let the various probabilities of $x, y, . .$ be equal, i.e. the make-up of each urn will be the same. Then instead of having n urns for one experiment, we may have just one upon which we make n experiments of drawing a ball, provided we replace it after drawing it. In this form the situation is more easily thought of as simply throwing a die n times—or throwing n dice once. It is clear that the average expected proportion of positive alternatives now becomes simply the probability of it.

The general form of Bernoulli's theorem is: If we have a field of n members all equally probable then the statement, "the frequency of a certain positive alternative approaches indefinitely close to its probability, as n approaches infinity", has a probability that approaches unity as n approaches infinity.

As with Poisson's theorem, this one also has a finite form, which would be given in a mathematical treatment, concerning the total number of positive alternatives instead of the frequency of them; but this has no additional metascientific interest.

II. Inverse Theorems

Bayes's Theorem

Bayes's theorem is often cited in different forms. It has traditionally been associated with the probability of causes. Suppose we have two boxes, with two drawers, each containing a coin;

in the first box each drawer contains a gold coin and in the second box one drawer contains a gold coin and the other a silver one. A box is chosen at random, a drawer opened, and a gold coin found. What is the probability that it came from the second box? It is very easy to work this out—the answer is 1/3—and a simple formula can be established for this sort of problem. Now if we interpret the boxes as causes and the drawing of the coin as an effect, the formula gives the probability that the effect is due to, say, the second of the two possible causes.

It is important to recognise that the theorem, to be used, requires us to know the prior probabilities of the causes; also we have to know that one or other of the supposed causes is the actual cause.

Another form of the theorem enables us to compare the posterior probabilities of two possible laws in the light of new evidence favouring each in different degrees. ('Prior' probability refers to the probability of a law before new evidence is available; 'posterior' probability refers to its new probability in the light of new evidence.) Here, too, there is a simple formula. If p_1, p_2 are the prior probabilities of two laws and q_1, q_2 the probabilities that a certain event is due to them, respectively, then, if this event happens, the posterior probability of the first law is, for instance, greater than that of the second law if $p_1 q_1$ is greater than $p_2 q_2$.

This leads to the form of the law that figures most in meta-scientific discussion. If p is the prior probability of a law and q the probability that a certain event is due to it, then, if this event happens, the posterior probability of the law is proportional to pq. The importance of this is that, since the factor of proportionality is known, it is obvious from the full formula that the posterior probability is greater than the prior probability. Hence this form of Bayes's theorem is often regarded as the basis of increasing the probability of a law in the light of experience.

All these forms of the theorem can be easily seen to be equivalent; but that does not concern us. The theorem can be generalised, and the name "Bayes's theorem" is given to any of its forms.

The Inverted Bernoulli Theorem

The theorem just discussed is all that is strictly due to Bayes, though what follows is often called by his name. Bernoulli's theorem was inverted by Laplace and Poisson. The result may be expressed as follows.[1] If in a certain field a positive alternative occurs r times out of n, then the statement, "the probability of the alternative lies in the interval $(r/n + \varepsilon)$, where ε decreases as n increases", has a probability that approaches unity as n approaches infinity.

Bernoulli's theorem itself asserts that, given the probability p of an alternative, then the frequency is probably close to p if n is large—an argument from probability to frequency. Here if f is the frequency of the alternative in a large number n of trials, then f is the most probable value of the probability of the alternative— an argument from frequency to probability.

The conditions under which the theorem holds are:[2] (i) the probability of a positive alternative at any point is independent of the frequency of that alternative on previous occasions; (ii) it is independent of its probability at any other point, and (iii) all values for the probability are equally likely.

The import of the theorem is this. From observations we infer the probability of an alternative—we are arguing back from observations to conditions likely to have created those observations. Hence the theorem has traditionally been associated with the probability of causes. Suppose we have a number of urns with different known proportions of white and black balls, where drawing a white one is the positive alternative. If we draw a large number of balls from one urn, replacing the ball each time after it is drawn, and if we do not know the contents of the urn used, we infer from the relative frequency of white balls that the number obtained is the probability of the positive alternative. This is connected with the probability of causes, because it is then probable that the urn from which the balls were drawn is the one whose contents are in the proportion that defines the probability of the positive alternative. More concretely, if the frequency of draws is $1/3$, the probability of getting a white ball is $1/3$; hence the urn used is probably the one in which white balls are in a proportion nearest to one-third of the contents.

The purpose of this theorem is sampling: from the frequency of an alternative in a sample we infer the frequency in the larger whole from which the sample was taken.

---

[1] Keynes, *Op. cit.*, p. 370.
[2] C. D. Broad, "Hr. von Wright on the Logic of Induction (II)", *Mind*, N.S. Vol. LIII, No. 210, London, 1944, p. 101.

CELEBRATED THEOREMS NOW FOUND IRRELEVANT

Bayes's Theorem Applied to Future Events

Given the prior probabilities of a set of mutually exclusive laws one of which must be true, the probabilities that a certain observed event is due to them respectively, and the probabilities that they should enable us to predict an event successfully, then it is possible to develop a formula for the probability that the predicted event should happen.

In this form the application is not of much interest here, because of the assumption that one of the laws must be true. But it leads to

Laplace's Rule of Succession

If a field consists of n members with prior probabilities that are independent of each other and equally likely, and if all possible values of the prior probability of the alternatives are equally likely, then, given that there are r instances of a positive alternative, the probability that the next member after n will be a positive alternative is $(r + 1)/(n + 2)$.

That is to say, if a die has been thrown n times and there have been r aces, the probability that the next throw will produce an ace is $(r + 1)/(n + 2)$.

When the positive alternative has always turned up in the past, r is equal to n and the probability of success next time is $(n + 1)/(n + 2)$.

Often it has been assumed that all values of the prior probabilities of the alternatives are equally likely when these probabilities are unknown. Curious consequences have been deduced from this. It follows, for instance, that if a positive alternative has occurred once in one trial, then the probability of its happening next time is $\frac{2}{3}$—which is unduly high. Again, if in one trial the positive alternative has failed to occur, still its probability of happening next time is $\frac{1}{3}$—again rather high. And the probability of the positive alternative the first time before any trials have been made at all is $\frac{1}{2}$. But these conclusions contradict one of the conditions of the theorem, not always stressed, that the alternative is equally probable at any time irrespective of what has happened before; for the theorem shows that the probabilities at different trials are not independent. Thus if the prior probability of an alternative is $\frac{1}{2}$, and after it has happened its probability is $\frac{2}{3}$, then the probability of its happening twice running is $\frac{1}{2} \times \frac{2}{3}$ and not $\frac{1}{2} \times \frac{1}{2}$ as it ought to be if the probabilities of the two occurrences were really independent.

Again, if the prior probability based on ignorance is $\frac{1}{2}$, consider an urn with white, red, and yellow balls in unknown proportions. The probability of drawing the positive alternative, white, as opposed to the negative alternative, red or yellow, is $\frac{1}{2}$; so is the probability of red; and the same for yellow. Hence the probability for drawing one or other is $\frac{3}{2}$!

In defence of the theorem, Keynes contends that it is true if n is infinitely great.[1] Again, Jeffreys tries to defend it by dividing cases, to which the theorem might be thought applicable, into two classes, to one of which it is applicable and true and to the other of which it is simply inapplicable.[2] But it is hard to see how even with the appropriate class the above contradictions are overcome.

Such at any rate is an undeservedly famous theorem upon which it has sometimes been hoped to build the probability of induction. The form discussed concerns only the probability of the next examined instance; but Laplace also gave a similar rule for the probability that all future alternatives would be positive: if r balls have been found to be white and there are n balls, the probability that all the balls are white is $(r + 1)/(n + 1)$. This is open to similar objections.

Having outlined these theorems, I propose to prove Tchebysheff's theorem, as the reader may wish to have at any rate one example of a theorem in probability proved; moreover the highly important Law of Great Numbers may then be very simply derived. The proof that follows is simpler than the one given by Tchebysheff,[3] though like his it depends only on elementary processes.

Proof of Tchebysheff's Theorem

Let there be n independent magnitudes $x, y, \ldots$, where x can take the l values $x_1, x_2, \ldots x_l$, the probabilities of their occurrences being respectively $p_1, p_2, \ldots p_l$; y can take the m values

---

[1] Keynes, *Op. cit.*, p. 378.
[2] Jeffreys, *Op. cit.*, p. 30.
[3] P. L. Tchebysheff (Chebuishev), *Œuvres*, Tome I, St. Pétersbourg, 1899, pp. 687–93.

$y_1, y_2, \ldots y_m$, the probabilities of their occurrence being respectively $q_1, q_2, \ldots q_m$; and so on $(\sum_1^l p_\lambda = 1, \ \sum_1^m q_\mu = 1, \text{ etc.})$

Put $\sum_1^l p_\lambda x_\lambda = a_1$, $\sum_1^m q_\mu y_\mu = a_2$, etc., and $\sum_1^l p_\lambda x_\lambda{}^2 = A_1$, $\sum_1^m q_\mu y_\mu{}^2 = A_2$, etc., that is a_1 is the mean of x, A_1 the mean of the square of x, both weighted by their probabilities, i.e., a_1, A_1 are theoretical mean values respectively of x, x^2, and so on.

It will be convenient to give an occurrence of specific values of the x's, y's, and so on a name; it may be called a "complete row of simultaneous values" or more simply a "row". Then $(x_\lambda + y_\mu + \ldots)$ is the value of the row, and $(x_\lambda + y_\mu + \ldots)/n$ is the average value of the quantities making up the row; this latter may be called the "row-average" (it becomes in a special case the frequency of a given alternative, which will be discussed in a corollary). It is required to find the probability that the row-average will lie in a certain interval round $(a_1 + a_2 + \ldots)/n$ or $\sum_1^n a_i/n$.

We may first of all consider all possible rows—including different rows that happen to have the same row-average. It is convenient to think of them as forming a table in which all the possible rows are arranged in a column. Let this column consist of r rows. The position may be illustrated by considering a throw of n dice; this would form a row; and the column would consist of all possible throws. To make the illustration perfectly general we should consider not n dice but n solids, not necessarily with the same number of faces and not necessarily regular; each face would be given some numerical label.

In the initial stages we closely follow Tchebysheff's method. We require the theoretical mean value σ^2 of the sum of the squares of the deviations of the row-averages from $\sum_1^n a_i/n$. This is arrived at by weighting the squares of all the r row-average deviations by their probabilities. Its value is

$$\sum \left(\frac{x_\lambda + y_\mu + \ldots}{n} - \frac{\sum_1^n a_i}{n} \right)^2 p_\lambda q_\mu \ldots$$

where the summation extends over the whole column, i.e. has r terms through the variation of λ, μ, $\ldots$

To evaluate this expression, we have

$$\sum_{1}^{l}(x_\lambda{}^2-2a_1x_\lambda+a_1{}^2)p_\lambda = \sum_{1}^{l}p_\lambda x_\lambda{}^2 - 2a_1\sum_{1}^{l}p_\lambda x_\lambda + a_1{}^2\sum_{1}^{l}p_\lambda$$
$$= A_1 - 2a_1{}^2 + a_1{}^2$$
$$= A_1 - a_1{}^2.$$

And $\Sigma q_\mu r_\nu \ldots = 1$, where the summation involves the whole range of possible values of $\mu, \nu, \ldots$ Hence

$$\Sigma(x_\lambda{}^2 - 2a_1x_\lambda + a_1{}^2)p_\lambda q_\mu \ldots = A_1 - a_1{}^2,$$

where the summation includes not merely those terms given by $\lambda = 1, 2, \ldots$, but these terms repeated for each of the values of $\mu, \nu, \ldots$ And hence

$$\Sigma\left[(x_\lambda - a_1)^2 + (y_\mu - a_2)^2 + \ldots\right]p_\lambda q_\mu \ldots = \sum_{1}^{n}A_i - \sum_{1}^{n}a_i{}^2.$$

Moreover,

$$\sum_{1}^{l}2(x_\lambda - a_1)(y_\mu - a_2)p_\lambda = \sum_{1}^{l}2(x_\lambda y_\mu - a_2x_\lambda - a_1y_\mu + a_1a_2)p_\lambda$$
$$= 2(y_\mu\sum_{1}^{l}p_\lambda x_\lambda - a_2\sum_{1}^{l}p_\lambda x_\lambda - a_1y_\mu\sum_{1}p_\lambda + a_1a_2\sum_{1}^{l}p_\lambda)$$
$$= 2(a_1y_\mu - a_1a_2 - a_1y_\mu + a_1a_2)$$
$$= 0$$

Therefore

$$\sigma^2 = \frac{\sum_{1}^{n}A_i - \sum_{1}^{n}a_i{}^2}{n^2}.$$

Having obtained a similar result, Tchebysheff introduces his characteristic method, without however using the concept of the standard deviation, and derives the theorem: There is a probability greater than $1 - t^2/n$ that the row-average lies in the closed interval

$$\frac{\sum_{1}^{n}a_i}{n} \pm \frac{1}{t}\sqrt{\frac{\sum_{1}^{n}A_i - \sum_{1}^{n}a_i{}^2}{n}}$$

By putting $t^2 = (\sum_{1}^{n}A_i - \sum_{1}^{n}a_i{}^2)/n\varepsilon^2$, we may express the theorem in the form: There is a probability greater than $1 - (\sum_{1}^{n}A_i - \sum_{1}^{n}a_i{}^2)/n^2\varepsilon^2$ that the row-average lies in the closed interval $(\sum_{1}^{n}a_i/n \pm \varepsilon)$.

But, by exploiting the formation of a^2, this form of the theorem may be obtained by a more direct method.

We wish to consider those row-averages that deviate from $\sum_1^n a_i/n$ by more than a given amount. Consider those rows for which the quantity

$$\left| \frac{x_\lambda + y_\mu \cdots}{n} - \frac{\sum_{}^n a_i}{n} \right|$$

exceeds a given positive number ε. Let w_j be the probability of the occurrence of a certain one of these rows, and let δ_j be the deviation of the row-average resulting from this particular row. Then we have

$$\sum \varepsilon^2 w_j < \sum \delta_j^2 w_j$$

and therefore

$$\varepsilon^2 \sum w_j < \sum \delta_j^2 w_j$$

in which $\sum w_j$ is clearly the probability of the occurrence of a deviation whose absolute magnitude exceeds ε. Now, if any special condition is imposed upon the deviations, the mean of the sum of the squares of the deviations marked off by the condition will obviously be less than or equal to the mean of the sum of the squares of all the deviations. Thus

$$\sum \delta_j^2 w_j \leq \sigma^2.$$

From this together with our last inequality we obtain

$$\sum w_j < \sigma^2/\varepsilon^2.$$

Thus the probability of the occurrence of a deviation whose absolute magnitude exceeds ε is less than σ^2/ε^2.

Therefore the probability that a deviation in absolute magnitude should be less than or equal to ε is greater than $1 - \sigma^2/\varepsilon^2$.

That is, the probability that a row-average lies in $(\sum_1^n a_i/n \pm \varepsilon)$, end-points included, is

$$1 - \frac{\sum^n A_i - \sum^n a_i^2}{n^2 \varepsilon^2}.$$

If we replace σ^2/ε^2 by t^2/n, we obtain the form in which Tchebysheff proved the theorem.

Corollary I

If each of the variables $x, y, \ldots$ can take only the values 1, which we shall call a "positive alternative", and 0, which we shall call a "negative alternative", and if the probability of a positive alternative in any variable is p, and the probability of a negative alternative is q, so that $q = 1 - p$, then $\overset{l}{\underset{1}{\Sigma}} p_\lambda x_\lambda$ becomes $p(1) + (1 - p)(0)$ or p. Hence $p = a_1$; similarly $p = a_2$; and so on. Also $p = A_1 = A_2 =$ etc. The row-average $(x_\lambda + y_\mu + \ldots)/n$ becomes the frequency of positive alternatives in a row of n trials, which may be denoted by f_n.

We thus derive the simple result, which might be called "Tchebysheff's frequency theorem": Given the probability p of a positive alternative and a range ε on either side of it, and given that in a sequence of n trials the positive alternative has the same probability throughout, then there is a probability greater than $1 - pq/n\varepsilon^2$ that the frequency f_n lies in the interval $(p \pm \varepsilon)$, end-points included.

It will be observed that σ^2, whose general value was established without the aid of the differential calculus, reduces in this special case to the well-known value pq/n.

By contrast with Tchebysheff's result, the corresponding probability in Bernoulli's theorem expressed in the present notation has the approximate value $\mathrm{erf} \sqrt{\dfrac{n}{2pq}}\,\varepsilon$ or $\mathrm{erf}\ \dfrac{1}{\sqrt{2}}\ \dfrac{\varepsilon}{\sigma}$, provided n is large. The meaning of this function cannot be explained here, but all that is needed is to remark that Tchebysheff's result permits of a lower estimate of the probability than Bernoulli's, and that it holds even when n is not large.

Corollary II

If n approaches infinity, it is practically certain that f_n lies in $(p \pm \varepsilon)$.

This is the Law of Great Numbers in its simplest form.

What are the theorems we require for subsequent metascientific discussion? Of the direct theorems, it is sufficient to retain the Tchebysheff frequency theorem, including the Law of Great numbers, which generally occurs in discussions of the subject. Of the inverse theorems, it is usual to discuss two: the inverse Bernoulli theorem itself, and one form of Bayes's theorem, namely the form that expresses the posterior probability of a hypothesis in the light of new evidence (*e.g.* confirmed prediction) in terms of the prior probability and the probability of the evidence (prediction) in relation to the hypothesis.

Thus there are only three theorems that are commonly regarded as having a bearing on induction.

CHAPTER XXI

THE MEANING OF PROBABILITY

It is quite possible to develop the mathematical theory of probability and also the logical foundations of this theory without giving much attention to the definition of "probability"; different definitions may cause slight modifications in the development but nothing fundamental. This does not mean that all definitions are equivalent but that the development is not fully rigorous. The importance of finding the correct definition is partly theoretical, but it also bears on the scope of probability. A prime condition that the definition must obey is that it shall be compatible with the mathematical theory and its logical foundations.

Definitions based upon the following ideas have been proposed: (1) equal likelihood; (2) intuitive relation; (3) degree of rational belief; (4) frequency (various forms); and (5) range.

(1) This is the classical approach due to Laplace, now universally rejected. In the loose presentation of simple problems it may nonetheless be used. A die can fall in six ways, an ace in one way; thus the ace can occur in one way out of six; then the probability of an ace is $\frac{1}{6}$—provided all the ways are *equally probable*. The definition may be expressed thus: the probability of a positive alternative is the ratio of the number of ways in which it can occur to the number of possible equiprobable alternatives. To this all manner of objections have been raised.

Certain paradoxes have been ascribed to it. Suppose that an equilateral triangle is drawn in a circle, and that a chord is drawn at random; what is the probability that it will be less than a side of the triangle? First, consider all possible chords drawn from one vertex of the triangle. One-third of them fall outside the triangle on the right, one-third on the left, and one-third inside. Only the last third are greater than a side of the triangle, and the first two-thirds are less than it. All chords are equally likely. Hence the probability of drawing a chord less than the side is $\frac{2}{3}$. Second, consider all chords drawn parallel to a side of the triangle. Half of these will lie between the side and the circumference, the other half between the side and the centre. All such chords are equally likely. Hence the probability of drawing a chord less than the side is $\frac{1}{2}$. Both answers cannot be correct, unqualified.

Again, suppose we have a glass containing water and wine, and suppose we know that there is as at least as much water as wine but not more than twice as much. First, since all amounts of water between these limits are equally probable, it is just as probable that the water is one to one and a half times as much as the wine, as that there should be more water than this. But, second, the wine has equally probable ranges from half the volume of the wine to an equal volume; hence it is just as probable that the wine is half to three-quarters of the wine as more than this. The dividing line from the first point of view gives a ratio of water to wine equal to $\frac{3}{2}$, but from the second point of view gives a ratio equal to $\frac{4}{3}$. Here again both results cannot be true without qualification.

Another difficulty is to extend the principle to cases where the alternatives are not all equally probable, as with a loaded die.

Again, what is the criterion of equiprobability? Some would say, for a true die, that it is supposed carefully made and tested to see that its centre of gravity is at the geometrical centre, which ensures that all alternatives are equally probable. The conclusion is true, but it cannot serve as a basis for a definition because it rests upon the statement that for a true die all alternatives are equally probable, and we still do not know what is meant by "equally probable". One may have at the back of one's mind that if the die were thrown a number of times, the proportions of each spot would be equal. Then we have extended our definition to something different and might as well say so, or we have introduced an empirical element into the definition, which was clearly intended to be of an *a priori* kind. The empirical statement, or something like it, is true, so that we may use the Laplacian notion for practical convenience in solving problems of a certain restricted kind.

(2) Keynes[1] described probability as an indefinable relation of 'degree of rational belief' intuitively perceived to hold between a given alternative and the information at our disposal about its field. When he wrote there was no serious rival to this view. The frequency account, it is true, existed but not in a well-developed or plausible form and he brought many objections against it. Of

[1] J. M. Keynes, *A Treatise on Probability*, London, 1921, Ch. I.

late, this view has been treated very carefully by several writers and it has gained many adherents; but the very possibility of a reasonable alternative to Keynes's conception has removed it from serious consideration.

One of the chief reasons for regarding his view as unsatisfactory is that probability becomes subjective in the sense that one and the same alternative in relation to the same relevant information could be given different probabilities by different judges. Another is that there is no way of passing from mathematical theorems based on it to frequencies in the actual world: there is no reason why actual frequencies should occur in the way the theorems would lead us to expect, *i.e.* why they should correspond to theoretical frequencies.

(3) "Probability" has been defined by Ramsey[1] as degree of rational belief. Keynes also held that his view made probability identical with degree of rational belief; but Ramsey takes this concept to be definable. He does not hold that the degree is to be found by introspection; he defines it by the behaviour of the believer. Thus a man believes that the probability of an ace is $\frac{1}{6}$, *i.e.* he believes to the degree $\frac{1}{6}$ that an ace will fall, if he would accept odds of 5 to 1 against it. Since beliefs are often not tested, Ramsey modifies this way of putting the matter by his suggestion that the degree of belief is measured by the behaviour of the believer in hypothetical circumstances—his degree of belief in an ace being measured by the odds he would accept.

Against Ramsey's view, there is the obvious objection that action is not always determined solely by the degree of belief, and this for two entirely different reasons.

Suppose you find some mushrooms that may be poisonous though this is not very likely—you assess the probability of their being poisonous at $\frac{1}{100}$. On the other hand there are also gooseberries to be had, but they often disagree with you—you assess the probability of their giving you indigestion at $\frac{1}{2}$. Which will you eat if you are very hungry? Your action is determined not by the probabilities but by the values of the alternatives. The mushrooms are very unlikely to do you any harm, but if they do the result is disastrous; whereas the gooseberries are quite likely to give you a slight pain but this will pass. It seems to me that your possible actions can be compared numerically only by multi-

---

[1] F. P. Ramsey, *The Foundations of Mathematics and Other Logical Essays*, London, 1931, VII, VIII.

plying the probability of each alternative by what I would call a "coefficient of valuation". You would multiply the probability of death by poisoning by o and the probability of pain from gooseberries by 1. Then $1 \times \frac{1}{2}$ is greater than $0 \times \frac{1}{100}$ and hence act on the gooseberry alternative. This seems to me to answer to rational behaviour. Ramsey, it is true, discusses a similar point.[1] But it would seem that, if anything like this describes rational behaviour, then the notion of probability or of degrees of belief is *presupposed*; in short one bases rational behaviour upon rational belief—one does not identify them.

The other difficulty with Ramsey's view concerns the meaning of "rational belief". Now the only meaning I can find for "rational" in this connection is that the belief should correlate closely with the realities of the world. If a man has a belief to the degree $\frac{3}{4}$ that some disaster will overtake him if he walks under a ladder, the degree of his belief does not correspond to the proportion of disasters that actually happen when people walk under ladders. Moreover, some people do in fact act on 'hunches', *i.e.* they act without relevant information. Their belief amounts to certainty, but there is no reason to suppose that there is a good correlation between such beliefs and realities. Irrational beliefs would seem to be those that ignore the demands of reality for some psychological reason. Certainly people do act in accordance with irrational belief, and I would concede that Ramsey's view of degrees of belief is correct, subject to two qualifications; action is the outcome of belief weighted with coefficients of valuation; and belief must not be restricted to being rational. What, then, is to be the criterion of rational belief or believing in accordance with reality? It must be belief in the light of *past experience* (of what is objective), which would seem to lead to the frequency theory— unless we take rational belief as being due to some faculty of the rational mind that gives probabilities *a priori*, and thus return to something like Keynes's view.*

[1] *Id.*, p. 175.

* It is worth referring to a formula devised by Ramsey to give the degree of belief in terms of the valuation of alternatives. The interesting feature of his result is that it involves such valuations and nothing else. In his proof he introduces the number of times a specific positive alternative would occur. But this number is irrelevant to his proof, because he does not contrast it with the number of negative alternatives. He should have noticed this, for the number divides out and does not appear in his final equation. In short, his formula makes no reference to the probabilities of the alternatives. And, just as I have maintained that probabilities should be weighted by co-efficients of valuation, so I would hold here that a formula of valuation should be weighted by probabilities.

We are led, then, to reject the definition of "probability" given in terms of degree of rational belief.*

(4) It is difficult to see a future for any of these definitions. But this does not mean they should be ignored. So long as even the most plausible approach fails to be wholly satisfactory, one may get inspiration even from a false view.

The next account defines "probability" as the frequency of a positive alternative in a large number of trials. Thus if we throw a die many times, the probability of an ace is the ratio of the number of aces to the total number of throws. Though he disagreed with this definition, Keynes, who wrote before the frequency theory had been maturely developed, pointed out its many advantages:

There is no mystery about it—no new indefinables, no appeals to intuition. Measurement leads to no difficulties; our probabilities or frequencies are ordinary numbers, upon which the arithmetical apparatus can be safely brought to bear. And at the same time it seems to crystallise in a clear, explicit shape the floating opinion of common sense that an event is or is not probable in certain supposed circumstances according as it is or is not usual as a matter of fact and experience.[1]

The difficulty is that in various large numbers of trials the proportions of aces are seldom the same. Accordingly "probability" is defined by von Mises[2] in terms of the limiting frequency as the number of trials increases indefinitely. That is to say, we count the proportion of aces in a large number of throws (the frequency), count it again for a larger number of throws, and so on; we then have a sequence of numbers, which are the proportions as the number of throws is increased. If this sequence approaches a limit, its limiting value is the probability. Thus, if in 1000 throws

* Jeffreys (Harold Jeffreys, *Theory of Probability*, Oxford, 1939, pp. 332-3) holds that probability cannot be identified with degree of rational belief, because he maintains that the latter is a logically prior notion to the former; even if the probability is equivalent to a frequency, we need the notion of rational belief before we can use it. In the preceding discussion also the two have been maintained to be different; but I have contended that rational belief must be posterior and accounted for in terms of probability. As opposed to Jeffreys, I would urge that rational belief presupposes probability—the degree of belief that it is rational to bestow upon something depends upon the probability of that thing (*Cf.* G. H. von Wright, "On Probability", *Mind*, N.S. Vol. XLIX, No. 195, London, 1940, p. 281). The *capacity* for rational belief is of course presupposed by the use of probability.

[1] Keynes, *Op. cit.*, pp. 94-5.
Richard von Mises, *Probability, Statistics and Truth*, London, 1939.

of a coin the frequency of a head is ·512; in 2000 is ·492; in 3000 is ·505; in 4000 is ·497; in 10,000 is ·5001; and so on; the limiting value is ·5. This is called "limiting frequency". But it should be noted that the limiting value is not itself a frequency; it is the limit of a sequence of frequencies. I will therefore use the more appropriate name, "frequency-limit".

Von Mises points out, however, that a second condition is required—that the distribution of alternatives in a long sequence of trials should be *random*. This is easily illustrated as follows. Suppose you throw a coin a large number of times and record the order of heads and tails: H T H T H H H T H T T H T H T T . . . The proportion of heads may be seen to approach $\frac{1}{2}$. Now select every second result: T T H T T H H T. Over a long enough sequence of trials this may give the same limit. Or take the result immediately after three successive heads; again the same limit may be attained. Whenever the same limit emerges, the selection is *insensitive to place selection* or *random*.[1]

Thus in order that a probability should exist, we must have a sequence with a frequency-limit; and there must be only one limit for the frequencies of this sequence and for sub-sequences taken out of it.

This definition has been much discussed and some amendments have been offered.

The second feature of the definition raises the difficulty oɪ knowing when we have completed the task of testing for randomness, or of knowing how to test for it. Von Mises maintains that this is a mathematical problem, and he refers to the work of Copeland and Wald, which he holds satisfactorily solves the problem.[2] But this would not be widely accepted. The mathematical difficulty is this. If a selection is to be made, we can describe the new sequence obtained only if there is some mathematical rule for constructing it. But it is impossible to find a rule to cover all possible selections that are insensitive to place selection; whatever rule is suggested, there are always other ways of finding selections not covered by the rule. To get over this, Popper[3] has put forward a weaker condition than that given by von Mises. Suppose we construct a sub-sequence by selecting from the original sequence the successor to every head. Taking the sequence given above, this

[1] *Id.*, pp. 30–3.
[2] *Id.*, pp. 141–5 and bibliographical notes attached; see also Wright, *Op. cit.*, p. 274.
[3] K. R. Popper, *Logik der Forschung*, Wien, 1935, §§ 55–9.

would give T T H H T T T T, in which the proportion of heads may not approach $\frac{1}{2}$. For randomness, however, the proportion must approach $\frac{1}{2}$; and this may be expressed by saying that the sub-sequence is insensitive to the immediate predecessors of its members. (The same is required to hold if we choose the successor to every tail.) But further suppose we select the successor to every pair of heads (and again pairs of tails, pairs consisting of head-tail, and pairs consisting of tail-head), and yet again suppose we select the successor to three consecutive heads (and so on), the proportion of heads must in each case approach $\frac{1}{2}$ if the initial sequence is random. Thus the frequency-limit of an alternative is to be the same for all possible combinations of its predecessors. Let this be carried on indefinitely. If all the sub-sequences obtained have the same frequency-limit, then the initial sequence is in Popper's sense random, insensitive to place selection, or, as he puts it, 'free from after effect'. Von Mises would of course agree that the sequence must be insensitive to at least these place selections, but also insensitive to more besides, whereas Popper holds that this type of insensitiveness is sufficient. He holds that this is in fact all we seek when we seek randomness: for we require only that every member of a sequence is independent of the way in which its predecessors occur.* The advantage of this procedure is that it is possible to construct sequences that are free from after effect and to know that they are in fact free from after effect; and he shows[1] how this can be done. Clearly by introducing a weaker criterion of randomness Popper was deliberately allowing a probability sequence to be *sensitive* to all place selections other than those excluded by his criterion.† This procedure, which is preferable to that of von Mises, seems to be the only practicable one; the justification of it would appear to be that it provides a clear definition of 'randomness', which, moreover, is close to or identical with what we ordinarily mean by it—that the probability of an

---

* The gambler's fallacy of the 'maturing of the chances' implies that members of a sequence do influence their successors—after a long run of heads many people expect a long run of tails, a sequence that can of course happen, but it would not be random or free from after effect if averaging out had to come about or even if it were highly probable.

[1] *Id.*, S. 108–9.

† Von Wright has criticised it on the grounds that it, though necessary, is not sufficient to ensure randomness. For a sequence might be free from after effect, and yet it might be possible to select a sub-sequence with a different frequency-limit from that of the initial sequence, by selecting those members, for instance, whose ordinal positions are prime numbers. If such a sub-sequence had a different limit we should not, von Wright contends, regard the sequence as 'random'. (Wright, *Op. cit.*, pp. 271–2.)

alternative is not affected by its predecessors. The issue, however, is of technical rather than general metascientific interest.

The first feature of the definition also has its difficulties. How do we know that a sequence will have a frequency-limit? We cannot travel along a sequence the whole way to infinity. With von Mises it appears to be an axiom that the required limit exists (*i.e.* intuitively we should expect it, as in a sequence consisting of throws of a coin) and indeed that we can find it; but, however far along the sequence we go, the limit, even if it exists, may be unascertainable unless we go further. Popper[1] eliminates this limit axiom. He observes that an infinite sequence must have at least one point of condensation, *i.e.* a term with an infinite number of terms infinitely close to it in value. There must therefore be at least one 'condensation-frequency'.* If there is only one, this may happen to be the frequency-limit, but it need not be—there would then be a condensation-frequency but no frequency-limit. In either case he takes the condensation frequency, just as von Mises took the frequency-limit, to be the probability. Where there are more than one condensation-frequencies, Popper takes the first one to occur after the place at which the sequence is first shown to be free from after effect. This procedure does not, of course, make us sure to attain a condensation-frequency, but the task is easier; and the possibility of there being many points of condensation throws light on statistical experience that in fact we do not need to have such very long sequences in order to see their tendencies. The point at issue here is again one of technical rather than of general metascientific interest.

Some metascientific problems connected with the frequency theory are of great interest.

If probability is some form of *a priori* notion, then it is impossible to step from this notion to statistics. This difficulty involves any theorem about the proportion of positive alternatives that will probably occur in a large number of trials; it involves notably the Law of Great Numbers. To take a simple form of this: if a die is thrown long enough, it is probable that the proportion of aces will approach the limit $\frac{1}{6}$, and the degree of probability approaches unity, given that the probability of throwing an ace is $\frac{1}{6}$. Now if we start from the Keynesian concept of probability, we can prove this theorem; but there would be no reason to ex-

[1] Popper, *Op. cit.*, §§ 63–4.
* Popper does not use this expression.

pect *actual* results derived from physical experiments with dice to conform to the conclusion of the theorem. To express the point in another way, the theorem is a theorem about concepts and about a theoretical sequence and distribution of trials or theoretically expected proportions, but there is no reason why actual occurrences should be distributed in anything like a similar way.

On behalf of the frequency theory it is claimed that this difficulty does not exist; within this framework the Law of Great Numbers, for example, can be interpreted. The probability of an ace is the limit of the frequency (or condensation-frequency) with which an ace appears as the number of trials becomes longer and longer. Let this be tried and let the empirical probability be $\frac{1}{6}$. The theorem then states that if we repeat the experiments it is extremely probable that the proportion will again approach $\frac{1}{6}$. It is important to note that what "probable" means here is that if you repeat the whole experiment a large number of times the overwhelming majority will in fact produce aces in proportions approaching $\frac{1}{6}$. The great utility of statistics bears out that this is in fact so. Nonetheless there is an insuperable difficulty about this way of interpreting the Law of Great Numbers, which arises from not distinguishing carefully to what the theorem applies. The main difficulty is cogently put by Broad:[1]

How are we justified in passing from the empirical premise that the frequency with which a certain die has fallen with 6 uppermost in the N times which, so far as we know, it has been thrown is so-and-so, to the conclusion that, if it were thrown infinitely many times, the frequency would approach indefinitely near to the limiting value so-and-so? Again, how can we establish empirically the very sweeping universal negative proposition that there is *no* way of selecting an infinite subclass from the original class of throws which would have a different limiting frequency for the same alternative? If we have any rational ground for believing such conclusions on such evidence, must it not involve principles of 'probability' in some important sense of "probability" not contemplated by von Mises? This would not necessarily be any objection to von Mises' definition; for he is admittedly confining his attention to 'probability' in the sense in which it can be measured and made the subject of a calculus. But it would show that we should have no reason to believe any propositions about probability,

[1] C. D. Broad, Critical Notice of von Mises' *Wahrscheinlichkeit, Statistik, und Wahrheit,* Wien, 1936, *Mind,* N.S. Vol. XLVI, No. 184, London, 1937, p. 487. *Cf.* R. L. Goodstein, "On von Mises' Theory of Probability", *Mind,* N.S. Vol. XLIX, No. 193, London, 1940, p. 61.

in his sense, unless there are logical principles of probability, in another sense.

It is desirable to make the difficulty still more explicit. If we take an actual empirical sequence of enormous length, in which a frequency-limit is found, the Law of Great Numbers is true of sub-sequences drawn from the original one. In fact the Law is here a purely mathematical theorem and a tautology. But, if we apply it to another sequence, outside the original one or a prolongation of it, we are making an empirical application of the theorem, which does not hold tautologically in the new field, *i.e.* we are making an empirical interpretation of the theorem. Put another way, when applying it to sub-sequences we are dealing with theoretical groups of distributions, of which the Law must hold tautologically; when applying it outside we are dealing with fresh material which might be completely at variance with the claims of the theorem.

Thus it is clear that, like the *a priori* interpretation of probability, the frequency definition fails to offer any guarantee that unexamined parts of a sequence will closely resemble in respect of proportions the examined parts.

The problem of applying probabilities based upon present and past experience to the future is not likely to be solved by introducing a new sense of "probable" for the contention that probabilities already found will continue to hold. The most fruitful approach seems to be one that was first suggested by Popper.[1] This is that the probability of an alternative, found by any means such as by the frequency method, is adopted as a *hypothesis* about the future behaviour of a sequence. Following this von Wright[2] adds that randomness may be regarded as a hypothesis. This is to the effect that if we make selections we shall in fact find them random; the hypothesis is equivalent to the assertion that the members of a given sequence are due to chance in the sense that we do not know their causes. We work on this hypothesis until we find it falsified: if we find a selection non-random, or find a cause of certain members of the sequence, then the sequence is no longer suitable for probability treatment.

In adopting a probability as a hypothesis we must clarify one point. Suppose certain observed frequencies lead us to say that the probability of a positive alternative is p; then the Law of Great

---

[1] Popper, *Op. cit.*, §§ 63–4.
[2] Von Wright, *Op. cit.*, pp. 275–6; *Cp.* Goodstein, *Op. cit.*, pp. 60–2.

Numbers asserts that it is extremely probable that the proportion of positive alternatives that will be found will approximate to p. This has to be transformed into a hypothesis. The question then is whether this hypothesis will concern what we *expect* to happen or will concern what *will* happen. Is the hypothesis of the form, "*We expect* that in the overwhelming majority of cases the proportion of positive alternatives will be approximately p" or of the form, "In the overwhelming majority of cases the proportion of positive alternatives *will be* approximately p". The former merely makes a probability statement in the language of "expectation" and commits us to nothing, for the expectation is not shown to be ill-conceived, nor need it be rescinded, by subsequent eventualities. Thus if only a small proportion turned out to be approximately p, what we expect would not have occurred but the expectation is not falsified. If a man habitually inserts the word "probable" into his statements with the aim of playing safe, he can claim that, even when the facts turn out otherwise from what he thought would probably happen, he did not make a false statement because he did not categorically predict. Now this way of using "probably" not only indicates fear of taking a risk; it precludes our using the word in a more valuable way. It is indeed correct to insert the word "probably" into a statement, but this is useful only if the aim is to convey, say, some information about the approximate proportions that *will* occur—we must commit ourselves about the future. Accordingly we must say that *a probability hypothesis is to be interpreted as leading to categorical predictions about the approximate* proportion of positive alternatives that* will *occur in the vast majority of cases.*†

Interpreted in this way a probability hypothesis is falsifiable but therefore usable. Thus a frequency hypothesis about proportions and randomness makes a claim on the future, just as do the hypotheses of natural science.

But this treatment involves a consequence for induction that would be displeasing to many of those who support the frequency

---

* Naturally the problem of drawing the line occurs here: *i.e.*, a decision has to be made about the size of the deviation between fact and prediction that shall be counted as falsifying the hypothesis. But the same problem besets not only probability hypotheses but quantitative predictions based on ordinary scientific hypotheses. If an eclipse is a second out or an hour out, is the relevant hypothesis falsified?

† A qualification may be added. Despite the intention to make a categorical prediction, one may make a mental reservation about the possibility of the prediction's going wrong—but this can happen also where predictions from ordinary scientific hypotheses are concerned.

theory; for it becomes impossible to justify induction by means of a theory of probability that makes, as it were, inductive claims or that might be judged to require the support of an inductive principle.

The frequency theory has been widely held to be too narrow on two grounds: it does not allow to speak of the "probability of a single event" in a categorical sense or of the "probability of hypotheses". According to the frequency theory "the probability of a single event" is merely a condensed way of speaking about large numbers of events—the phrase cannot refer literally to a single event. There is, I think, a genuine problem here. As to the 'probability of hypotheses', we shall see that the conception does not survive analysis and that there is unlikely to be any future for it.

(5) The frequency definition provides an objective concept of probability. Another objective concept is provided by a definition in terms of *range of possibilities (Spielraum)*.* The idea is this: the probability that a thing possessing the property h should have the property a is identified with the ratio of the range of things that have the properties ha to the range of things that have h. Its merit is that it is the kind of notion that the mathematician has at the back of his mind, and it can serve as a basis for the mathematical theorems on probability while being completely free of subjective features. Moreover the range definition was perhaps what Laplace was driving at[1]—though there is no reason to suppose he had any inkling of the main difficulty and how to tackle it. Be that as it may, the range definition includes what is intuitively satisfactory about the one given by Laplace. The most detailed version is that developed by Kneale. It is as follows.

---

* This was first put forward in 1886 by von Kries in a rather vague empirical form (see Keynes, *Op. cit.*, p. 87). Logical definitions closely allied to one another were given by Wittgenstein (1922), Waisman (1930), and Hailperin (1937). For references see *e.g.* G. H. von Wright, *The Logical Problem of Induction*, Helsinki, 1941, pp. 150–1, 234. Von Wright makes the point that there are two different forms of range theory, one that is logical and one that he distinguishes roughly as 'empirical'. For a fuller exposition of the differences between the different types of range definition see C. D. Broad, "Hr. von Wright on the Logic of Induction (III)", *Mind*, N.S. Vol. LIII, No. 211, London, 1944, pp. 205–7. The 'empirical' form has been developed independently by Kneale (William Kneale, *Probability and Induction*, Oxford, 1949, §§ 34–5). Part of the logical form has been sketched by Russell under the title of "finite-frequency theory"; Russell's work, however, appears to be fusion of both range and frequency approaches, for though he begins with the equivalent of a range definition in connexion with finite classes he leans towards the frequency theory when he comes to infinite classes (Bertrand Russell, *Human Knowledge: its Scope and Limits*, Pt. V, Ch. III, London, 1948).

[1] *Id.*, p. 170.

Kneale's presentation begins with the concepts of *possibilities* and *equal possibilities*. Thus we can assert that "there are more possibilities of an undergraduate's being a member of University College than of his being a scholar of that college."[1]

Now there is, I believe, a very good sense in which the alternatives of being this, that, or the other individual undergraduate can be called equal possibilities or equipossible cases under the concept of a present undergraduate.[2]

The objects that can have the property of 'being a present undergraduate of University College' are just those persons who are in fact undergraduates of University College and no others; they are ultimate alternative objects upon which the cap ('being a present undergraduate of University College') fits. The situation is not the same if the property is 'being a member of University College or of Merton College'. 'Being a member of University College' is possible and 'being a member of Merton College' is possible. But they are not equally possible: 'being a member of University College or of Merton College' is a cap that does not have the same possibilities of fitting members of University College as of fitting members of Merton College (though it has of course the same possibilities of fitting any individual who is a member of one or the other). Thus alternatives ('being this present undergraduate of University College', 'being that one', and so on) under a description ('being a present undergraduate of University College') are equipossible if they are ultimate alternative units under that description.

Alternatives are also equipossible, moreover, if they are, say, disjunctions of the former ultimate alternatives. For instance, if a college happens to be composed of pairs of brothers and no one else, then 'being a member of that college' describes one of any pair, so that 'being a member of a certain pair' is a unit and all such units are disjunctions of ultimate units (namely individual persons); and all instances of membership of a certain pair are equipossible.

Thus two alternatives are equipossible if and only if one or other condition is satisfied.

"Probability" may now be defined in terms of equipossible alternatives. Suppose we are concerned with the probability that

[1] *Id.*, p. 170.
[2] *Id.*, p. 171.

an undergraduate knows Greek. Let 'being an undergraduate' be denoted by "h", and 'having knowledge of Greek' by "a". The probability required, denoted by "P (a, h)", is concerned with the possibilities of finding the conjunction ah. Let "N(ah)" denote the *number* of instances of ah, and "N(h)" the number of instances of h. Then if the alternatives under h are equipossible, the probability of an instance of ah is defined by

$$P(a, h) = \frac{N(ah)}{N(h)}.$$

In words this is: Given that a property h fits equipossible alternatives, then the probability that an instance of h shall be accompanied by some other specified property a is the ratio of the number of conjunctions, each consisting of an instance of the given property and an instance of the specified property, to the number of instances of the given property.

Now this definition is inapplicable when the field of possibilities under h is open, *i.e.* when h characterises an infinite class. The class of present undergraduates of a college is closed; but a class may be open like that of Christmas days. When the field of possibilities of h is infinite it is convenient to speak of "the *range* of h". What is now necessary is to replace the number of instances of h, since this is no longer finite, by the range of h. (We cannot speak of the number of points on a line but we may speak of the range of such points.) Now this will not assist us unless the range can be referred to in finite terms. We must therefore go further and speak only of the *measure of the range* of h. (And similarly for ah.)

Now it may be that though the range of h is infinite it may be divided into a finite number of equal sub-ranges. Then the range is measured by the number of these sub-ranges; and these are taken as equipossible alternatives. Hence if R(h) is the measure of the range of h and R(ah) the measure of the range of ah, in the sense explained, the sub-ranges being the equipossible alternatives, then the definition of "probability", consistent with the previous one, is

$$P(a, h) = \frac{R(ah)}{R(h)}.$$

For instance, though the number of shades of colour is infinite, we may divide the range of colour into seven equal sub-ranges, those of the rainbow. Then if we ask for the probability that something is indigo or blue, where there are two sub-ranges, we see that it is $\frac{2}{7}$.

But it may not be possible to divide an infinite range into finite sub-ranges. For instance, there are infinitely many absolutely specific shades of colour, and if we are concerned not with the probability that something is, say, blue, but with the probability that it is some absolutely specific shade, then we cannot find a finite set of sub-ranges to suit our purpose. But, so long as it is possible to measure infinite ranges, in the sense of being able to *compare* the sizes of infinite ranges, then "probability" can be defined by the equation just given; and this is a purely mathematical task.[1]

It should be added that, though "probability" can be defined in this way, the procedure does not imply that we can in a practical example carry out the steps and measure the probability.

These approaches may be briefly commented upon. The first three are most unsatisfactory. The frequency definition and the range definition are the only ones that can be regarded as reasonably successful.

The question arises whether at one point the range definition does not presuppose the frequency approach. The basis of the range definition is equipossible alternatives. The plausibility of the approach lies in the use of the concept of possibilities. But 'equipossible' alternatives must be interpreted as 'equiprobable' alternatives, and the only way to find out whether ultimate alternatives were equiprobable would be to inspect their frequencies. On the other hand, one could take the view that the foregoing consideration concerned only the practical assessment of a probability and that for purposes of definition 'equipossible' was an unanalysable concept.

It would appear that both the frequency and the range definitions are admissible. But there is nothing paradoxical in there being more than one; for Popper has indicated[2] that all we require is a definition that satisfies the axioms of the mathematical theory of probability, that in fact definitions must be regarded as interpretations of these axioms, that many such interpretations may be possible, and if so that they must be in a sense equivalent.

---

[1] Kneale gives an account of this (*Id.*, pp. 177 ff.), which is more clearly set forth by C. D. Broad, Critical Notice of Kneale's *Probability and Induction*, *Mind*, N.S. Vol. LIX, No. 233, Edinburgh, 1950, pp. 102–4.
[2] K. R. Popper, "A Set of Independent Axioms for Probability", *Mind*, N.S. Vol. XLVII, No. 186, London, 1938, p. 275.

CHAPTER XXII

THE PROBABILITY OF A HYPOTHESIS

WHEN it was realised that inductive inference could not be certain and indeed ought not to be so, it was natural to suppose that it was probable and to hope to justify it by means of probability. Various attempts have been made to effect this. In this chapter we shall be concerned with the idea that a generalisation or hypothesis can be characterised as 'being probable', so that a prediction derived from it can be probable, and with the idea that confirmation of a generalisation renders that generalisation probable or more probable than it was.

We shall first consider Keynes's ingenious contribution to the subject.[1] It is built upon Bayes's theorem, which connects prior and posterior probabilities. Of this theorem Jeffreys has said:[2] "It is the chief rule involved in the process of learning from experience."

Its bearing on induction is that it purports to answer the questions: can the probability of a generalisation be increased by further evidence, and can its probability be indefinitely increased towards certainty?

Let g be a generalisation, h the information upon which it is based, and c the confirmations of g that have been obtained. It conduces to brevity to use a probability notation. $P(g, h)$ is the probability of g upon the data h—the 'prior probability' of g. $P(g, hc)$ is the probability of g given the information h and given that confirmations c have been obtained—the 'posterior probability' of g after confirmation. Bayes's theorem tells us that $P(g, hc)$ is greater than $P(g, h)$, i.e. that the probability of g is increased by confirmation, and further elaboration shows that $P(g, hc)$ increases indefinitely close to unity as confirmation increases. Now this is true only if two conditions are satisfied: (i) the probability of c, given h and given that g is false, must be infinitesimal; and (ii) the prior probability of g must be a finite quantity greater than zero. All this can be shown mathematically.

(i) It certainly seems plausible that a sequence of confirma-

---

[1] J. M. Keynes, *A Treatise on Probability*, London, 1921, pp. 235–8.
[2] Harold Jeffreys, *Theory of Probability*, Oxford, 1939, p. 29.

tions should be extremely improbable if the generalisation is false. But von Wright has pointed out that this is not so, and that indeed a sequence of confirmations may even be infinitely probable in spite of the falsity of the generalisation.[1] A particular example suffices to show this. Suppose that *g* is false because one exception to it has been found; and suppose that on a fairly large number of occasions it has conformed with fact. Then by a statistical inference it is most probable that confirmation of *g* will be received on the large majority of occasions. Likewise such confirmation may become extremely probable. And similar examples could be constructed to show that the degree of probability could assume any value.

This condition is not, however, of metascientific interest. We turn to the second one, which is interesting from this point of view.

(ii) There is no obvious reason why a generalisation should have a prior probability at all. Keynes was aware of this, and in order that there should be one he introduced the Principle of Limitation of Independent Variety. The point of doing this is that, *if a limitation is imposed upon the number of properties in an inductive group and upon the number of groups into which a property can enter, so that there is only a finite number of ways in which a property can occur, then there is a finite probability that a given property will occur in a specified group.* Broad worked with a similar conception: in order to explain the stability of inductive generalisations, he first postulated 'natural kinds', but later when he based induction on the theory of probability he introduced the concept of *loading*—that is to say, properties occur together with high frequency because the distribution of properties throughout the universe is loaded so as to produce this result, rather like the way in which a die may be loaded to produce a high frequency of aces.[2]

The Keynes-Broad procedure is that induction is justified by the postulate, and the only problem remaining is to find out if the postulate is true. They showed that the postulate need not be held to be certain; it will serve its purpose if it is probable, and then further experience would increase its probability.[3] This also can be demonstrated mathematically.

Now this result, just as the conclusion derived first of all from Bayes's theorem, is true only if a certain condition holds. The

[1] G. H. von Wright, *The Logical Problem of Induction*, Helsingfors, 1941, pp. 124–5.
[2] C. D. Broad, "The Principles of Problematic Induction", *Proc. of the Arist. Soc.*, N.S. Vol. XXVIII, London, 1928, pp. 12–8.
[3] Keynes, *Op. cit.*, pp. 258–64; Broad, *Op. cit.*, pp. 42–4.

application of Bayes's theorem required that the prior probability of g should be finite and greater than zero. Likewise here the result requires that the postulate in relation to facts that support it should have a finite probability greater than zero.

The procedure is very ingenious and it certainly makes the *a priori* demand on nature very small—not the truth but the mere probability of the postulate. But, as Keynes admitted, a peccadillo remains a peccadillo even when its consequences are very small: it is as difficult to find any reason for giving the postulate a small finite probability* as to show that it is certain. For this reason, this line of argument was avoided in Part II, where the conclusion was reached that the 'postulate' is but a descriptive summary of the most abstract scientific results.

This valiant attempt to dispense with the Law of Uniformity of Nature, while working in the spirit of Mill, has not received so much attention as it deserves—the attitude being that no meaning can be given to "prior probability of a generalisation" and hence that there is nothing to be hoped for from this approach. But it is one of the high-lights among the attempts to grapple with the problem of induction and might yet be put to some important use or other; it therefore seems to me to be worth retaining in our study of the subject and that it ought not to be relegated to the limbo of useless historical misfires.

For those interested, the relevant mathematical derivations are given in an appendix to the chapter, as they are not readily available in a simple and satisfactory form.

We may now briefly mention Reichenbach's proposal to define the probability of a generalisation through the proportion of true predictions it would lead to. The Reichenbach-Hempel version of this is as follows.[1] Given a generalisation g, consider the initial conditions. Thus if g is Charles's law, one set of initial conditions could be that the temperature of the gas in a given piece of apparatus was $17°C$. and the volume $2 \cdot 8$ c.c. Let this set of conditions be i_1. From g and i_1 we can deduce the prediction that the volume will be $2 \cdot 9$ c.c. if the temperature is raised to $27°C$. Let this prediction be c_1. Again, the initial conditions (i_2) could be that the temperature and volume are at some other specified levels and

---

* Broad thought it reasonable to suppose the postulate has a finite probability—*Id.*, p. 43.

[1] Ernest Nagel, *Principles of the Theory of Probability, Inter. Enc. of Unified Science*, Vol. I, No. 6, Chicago, 1939, p. 63.

we could predict (c_2) what would happen to the volume if the temperature were raised to a specified degree. In this way we get predictions c_1, c_2, . . .* Now some of the c's may be true and some false. Consider those that are true (r) out of the total (n). Then "the probability of g" is defined as the frequency-limit of r/n.

This is applicable as a measure of the probability of a statistical generalisation, but not of an ordinary one; for, if one of the n predictions is false, so is the generalisation, and therefore its probability is zero.

Reichenbach has put forward another proposal.[1] For a reference class consisting of all statistical generalisations that have some characteristic in common with g; then the "probability of g" is defined through the proportion of these generalisations that have probabilities, estimated by Reichenbach's first method, above a specified positive value.

This procedure would at best give a probability for confirmation of g, and thus give a meaning to "the probability of a statistical generalisation". But this is not the goal in question. Most of those who have discussed the theme have been interested in the probability of a generalisation being *true*. One contrary instance would render this probability zero; but one contrary instance could leave the probability of a statistical generalisation as high as 100%. Thus the two goals are entirely different, and Reichenbach's method throws no light on the nature of the probability of a non-statistical and unfalsified generalisation. If this exists at all it can concern only the facts that are relevant to the generalisation and the proportion of unfalsified generalisations known to us.[2]

"The probability of a statement" is definable, just as is "the probability of an event", provided the statement is particular; but when it is a universal and states a hypothesis, the possibility of definition becomes questionable. Almost certainly, as Popper maintains[3] (and in this he has been followed by Carnap, Russell, and others), it cannot be done, and we must be content to speak

---

* From a given set of initial conditions, it is true, we could make an infinity of predictions; but, since it is convenient to have the number of predictions the same as the number of sets of initial conditions, we have only to say that a set of initial conditions is repeated for every prediction based upon that set.

[1] Nagel, *Op. cit.*, p. 65.

[2] Cf. C. D. Broad, "Hr. von Wright on the Logic of Induction", *Mind*, N.S. Vol. LIII, No. 211, London, 1944, pp. 204-5.

[3] K. R. Popper, *Logik der Forschung*, Wien, 1935, S. 193.

of degree of 'acceptability' or 'credibility' of hypotheses without holding that this concept satisfies the axioms of probability.

APPENDIX TO CHAPTER XXII

The Probability Calculus and Keynes's Principle

LET a and b be alternatives, which may be interpreted as events or statements, and let h be information relevant to their probabilities. We shall use "$P(a, h)$" to denote the probability of a upon the data h. We shall be concerned with the probability of the conjunction ab, read "a and b", and with that of the disjunction $a \lor b$, read "a or b". $\sim a$ is read "not -a".

We first establish the two fundamental theorems concerning addition and multiplication, following Jeffreys' simple presentation;[1] derive Bayes's theorem; and then proceed to the probability of a generalisation and of the Principle of Limitation of Independent Variety. Postulates which are required in a rigorous treatment will be omitted.

The Addition Theorem

We need a fundamental convention that if a and b are mutually exclusive, then the probability that one of them occurs is equal to the probability of the one plus the probability of the other. Thus

$$P(a \lor b, h) = P(a, h) + P(b, h). \tag{1}$$

Now consider the alternative a or b, both of which might happen. The two possibilities ab and $a \sim b$ are mutually exclusive, so that by (1) we get

$$P(ab \lor a \sim b, h) = P(ab, h) + P(a \sim b, h) \tag{1.1}$$

But the alternatives of the left-hand side can happen only if a happens, *i.e.* the left is equal to $P(a, h)$. Therefore

$$P(a, h) = P(ab, h) + P(a \sim b, h). \tag{1.2}$$

Similarly $\qquad P(b, h) = P(ab, h) + P(b \sim a, h). \tag{1.3}$

By addition

$$P(a, h) + P(b, h) = 2P(ab, h) + P(a \sim b, h) + P(b \sim a, h). \tag{1.4}$$

But $a \lor b$ holds only if one of the following happens: ab, $a \sim b$, $b \sim a$; therefore $\quad P(a \lor b, h) = P(ab, h) + P(a \sim b, h) + P(b \sim a, h). \tag{1.5}$

---

[1] Harold Jeffreys, *Scientific Inference*, Cambridge, 1931, Ch. II; *Theory of Probability*, Oxford, 1939, Ch. I.

(1.4), (1.5) give
$$P(a \lor b, h) = P(a, h) + P(b, h) - P(ab, h) \qquad (1.5)$$

which is the general addition theorem for alternatives that do not exclude one another; when the alternatives are exclusive, the last term in (1.5) is zero.

The Multiplication Theorem

Consider a straight line AY of finite length n, and let there be two overlapping lengths AB, XY marked on it. Let AB $= m$ and let the overlap be k.

Suppose any point is marked on the line at random. The probability that it should lie in AB is m/n. If a stands for the occurrence of the point in AB, the probability of a is given by
$$P(a, h) = m/n. \qquad (2)$$

On the supposition that the point lies in AB, the probability that it lies in XB is k/m. If b stands for the occurrence of the point in XY, then the probability that it lies in XB on the supposition that a is true is $P(b, ah)$. Thus
$$P(b, ah) = k/m. \qquad (2.1)$$
Finally, the probability that a and b are both true, i.e., that the point actually lies in XB, is k/n. Thus
$$P(ab, h) = k/n \qquad (2.2)$$
$$= (m/n)\ (k/m) \qquad (2.3)$$
so that $\qquad P(ab, h) = P(a, h) \ . \ P(b, ah). \qquad (2.4)$

That is to say, the probability of the combination of two events is equal to the probability of one of them multiplied by that of the other upon the supposition that the one has occurred. This is the general multiplication theorem. Where the alternatives are independent (2.4) becomes the simplified rule, $P(ab, h) = P(a, h) \ . \ P(b, h)$. Notations of the present type, designed for the foundations of the subject, bring out the difference that arises when the occurrence or otherwise of the first alternative has a bearing on the occurrence of the second. Thus here the probability that the point lies in XB is equal to the probability of its lying in AB multiplied by that of its lying in XB upon the assumption that it does lie in AB.

Bayes's Theorem

By the symmetry of a, b in (2.4) we have also the parallel result:
$$P(ab, h) = P(b, h) \ . \ P(a, bh). \qquad (3)$$

Dividing (2.4) by (3) we get

$$P(a, bh) = \frac{P(b, ah)}{P(b, h)} \cdot P(a, h) \tag{3.1}$$

which is one form of Bayes's theorem. If b is more probable upon the supposition of a than without that assumption, then the fraction is greater than unity. Consequently the probability of a in relation to fresh information b, i.e. $P(a, bh)$, is greater than it was without the information b, when the probability was $P(a, h)$. In particular, if b is a consequence of a its occurrence affords evidence for a. $P(a, h)$ is the prior probability of a, and $P(a, bh)$ is its posterior probability.

Conditions for Increasing Probabilities of Generalisations.[1]

If g is a generalisation and c a set of predictions derived from it, Bayes's theorem (3.1) assumes the form:

$$P(g, hc) = \frac{P(c, hg)}{P(c, h)} \cdot P(g, h). \tag{4}$$

Now c must be true, given that g is true, so that $P(c, hg) = 1$. Hence

$$P(g, hc) = \frac{P(g, h)}{P(c, h)} \tag{4.1}$$

provided $P(c, h)$ is not zero.

Write $cg \vee c{\sim}g$ for c (that is to say the assertion that c is true is equivalent to the assertion that either c and g are true or c and not-g are true); thus

$$P(c, h) = P(cg \vee c{\sim}g, h) \tag{4.2}$$
$$= P(cg, h) + P(c{\sim}g, h). \tag{4.3}$$

Substitute in the denominator of (4.1):

$$P(g, hc) = \frac{P(g, h)}{P(cg, h) + P(c{\sim}g, h)} \tag{4.4}$$

$$= \frac{P(g, h)}{P(g, h) \cdot P(c, hg) + P({\sim}g, h) \cdot P(c, h{\sim}g)} \tag{4.5}$$

$$= \frac{P(g, h)}{P(g, h) + P({\sim}g, h) \cdot P(c, h{\sim}g)} \tag{4.6}$$

$$= 1 - \frac{P({\sim}g, h) \cdot P(c, h{\sim}g)}{P(g, h) + P({\sim}g, h) \cdot P(c, h{\sim}g)} \tag{4.7}$$

[1] J. M. Keynes, *A Treatise on Probability*, London, 1921, pp. 235-7.

(where (4.5) is obtained by the multiplication rule (2.4), and (4.6) is obtained by putting $P(c, hg) = 1$). It is convenient to write this in a different form, by dividing above and below by $P(c, h\sim g)$:

$$P(g, \ hc) = 1 - \cfrac{P(\sim g, \ h)}{\cfrac{P(g, \ h)}{P(c, \ h\sim g)} + P(\sim g, \ h)} \qquad (4.8)$$

We saw that (4.1) was subject to the condition that its denominator was not zero. Moreover $P(c, h)$ is not unity. Hence, on the assumption that $P(g, h)$ is finite, (4.1) gives,

$$P(g, \ hc) > P(g, \ h). \qquad (4.9)$$

Thus the probability of a generalisation upon hc, *i.e.* upon the original information and confirmation, is greater than that of the generalisation upon the original information alone—the posterior probability is greater than the prior probability—provided the generalisation has a prior probability.

Now in order that g should become practically certain, as the set of predictions (n, say) increases indefinitely, the main denominator of (4.8) must approach zero. Thus in order that

$$P(g, \ hc) \longrightarrow 1, \text{ as } n \longrightarrow \infty \qquad (4.10)$$

it is necessary and sufficient that

$$P(c, \ h\sim g) \longrightarrow 0 \qquad (4.11)$$

and

$$P(g, \ h) > \varepsilon > 0 \qquad (4.12)$$

where ε is a positive number, however small.

This completes our account of the conditions, first enunciated by Keynes, for increasing the probability of a generalisation.

Keynes,[1] later correctly criticised by Nicod[2], attempted to analyse (4.11) further by splitting c into a conjunction of n predictions $c_1 c_2 c_3 \ldots c_n$. Then

$$P(c, \ h\sim g) = P(c_1 c_2 \ldots c_n, \ h\sim g) \qquad (4.13)$$
$$= P(c_1, \ h\sim g) \cdot P(c_2, \ hc_1 \sim g) \ldots P(c, \ hc_1 \ c_2 \ldots c_{n-1} \sim g) \qquad (4.14)$$

by repeated application of the multiplication rule (2.4). Keynes held that (4.11) was ensured provided

$$P(c_n, \ hc_1 c_2 \ldots c_{n-1} \sim g) < \eta < 1 \qquad (4.15)$$

---

[1] Keynes, *Op. cit.*, p. 237.
[2] Jean Nicod, *The Logical Problem of Induction*, Eng. trans. in *Foundations of Geometry and Induction*, London, 1930, pp. 275-7.

where η is a positive number, however small. But Nicod pointed out that this, though sufficient, is not necessary; for it is *possible* for $P(c, h \sim g)$ to approach zero even if the probability in (4.15) approaches unity. Thus if, for example, this probability is $n/(n+1)$ which approaches unity, the product (4.14) becomes $1/(n+1)$, which approaches zero, as n approaches infinity. On the other hand we cannot substitute the condition

$$P(c_n, hc_1 c_2 \ldots c_{n-1} \sim g) < 1. \qquad (4.16)$$

This condition is obviously true; but it is not sufficient to ensure (4.11). Thus if, for example, this probability is $(n+1)/ne^h$, which is less than unity, the product (4.14) becomes $(n+1)/e^{1 + \frac{1}{2} + \frac{1}{3} + \cdots \frac{1}{n}}$, which approaches $e^{-\gamma}$ (approximately ·56), where e is the exponential and γ is Euler's constant, as n approaches infinity. Hence the condition (4.16), though necessary, is not sufficient.

Von Wright has pointed out that, in general, (4.11) is not satisfied.[1]

Keynes's Basis for the Prior Probability of a Generalisation.[2]

I follow Broad's treatment[3] with minor modifications. Let L be the Principle of Limitation of Independent Variety, C a set of predictions derived from it, and H the information on which it is based. We assume that $P(L, H)$ is finite, *i.e.* that

$$P(L, H) > \varepsilon_1 \qquad (5)$$

where ε_1 is some positive number, however small.

Assuming that $P(C, H)$ is neither zero nor unity, we have by Bayes's theorem (3.1) that

$$P(L, HC) > P(L, H) \qquad (5.1)$$

so that
$$P(L, HC) > \varepsilon_1 > 0. \qquad (5.2)$$

Now consider a generalisation g. Because L has been so constructed as to impose a limitation upon groups of properties, we have

$$P(g, L) > \varepsilon_2 > 0 \qquad (5.3)$$

where ε_2 is some positive number. By the multiplication rule (2.4) it is clear that

$$P(gL, HC) = P(g, HC) \cdot P(L, gHC) \qquad (5.4)$$

so that
$$P(g, HC) > P(gL, HC). \qquad (5.5)$$

Expanding the expression on the right by the multiplication rule once

[1] G. H. von Wright, *The Logical Problem of Induction*, Helsingfors, 1941, pp. 124–5.
[2] Keynes, *Op. cit.*, pp. 259–60.
[3] C. D. Broad, "The Principles of Problematic Induction", *Proc. of the Arist. Soc.*, N.S. Vol. XXVIII, London, 1928, pp. 42–4.

more, this time in the form P(L, HC).P(g, LHC), which is greater than or equal to P(L, HC).P(g, L), we conclude that

$$P(g, \text{HC}) > \varepsilon_1 \varepsilon_2. \tag{5.6}$$

Thus, subject to the condition (5), any generalisation has a prior probability in relation to certain facts. It may be noted that the facts that give g a prior probability are not necessarily to be identified with those upon which g has been based. Moreover the prior probability of all generalisations would be the same.

By an argument similar to that of the preceding section it is easy to obtain the conditions in which L would become practically certain.

No satisfactory reason has been offered for (5). If we reject this and (5.6) as a basis for increasing the probability of a generalisation, Keynes's condition (4.12) remains unjustified. And we have seen that his other condition (4.11) can be false.

CHAPTER XXIII

PROBABILITY AND INDUCTION

THE topic to be discussed here is closely connected with that of the previous chapter. It differs in that it is concerned not with the probability of a generalisation but with the justification of a probability inference from present observation to future ones. The only theorems that seem to be relevant to such a project are the Bernoulli-Poisson Law of Great Numbers (or the more general Tchebysheff Frequency Theorem); inverse theorems, the Probability of Causes or the Inverted Bernoulli Theorem, and Bayes's Theorem in the form connecting prior and posterior probabilities.

This last, however, can be utilised only in connexion with generalisations; it was discussed in the previous chapter. The other inverse theorems cannot be used in connexion with any approach to induction so far made, for they involve the conditions that the number of possible causes of an event is finite, that one of them must be the cause, and that their probabilities are known; and these conditions are not satisfied. In this chapter, therefore, we shall be concerned solely with Tchebysheff's theorem or with its special form the Law of Great Numbers.

Two approaches will be considered: one that attempts to base induction on the frequency theory, and the other that attempts to base it on the theory of sampling.

If "probability" is taken to be some *a priori* notion, our theorem is inapplicable to actual states of affairs. But, if we restrict ourselves to the frequency or range interpretation of probability, the theorem is applicable but there is no guarantee that it will always hold good. More precisely, when we have found a frequency-limit that satisfies the condition of randomness or a set of equi-possible ranges of an alternative, the theorem tells us that most probably approximate conformity will continue to be found. *But this is true only if the new observations fall within the field from which the frequency or range-ratio has been estimated. It is not true for observations beyond this field.* Thus if a probability is derived from a long sequence of throws of a coin, our theorem must be true of a sequence sliced out of the given one, but it is not necessarily true of a prolongation of that sequence. If it were, we could justifiably make inductive statements about the future on the strength of past observations, *i.e.* extrapolate into the future, for this theorem would render such probable predictions tautological.

Indeed the attempt to base induction on probability involves holding that untried portions of a sequence will behave much like an examined portion, and this amounts to making an inductive claim. In other words, if induction could rightly be said to presuppose an inductive postulate, this use of probability theory would in the same way need an inductive postulate (to the effect that unknown portions of sequences would have approximately similar frequencies as known ones). Thus so far from solving the problem of induction by means of the theory of probability, it is clear that the application of the theory would rest on induction.

Thus induction cannot be justified by the frequency theory and the Law of Great Numbers.

An ingenious attempt has been made by Williams[1] to show that inductive inference is logical; he bases it on the theorem we are considering alone, which he rightly interprets as a tautology, and he claims that no empirical assumption is involved. (It would be well to be explicit about which theorem is to be used. It could be Tchebysheff's frequency theorem or Bernoulli's theorem; they make much the same assertion, differing only in the actual measure of the probability involved. They are concerned with a sequence of a finite number of members, moreover, and the Law of Great Numbers is no more than the form either theorem takes when the number of members in the sequence is allowed to become very great or approach infinity. For purposes of the present discussion, therefore, it is a convenient and harmless vagueness to refer simply to 'the' theorem, without differentiating which is being used.)

As a preliminary step Williams introduces the 'proportion syllogism', which is

$$r/n \text{ of M are P}$$
$$\underline{\text{S is an M}}$$
$$\text{The probability is } r/n \text{ that S is P.}$$

---

[1] Donald Williams, *The Ground of Induction*, Cambridge (Mass.), 1947, mainly Ch. IV.

Thus if $\frac{4}{5}$ of the balls in an urn are black and one is drawn, the probability is $\frac{4}{5}$ that it is black.[1] This bears an obvious analogy to the classical syllogism

All M are P

S is an M

S is a P.

Williams discusses the relation most persuasively to show that between an invalid and valid syllogism the proportion syllogism takes a logical place with an intermediate logical cogency denoted by a proportion:[2] this may assist one to assume the right frame of mind, but it is not strictly necessary to his argument. In fact the proportion syllogism is a tautology. Moreover it does not require M to be large.

Now the proportion syllogism cannot at once be used for the purpose in hand. Suppose we have a set of M members, which may be called a "population", and examine a set of S members of M, which we may call a "sample". From our knowledge of the number and composition of S we wish to make an inference about the composition of M. That is, we wish to make the inductive inference:

r/n of S are P

Probably, approximately r/n of M are P.

Thus suppose that of 50 balls drawn from an urn 40 are black, then it is probable that approximately $\frac{4}{5}$ of the balls in the urn are black. But this cannot be established by the proportion syllogism. What the proportion syllogism can do is to make an inference about the composition of S from our knowledge of the number and composition of M. In order to make use of this we proceed as follows.

The first step[3] makes use of the probability theorem.

Consider a sample of a population M, and consider all other possible samples of the same size that could be formed from M. Then given the size of the sample and the size and composition of M, it is easy to find by the algebra of permutations and combinations the proportion of samples of the same size that have the same

---

[1] *Id.*, *pp.* 12–3.
[2] *Id.*, p. 36 *et passim.*
[3] *Id.*, Ch. IV.

composition as M. More important, we can find the proportion *s/m*, say of samples that have *approximately* the same composition as M, where the degree of approximation is specified, or, as we may say, the proportion of samples that 'match' M. This may be otherwise expressed by saying that we can find the probability *s/m* of a sample 'matching' M.* And when S is large the vast majority of samples will 'match' M, or it is overwhelmingly probable that a sample will 'match' M. (It must be stressed that 'matching' is an approximation relation.) Williams points out, moreover, that M need not be a finite or closed class. We may call these inferences types of "sampling inference".

All this is an application of our probability theorem and is tautological. There is therefore no difficulty in accepting the results. In the typical conclusion, "The probability is *s/m* that a sample has approximately the same composition as the population", the degree of approximation and the degree of probability are connected by a precise relation such that for any assigned approximation the degree of probability can be calculated, and for any assigned probability we can calculate the degree of approximation. Indeed the degree of probability is quite high even when the approximation is close for even moderate-sized samples and populations.

The second step is to apply the proportion syllogism to this result:

> *s/m* of equal sized samples 'match' M
> S is one such sample
> _____
> The probability is *s/m* that S 'matches' M.

And, if the sample is large, we have

> Nearly all equal sized samples 'match' M
> S is one such sample
> _____
> The probability is overwhelming that S 'matches' M.

Finally, Williams notes, if S 'matches' M, then M 'matches' S. Hence from a knowledge of the composition of S we can deduce the probability that M 'matches' S.

One or other of these inferences is needed in order to apply the sampling inference to a concrete case when we are confronted with an actual sample. Once again the inference is tautological. It is

---

* The proportion or probability *s/m* is a minimum, but this has no bearing on the discussion. Probability will therefore not be qualified as minimal in what follows.

the expansion of the inductive argument we set out to justify, namely

S has a certain ascertained composition
_____
Probably M has approximately this composition

or

r/n of S are P
A specified object is an M
_____
The probability is approximately r/n that the object is P.

Thus if 50 black balls have been drawn from an urn and 40 are found to be black, then the probability is approximately $\frac{4}{5}$ that the next one to be drawn will be black.

It remains to remark that this procedure covers 'laws of nature'. The only alteration needed is to replace the observed fraction r/n by 100%, and if the sample of observations is of reasonable size then it is overwhelmingly probable that the next observation will conform. Thus if 100% of observed crows are black, it is overwhelmingly probable that the next crow to be observed will be black.

This nice treatment of the subject unfortunately suffers from familiar difficulties.

We have seen that our theorem can be applied to portions of a sequence but not outside it. This is essentially the idea that Williams has tried to use; for he has based his argument on the 'sampling inference', which is an application of the theorem from the population to the sample (analogous to an application from a sequence to a portion of it). But doubts about whether he has in fact done this arise when we ask with regard to an inductive argument what the population is. For his procedure to work, the population of crows, for example, must be the set of crows, past, present, and to come.

Before proceeding with the difficulty involved, we may point to one successful achievement of his argument—it is at least a partial success. *It goes some way at least to justifying inductive interpolations within the present.* For instance, if all crows in an observed sample are black, his argument asserts that it is overwhelmingly probable that all present crows are black. A doubt may be raised even about this; but the difficulty is easier to see in the problem of justifying inductive conclusions about the future.

The main difficulty with regard to a population concerns the justification of inductive extrapolations into the future. Williams is of course correct in holding that his argument is valid no matter what the composition of the population is. But the tacit assumption made here is that the population exists. To justify inductive extrapolation, the 'population' must contain members that will in fact exist but that do not yet exist. Now this places a severe limitation upon the number of obtainable samples of the 'population'; for the number is reduced to what we can at present inspect. Does he not require some guarantee that the 'population' that includes what is to come shall 'match' the present population?

Williams would perhaps reject this criticism, on the ground that it is equivalent to demanding that a sample should be *random*, which he claims is not necessary. Let us consider this.

We have to consider the question of randomness in two contexts: (i) inductive interpolations in the present; and (ii) extrapolations into the future.

(i) Is it correct to claim that no attention need be given to randomness, when, for example, all observed crows are black and we infer with overwhelming probability that all existing crows are black? There was a time when this type of inference was made in connexion with the observation that all observed swans were white. Black swans were later found in the antipodes. But this does not necessarily invalidate a probability inference. The question is whether the original sample of white swans was a 'fair' one or random.

Williams' answer[1] is that we make probability inferences just because we lack full knowledge: that to *know* a sample was random would be to *know* it 'matched' its population, which would obviate the need for the probability inference; that therefore we do not even *assume* that a sample is random—if it is not we shall be unlucky in our prediction, as with the black swans—but that it is of the nature of the sampling inference that we make the best inference we can despite our ignorance, or make a probability prediction in relation to such knowledge as we have and not in relation to knowledge we wish we had.

This is most persuasive. It even accords more closely than might be expected with practical statistical work. We know in practical affairs that we must take random samples. But this is because we utilise existing knowledge. If we know of some circumstance that would influence a sample, we must look for a sample that would

[1] *Id.*, pp. 66–72, 140–3.

be uninfluenced by it. Thus if we wish to find out the number of men who generally are at home in the middle of the morning, it would be unwise to make investigations on a Sunday. Now all this is only to say that *we avoid using a sample that is influenced in a known way*. What is commonly regarded in practical work as a random sample is simply a residual one, after we have eliminated the multitudes of those that are influenced in multitudinous ways known to us. Now, for Williams' argument, we must suppose that such precautions have been taken. The samples he is concerned with are therefore random in the practical sense. If we demand that they should be random in a further sense, it is either a demand for knowledge of 'matching' or for additional knowledge about the influences that might affect the sample—the one would render statistical inference superfluous, the other is worthy in the interests of efficiency but does not come into conflict with Williams' argument. After all, *probability is used when all available knowledge has been taken account of and found insufficient*.

The question might be raised whether Williams' argument presupposes that samples are equally likely to be available for inspection. This is in effect the same point in a different form. If we know there is some influence that is likely to push an unfair sample before us, we refuse it. We utilise a sample only after ascertaining that, *so far as our knowledge goes*, there is no such influence. (At worst, this objection would only show that our inductions might be unreliable in practice, but not that Williams' justification was invalid.)

An important detail about the statistical inference may be made clear by further consideration of the practice that a sample is random *provided our knowledge does not indicate that the sample is not random*. It might seem that a sample would not be a fair one unless we took all possible practical steps to rule out unfair samples; but there is a confusion here. This is so in practice, but to apply the statistical inference all samples are usable, even unfair ones. If we use an unfair one, knowing it is unfair, then our probable prediction of the composition of the population will be wrong as regards what is predicted but its probability will not have been falsified. Thus a sample does not have to be fair from the theoretical point of view. The reason why an unfair sample is avoided in practice is this. We know the propertion of samples that will 'match' the population, and this is our main interest; but we must not forget that some samples will not 'match'. If we have a sample we believe to be unfair, then it is unlikely to 'match'; it is likely to be one of those that do not 'match'. Hence we should not use it. But, in the absence of any knowledge that it is unfair, the probability is that it is not unfair and that it will 'match'.

I conclude, then, that Williams' view of randomness is justified, which suggests that his argument, interpreted as an inductive interpolation about the present, is valid. This would be true, however, only on the assumption that our samples are in fact samples of the present population. Unfortunately the inductive problem is here once again in a disguised form. Induction is concerned not with the *practical* problem of sampling, but with the theoretical one of making an inference about unexamined things in view of the possibility that the universe might play some trick that would wreck our best calculated expectations. But the difficulty is more easily seen in the context of inferences about the future.

(ii) We turn, therefore, to inductive extrapolation about the future. In this context it is difficult to agree that a present sample is random. The whole point behind the need to justify induction has always been that the nature of things or the nature of the universe might change; and one difficulty of justifying induction has always been that we have no knowledge about the future *at all* and can therefore offer no reason for holding that such changes will not occur. If this is the problem of induction and the main difficulty of solving it, then it is equally a problem, with its concomitant difficulty of solution, in a corresponding form for Williams; for, in the event of change in the nature of things or of the universe, a present sample would be no guide to the composition of a population that embraces the future.

Why is this? We saw, in connexion with inductive interpolation, that in a sense any sample is fair—why not here? One way of putting the reason is that a present sample is a fair one by which to judge the present population as a sub-population of the total population that embraces the future; hence we should have to argue that the sub-population was a sample that most probably 'matches' the whole population; but can it be a good statistical guide?

Suppose, for example, we draw a sample of balls from an urn, but know that there is a peculiar feature of the population, namely that, because of a division of the urn into two compartments only one of which is accessible to us, we can take samples only from one compartment. We can estimate the sub-population that is accessible; but can we estimate the whole population? It is true that in the absence of knowledge of factors influencing a sample we rightly use that sample as a guide and that with such knowledge we rightly reject the sample. But here the position is that we do not know whether or not there is an influence at work and we think it possible there may be. In view of this doubt we cannot regard the sample as a guide that has the required statistical reliability.

In other words, if some balls in an urn were sewn into a pocket, we could not get a fair sample—or rather we could not get a sample at all. Likewise the 'iron curtain' between the present and the future invalidates inductive extrapolation about the composition of things behind the curtain—we cannot sample them from this side.

For this reason there is an unjustified step in inductive extrapolation or statistical inference from present sample to future population. Thus Williams' ingenious and delightful idea fails at the last hurdle.

It would seem to be impossible to justify induction by probability considerations. As Hume said, though he had little to contribute on probability,

Nay, I will go further, and assert, that he could not so much as prove by any *probable* arguments, that the future must be conformable to the past. All probable arguments are built on the supposition, that there is this conformity betwixt the future and the past, and therefore can never prove it.[1]

Two hundred and fifty years later this was reiterated by Heymans: the theory of probability cannot explain the procedure of induction,

because the same problem which is concealed in the one is also concealed in the other. For in both cases the inference goes beyond what is given in the premisses.[2]

---

[1] David Hume, *An Abstract of A Treatise on Human Nature*, Cambridge, 1938, p. 15.
[2] Heymans, *Gesetze und Elemente des wissenschaftlichen Denkens*, 1890–4, S. 290*fg.*, quoted from Popper, *Op. cit.*, S. 196–7.

PART IV

CHAPTER XXIV

TRANSFORMATION
OF THE PROBLEM OF INDUCTION

THE problem of induction was known to Aristotle; but the full extent of its difficulty first came to light in Hume. How can we make an inference from examined instances to an unexamined instance or to all instances examined and unexamined? We have found hitherto that brass has expanded when heated, but how can we infer that the next piece of brass to be examined will do so too or that all pieces of brass will? As Hume put it, how do we know that the sun will rise to-morrow, simply from our knowledge that it has done so regularly in the past? There is nothing contradictory in supposing that past regularities will suddenly not be repeated.

Mill's attempt to justify the inference from past to future by means of the Law of Uniformity of Nature or the Law of Universal Causation fails for a number of reasons. Keynes made a subtle attempt to evade the difficulties created by introducing such a Law. His Principle of Limitation of Independent Variety comes very close to doing what is required of it; but though it comes extremely close a gap remains—a gap that there is no reasonable expectation of closing.

As is often the way with an old problem, discussion down the ages leads to an alteration of its formulation: the problem is seen or believed to turn on some more narrowly defined issue. The inductive issue that became the focus of discussion for many years, perhaps from the time of Kant to the present day, concerned the causal relation. Philosophers would try to understand the nature of causing by analysing the statement "X causes E". This produced a sharp controversy and led to the clearer realisation that there were two uncompromising attitudes. On the one hand, idealists, realists, intellectualists, and metaphysicians generally held in common that there exists a single, simple, and necessary relation connecting the essence of X with the essence of E, not unlike (though not wholly like) the relation of entailment which connects premisses and conclusion of a deductive inference. (If this were true, the problem of induction would have been overcome, it was supposed; but this is doubtful.) On the other hand, logical analysts and logical positivists of various hues held in common that the relation connecting X and E was not one of necessary connexion, that it was in no way like that of entailment, that there was no essence of X or of E to be connected, and that the relation, though perhaps single and simple, was just one of constant conjunction—that is, that instances of X and of E accompanied one another with *de facto* regularity. (If this were true, the problem of induction, according to most of these thinkers, would be dissolved or resolved, and stand in no need of justification.)

The objections to both views are claimed in this book to be overwhelming. Now, if the study of the statement, "X causes E", properly represents the problem of induction, and if it is agreed further that no other interpretation of this statement is possible within the framework of induction except the two described, then it follows that "X causes E" cannot be satisfactorily interpreted and that therefore inductive inference cannot be justified.

"X causes E" may be interpreted by reference to all possible types of statement in which "cause" occurs, and this would involve reference to all possible types of statement of which the comparison and contrast would lead us to single out a factor as a cause. In this way we could in principle get a definition from usage, though this would be complicated to write down. What would be noticed about it, however, is that it would refer to a *class of instances* of X (and a class of instances of E)—and indeed these would be classes of instances *resembling* one another, not of identical instances. Thus it would turn out that "X causes E" is in fact a universal statement, "All resembling instances of X . . ." And this points to the way hypotheses are used in the hypothetico-deductive system.

Thus Hume's problem in its original form, whether discussed in terms of inferences from the past to the future or in terms of the causal relation, is answered—inductive inference cannot be justified.

The attempt was then made to modify the problem and treat inductive inference as a species of probable inference. But all such attempts foundered because probability inferences from the past to the future would require justification of exactly the same kind as that sought for the original form of inductive inference. And Keynes's ingenious attempt to make the Principle of Limitation of Independent Variety the basis of inductive probability inference fails, both because the conditions required for its success cannot be fulfilled and because it is highly doubtful if we can speak meaningfully of the probability of an inductive generalisation.

Thus inductive inference, even when interpreted as a species of probable inference, cannot be justified.

This does not in itself mean that the question about justifying induction was put in a wrong form or that a wrong question was asked. The form of question may have been correct and the answer to it simply disappointing. But, if the problem of induction is crystallised in the problem of interpreting "X causes E" and if there is no possible interpretation of this within the framework of induction, then there is good ground for supposing that the question was wrongly posed. There may indeed be no right form; but, if we think there may be one, we must reframe the question.

Doubt whether there is a correct form of the question arises out of the logico-positivist view that induction stands in no need of justification and that there is a peculiar confusion underlying the very idea of justifying such a procedure as induction.

"Why are you drinking that glass of water?"

"To assuage my thirst."

"Why do you think that drinking a glass of water will assuage your thirst?"

"It has always (or usually) done so."

"So your *reason* for expecting a certain sort of result from a certain sort of action is that that sort of result has always (or usually) ensued from that sort of action?"

"Yes."

"Then you know what the *reason* is for expecting your anticipations to be fulfilled?"

"Yes."

"Clearly, the philosopher who seeks to justify induction is looking for a 'reason' rendering the inference from past to future acceptable. You know the reasons for expecting your anticipations to be fulfilled. He is evidently looking for some deeper 'reason' to justify the reasons you give."

This 'reason' for inductive inference is held by logical positivists of whatever hue to be a strange thing to demand.

I wish to offer grounds for regarding it as a sensible demand, for regarding it as sensible to ask what reason there is for expecting the same sort of uniformities to occur in the future as have occurred in the past.

"You have mentioned that Socrates is mortal. Why is that?"

"Because, as you would doubtless agree, all men are mortal and Socrates is a man."

"Yes."

"Then you see my reason for asserting that Socrates is mortal."

"The reason being that all men are mortal and Socrates is a man?"

"Yes."

"I do not understand why that is a reason. Explain to me how the mortality of all men and the humanity of Socrates can be a reason for concluding that Socrates is mortal."

Aristotle thought this a sensible demand and gave as a quasi-answer his *dictum de omni et nullo*. But it has been shown to be a sensible demand only with the recent discovery of the answer to it—of the answer sought.[1] Formal Logic has justified the question.

"Why are you so depressed?"

"Because of the weather."

"Why does the weather make you depressed?"

"I have no idea."

"Then it would take perhaps prolonged psycho-analysis to find the reason."

"You mean the reason involves experiences, hallucinations, wishes, and fears I had long ago, which became connected both with the weather and my depression?"

Here, too, in certain cases the 'reason' for the reason has been found.

Thus I think that a reason should be sought to justify inductive inference, that this form of inference cannot be justified and that no reason for it can be found; but this is not at all the same as to assert that the 'problem of induction' is a pseudo-problem. The logico-analytical and logico-positivist techniques are excellent for showing a pseudo-problem for what it is; they can be used, but

[1] K. R. Popper, "The Trivialisation of Mathematical Logic", *Proceedings of the Xth International Congress of Philosophy*, Vol. I, Amsterdam, 1948.

they can and are likely to be abused, if the problem is a real one.

This opinion can of course be established only by finding the 'reason' justifying inductive inference. The foregoing argument—one of somewhat doubtful analogy—is in no way conclusive. It is an argument to suggest that it is worth bearing in mind simply as a working hypothesis that a 'reason' might be found.

While subscribing to the widely-held opinion that there are no grounds for inductive inference, I do so, not because the problem of induction is a pseudo-problem, but because inductive inference, with or without the support of probability, is simply invalid. What I wish to put forward is that the problem has an heir—that there is a genuine question underlying the aim of justifying induction that can be expressed in a form that may be susceptible of a satisfactory answer. Can we, then, find an heir to the problem of induction—a problem in the spirit of that problem, which shall be more suitable for investigation?

We have seen that many difficulties in the nature of the causal relation and inductive inference are obviated by using the scheme of explanation provided by the hypothetico-deductive system, according to which a hypothesis is accepted when it has been 'tempered' by severe testing and has not been falsified. Let us pursue this further.

What we obtain from a successful piece of scientific work is a hypothesis that has survived the ordeals of the severest testing that can be devised; thus all we can claim to possess is a hypothesis that is not, so far as we know, false. If we wish to say that it is then in high degree confirmed, this can be no more than a statement in new terms of what is asserted by the previous one. Humanly speaking, we are likely to slip into interpreting this as positive confirmation, but strictly we are provided with no reason for adopting the hypothesis. In other words, why should we rely on a hypothesis in the future simply because it has not let us down in the past? Is it rational to regard unfalsified hypotheses as having some measure of credibility?

The transformed problem is thus not one of justifying an inductive inference from particulars but of justifying our adoption of unfalsified hypotheses. But the new problem is not even to justify the belief that a hypothesis hitherto unfalsified should survive falsification tests in the future, but to show that the belief is more rational than any other. The method of dealing with this is to effect a comparison with falsified hypotheses. We may not be able to show that any belief is rational; but we may be able to show that one belief is *more rational* than another.

Consider a man who is confronted with a situation calling for a decision to act (including the special case of deciding to do nothing). If he favours a certain decision it must be based upon belief in the utility of a certain hypothesis. This, let us suppose, has survived falsification tests. Suppose now that he maintains there is no reason to trust the hypothesis. Thus if he feels ordinarily thirsty, he may distrust the hypothesis that if he drinks a glass of water his thirst will be assuaged. What course is now open to him? He may consider that if he does nothing his thirst will vanish in a few seconds, or he may consider that if he eats dry bread this will happen. Whatever alternative consequence to drinking water is envisaged, some hypothesis is involved. Thus all possible consequences of his action, those that are plainly absurd as well as those that are normal, are derivable from some hypothesis. Now the characteristic feature of those hypotheses ordinarily regarded as absurd is that they have *always* been falsified by past experience —we may conveniently refer to them as 'regularly falsified hypotheses'. Hence the man's choice is between one of a small set of hypotheses that have survived falsification tests and one of a large set of those that have been regularly falsified.

Our preliminary transformation of the problem, then, is this. Instead of justifying induction from particulars or even of justifying the belief that an unfalsified hypothesis can be trusted, we have to justify the choice of unfalsified hypotheses instead of regularly falsified ones.

In this form a specious air of self-evidence creeps in, for it seems obvious that it is rational to choose unfalsified hypotheses rather than those that have been falsified. But this would presuppose the belief that falsified hypotheses will continue to be falsified. However, just as it is a commonplace to point out that it is logically possible for long established uniformities to break down, we must now point out that it is logically possible for a well falsified hypothesis to be confirmed by all future tests. Hence, though the problem of induction is dead, it has an heir. The problem in its new form might seem to require not the Law of Uniformity of Nature but a law of uniformity of unconnectedness, *i.e.* that if two occurrences have ever been found not to go together, similar occurrences in similar immediate circumstances will be found not to happen together. I am not suggesting that there is such a law; I wish only to indicate that I approach the problem of induction initially not by asking whether we can trust an unfalsified hypothesis to hold but whether we can trust a regularly falsified hypothesis to fail.

Greater precision about falsified hypotheses is now required. Suppose we consider the falsified hypothesis that all gases explode. This might very well be confirmed at the next test or indeed by all tests over a long period; yet this would be due to our not having tempered the hypothesis by dividing gases into two classes, those that explode and those that do not. We should have replaced the hypothesis by one to the effect that all gases characterised in such and such a way explode. Again the falsified Newtonian hypothesis of gravitation should be referred to different fields of application, for if all our future tests concerned medium sized bodies moving with moderate speeds and not moving too far, we should get nothing but confirmation.*

It is evident that a hypothesis of this kind can be split into two hypotheses, one that is unfalsified, and one that has always been falsified—*i.e.* that has been falsified by every test. But the qualifications given are not sufficient. It is not always possible to split a hypothesis into two component parts, one of which has always been falsified and the other always unfalsified, or to distinguish two different fields of application characterised in the same way. For instance, the hypothesis that all swans are white has been falsified by the discovery of black swans. But it is impossible, so far as I know, to distinguish white and black swans as two different types, such that we could say that all swans of the one type are white and all of the other type are black. Then the hypothesis that all swans are white and the hypothesis that all swans are black are both falsified, and yet confirmation of either is to be expected.

Here our data tell us that some swans have been white and some black, and in certain examples we could name the proportions of each. If we have made a count we can describe the data by a statistical statement such as "$n\%$ of swans have been white", where n may have any value from 0 to 100 exclusive. And we may, if we wish, frame the statistical hypothesis, "$n\%$ of swans are

---

* The need for this qualification is not, however, a disadvantage to the view being put forward. Suppose that through ignorance we had omitted the necessary qualification, and obtained repeated confirmation of a previously falsified hypothesis, we should decide, not that the improbable had occurred (though we might keep this possibility at the back of our minds) but that the hypothesis required some analysis. The situation would be of exactly the same kind as when we have a well-confirmed hypothesis that suddenly comes in for repeated falsification—the sequence of events would be different, that is all.

white". If we wish to be more cautious we shall be content with saying, "some swans are white and some are black". We can always set up the statistical hypothesis, "$n\%$ of swans are white", where n may be known or unknown (though if unknown it is at any rate known not to be 0 or 100).

What we have, then, are (i) regularly unfalsified hypotheses, (ii) statistical hypotheses of the form, "$n\%$ of x's have the property φ", and (iii) regularly falsified hypotheses.

Suppose a person is confronted with a situation, such as the need to put a dog out of misery, in circumstances in which he can get no help; and suppose he happens to have a gun, a small dose of arsenic, and some water. He may consider acting on (i) the regularly unfalsified hypothesis that shooting a dog through the brain kills it, (ii) the statistical hypothesis that sometimes to give a dog a small dose of arsenic kills it, and (iii) the regularly falsified hypothesis that giving a dog water kills it. Obviously he adopts (i), the regularly unfalsified hypothesis. If he had no gun, he would prefer (ii), the hypothesis about a method that had sometimes worked, to (iii), the one that had never worked.

It is clearly rational to trust in (i) rather than in (ii) and in (ii) rather than in (iii)—and a fortiori in (i) rather than in (iii). Can this be justified? This seems to me to be a genuine heir to the problem of induction, to which it might be possible to give a positive and satisfactory answer. If not, this transformation of the problem of induction will not have been wasted, for it replaces an alleged method and mode of inference that bears no relation to the procedure of science by one that is true to that procedure.

I will now sketch a way in which this might be justified.

An unfalsified hypothesis is reliable or trustworthy if it continues to be unfalsified; a statistical hypothesis if it continues to be confirmed about as often as it was in the past; and a regularly falsified hypothesis if it continues to be falsified. Otherwise they are unreliable or untrustworthy. Now the universe may render hypotheses reliable or it may render them unreliable. Many kinds of universe can be conceived that could do either. If the universe has just enough order in it to render hypotheses reliable, we shall call it "favourable", and if not we shall call it "unfavourable".

If the universe were in fact rigidly deterministic, we should have no ground for using a regularly falsified hypothesis but excellent reason for using an unfalsified one—for supposing that an unfalsified hypothesis was a law. If the universe were chaotic we should have no ground for trusting a hypothesis whether regularly falsified or unfalsified (though we might be in for a run of good luck with either). If the universe were 'loosely jointed', then it would be most unlikely that a regularly falsified hypothesis would hold in the future, whereas there would be some possibility that an unfalsified hypothesis would be a law. Thus, in no sort of universe would there be any likelihood that a regularly falsified hypothesis would hold in the future. It is therefore rational not to adopt a regularly falsified hypothesis.

Now the only alternative procedure is to adopt an unfalsified hypothesis (or else a statistical hypothesis). Nonetheless it would not be rational to do this if there were also no likelihood that an unfalsified hypothesis (or a statistical hypothesis) would hold in the future. Indeed an unfalsified hypothesis would be most unlikely to hold in an unfavourable universe. Hence in such a universe there would be nothing to choose between an unfalsified hypothesis and a regularly falsified one. But, in a favourable universe, an unfalsified hypothesis would be likely to hold. Hence to choose an unfalsified hypothesis rather than a regularly falsified one is to gamble on whether the universe is favourable or not.

But what of statistical hypotheses in an unfavourable universe? Where the hypothesis is "$n\%$ of x's have φ", we can see that a future x is most unlikely to have φ, because the consequences of giving a dog arsenic, say, would not be limited to the dog's dying or the dog's living—the animal might cease to be a dog. Thus in an unfavourable universe a statistical hypothesis would have almost no chance of success (indeed it would be almost certain to fail in a bizarre way).

In a favourable universe, on the other hand, a regularly falsified hypothesis would be almost certain to fail, whereas a statistical hypothesis would probably succeed. Thus it would be reasonable to adopt a statistical hypothesis rather than a regularly falsified one. On the other hand, a statistical hypothesis would be most unlikely to be proved unreliable by a peculiar set of circumstances in which all future x's turned out to have φ. And an unfalsified hypothesis would be most unlikely to be falsified. Hence, if we are concerned to kill a dog, we are much more likely to succeed by adopting the relevant unfalsified hypothesis, that shooting dogs through the brain kills them, rather than the statistical hypothesis, that a small dose of arsenic sometimes does.

Hence in a sufficiently favourable universe an unfalsified hypothesis is more reliable than a statistical hypothesis, and a statistical hypothesis more reliable than a regularly falsified hypothesis. In an unfavourable universe all hypotheses are unreliable.

All this depends upon the notions of favourable and unfavourable universes. The aim is to devise these in such a way that the above conclusions hold. Further elaboration would, of course, require discussion of 'likelihood' and whether it is the same as 'probability' in the sense considered in Part III; but here I wish only to stress certain points about the approach. No attempt is being made to show that hypotheses are in an unqualified way likely to hold. A fundamental point to be borne in mind is that the existence of a favourable universe is not postulated. All that is needed is its *possibility*. There is also the possibility that the universe is in fact unfavourable. Then all predictions will be unreliable. But we do not *know* that the universe is *not* favourable; hence it is rational to use hypotheses on the *possibility* that it is favourable rather than beat the air, so to speak, on the possibility that it is unfavourable. It may be added that the least favourable sort of favourable universe would have to have severe limitation of independent variety, *i.e.* to be characterised in some such way as Keynes suggested (though there is no question here of putting this to the use he envisaged, for it is not being introduced as a postulate, nor are hypotheses being endowed with a probability).

There is no question of justifying induction or of presupposing induction, for there is in an important sense no *inference* from the past to the future at all. This differentiates the scheme from, for instance, Williams' attempt to infer by sampling what goes on behind the iron curtain that envelops the future. The difference arises from the use made of the hypothetico-deductive system. This permits of deriving valid conclusions. In other words we can make a valid prediction and discuss its fulfilment. But, if we adhere to the inductive procedure, we cannot make a valid inference at all. In order to use the sampling inference we have to add a hypothesis of the form, "All examined sets of x's are samples of the population of unexamined x's"; but, once the underlying assumption is made explicit, the method at once becomes hypothetico-deductive.

Finally I wish to stress the tautological nature of one of the main parts of the proposed solution, and to point out that nonetheless there is no question of 'reducing' induction to deduction.

The inferences are all deductive and tautological, for the concepts of favourable and unfavourable universes are designed with that end in view. But a fact enters the scene, which prevents there being a straightforward deduction alone. The fact is this: the universe may be favourable or it may be unfavourable. The tautologies are these: on the possibility of a favourable universe, there is a rational choice among hypotheses; else there is none. Thus our only real hope of success is to gamble on the universe being favourable. This is not deductive. Hence the solution as a whole is not deductive (though it contains a deductive part).

In short, if the universe has an unfavourable structure, the method of hypothesis is useless; if it has a favourable structure, the method can work. Thus the solution appears to say no more than: If the universe favours scientific procedure, scientific procedure is the most reliable, and, if not, not! This way of putting it may over-emphasise the trivial or tautological aspect of the solution. We must not, however, slur over the additional feature —the possibility that the universe is favourable.

Reichenbach's Solution

After developing the foregoing solution of the problem, I found that Reichenbach had already proposed a solution with a basic similarity to this one, though different in some respects. His solution, which is in terms of induction, is as follows.[1]

Reichenbach opens by pointing out, as against Hume, that to justify induction it is not *necessary* to prove the *truth* of an inductive conclusion (though if we could do this it would be *sufficient* to justify the inference). He gives the following illustration:

A man may be suffering from a grave disease; the physician tells us: "I do not know whether an operation will save the man, but if there *is* any remedy, it is an operation." In such a case, the operation would be justified. Of course, it would be better to know that the operation will save the man; but, if we do not know this, the knowledge formulated in the statement of the physician is a sufficient justification. If we cannot realize the sufficient conditions of success, we shall at least realize the necessary conditions.[2]

So far, there is complete agreement between the two approaches. Reichenbach, however, now develops his solution in terms of the

---

[1] Hans Reichenbach, *Experience and Prediction*, Chicago, 1938, §§ 39–40.
[2] *Id.*, p. 349.

frequency theory of probability: we do not aim at foreseeing the future;

The aim of induction is to find series of events whose frequency of occurrence converges toward a limit.[1]

Now the world may be too disorderly for limits to exist, and he therefore introduces the concept of a 'predictable' world. It will be observed that he has made essentially the same distinction between 'disorderly' and 'predictable' worlds as I have between 'unfavourable' and 'favourable' universes—but his are defined by frequencies:

Let us introduce the term "predictable" for a world which is sufficiently ordered to enable us to construct series with a limit. We must admit, then, that we do not know whether the world is predictable.[2]

This account has to be supplemented by the concept of *posit*. With a die we wager on an ace turning up in accordance with the probability of an ace being $\frac{1}{6}$, and this is an 'appraised posit' (what might be called a "probability hypothesis"). With inductive prediction, we make a 'blind posit', because, though we do not know its actual value, we know it is our best posit. Blind posits may be corrected by further experience; and hence, *if there is a limit at all*, we must in the end get closer to it. Clearly the idea here is essentially the same as the possibility of a predictable universe and the possibility of there being a limit.

If there are other methods of prediction, they must in the end lead asymptotically to the same limit—else they would be wrong. He thus arrives at the following:

if there is any method which leads to the limit of the frequency, the inductive principle will do the same; if there is a limit of the frequency, the inductive principle is a sufficient condition to find it.[3]

It is because other methods might be effective for prediction that we must say, not that the inductive principle is a necessary condition for the existence of a frequency-limit, but that the *applicability* of that principle is necessary. This again is like the present solution, in holding that, if the universe is favourable, scientific

[1] *Id.*, p. 350.
[2] *Id.*, pp. 350-1.
[3] *Id.*, p. 355.

method will be applicable. But I diverge here slightly, on the grounds that any effective method must be equivalent to scientific method.

Reichenbach also makes the point that he uses only tautological relations:

Although the inductive inference is not a tautology, the proof that it leads to the best posit is based on tautologies only.[1]

He adds that there is the additional factor of the 'best posit'. This corresponds to the present solution, which consists of tautologies plus the possibility of a favourable universe.

He stresses further that he does not postulate the existence of limits. There may be none, and then induction would be unsuccessful. But this should not deter us from using induction.

Only if we knew that the unfavourable case is actual, should we renounce attempts at prediction. But obviously this is not our situation. We do not know whether we shall have success; but we do not know the contrary either. Hume believed that a justification of induction could not be given because *we do not know whether we shall have success*; the correct formulation, instead, would read that a justification of induction could not be given if *we knew that we should have no success*.[2]

It will be seen that there is considerable identity in the two approaches: one adopts scientific procedure (for Reichenbach induction) on the possibility of a favourable universe (as the 'best posit' in a 'predictable' world); if the universe is unfavourable (unpredictable) scientific inference (induction) fails; we do not know we shall have success; we do not know we shall have no success. When he asserts that a necessary condition of success is the applicability of induction (I prefer to write "of scientific inference") I agree, though I have not put it that way.

Although Reichenbach has given the essentials of the solution, I have ventured to put forward the solution in the form in which I arrived at it, because his version has not won acceptance, and because this may be due to two features of it, which are different in my presentation.

First he identifies scientific inference with induction, whereas I hold that this is too narrow a description—even if there is such

[1] *Id.*, p. 359.
[2] *Id.*, p. 362.

a form of inference as induction. What is needed is to justify the hypothetico-deductive method. It is true that Reichenbach's work practically amounts to that, for his 'blind posit' is, or could be made, equivalent to a hypothesis. But, as with Williams' treatment, it is desirable to have the element of hypothesis made explicit. This difference is perhaps the less important one.

The second difference is that his solution is bound up with the frequency theory of probability. This is a pity. One may use the concept of probability without deciding which of the possible interpretations to put upon it. No doubt the frequency interpretation when further elaborated will be made satisfactory, but in Reichenbach's form it is not—at any rate not generally accepted. The point, however, is that the solution of the 'problem of induction' must be independent of the interpretation of probability. And perhaps one reason why his solution has not been well received is because of its close though irrelevant connexion with the frequency theory. So far as the mathematical procedure is concerned, Williams' tautologies are to be preferred, interpreting 'probability' in these how we will.*

It may be added that it is regrettable to speak, as Reichenbach does, of an inductive 'principle', for no such 'principle' operates in either scheme, his or mine.

Apart from these differences the basic idea is the same. The form of it that I arrived at, however, concerning the possibility of a weakest favourable universe, would seem to be preferable to that of a predictable world containing frequency-limits. I suggest that the idea, first seen by Reichenbach, is worth careful examination, and that it is worth making a serious attempt to grapple with the difficult tautologies involved.

---

* Possibly one reason why Reichenbach's solution has not gained acceptance—indeed its significance appears to have been missed—is that he added to it a conception of 'concatenated inductions', designed to strengthen inductive conclusions *after* induction has been justified; his emphasis on this may have distracted attention from the main theme.

LIST OF WORKS DIRECTLY CITED

Ayer, A. J., *Language, Truth and Logic*, London, 1936.
  The Foundations of Empirical Knowledge, London, 1940.

Berkeley, George, *Works*, ed. by Sampson, London, 1898, Vol. II, *De Motu*.
Braithwaite, R. B., "*La problème logique de l'induction*. By Jean Nicod", *Mind*, N.S. Vol. XXXIV, No. 136, London, 1925.
  "The Idea of Necessary Connexion", *Mind*, N.S. Vol. XXXVII, No. 145, London, 1928.
Bridgman, P. W., *The Logic of Modern Physics*, New York, 1927.
Broad, C. D., "On the Relation between Induction and Probability (I)", *Mind*, N.S. Vol. XXVII, No. 108, London, 1918.
  "The Relation between Induction and Probability (II)", *Mind*, N.S. Vol. XXIX, No. 113, London, 1920.
  "The Principles of Problematic Induction", *Proc. of the Aristotelian Soc.*, N.S. Vol. XXVIII, London, 1928.
  "The Principles of Demonstrative Induction (I)", *Mind*, N.S. Vol. XXXIX, No. 155, London, 1930.
  "*Wahrscheinlichkeit, Statistik, und Wahrheit*. By Richard von Mises", *Mind*, N.S. Vol. XLVI, No. 184, London, 1937.
  "Hr. von Wright on the Logic of Induction (II)", *Mind*, N.S. Vol. LIII, No. 210, London, 1944.
  "Hr. von Wright on the Logic of Induction (III)", *Mind*, N.S. Vol. LIII, No. 211, London, 1944.
  "*Probability and Induction*. By Wm. Kneale", *Mind*, N.S. Vol. LIX, No. 233, Edinburgh, 1950.

Carnap, Rudolf, *The Unity of Science*, London, 1934.
  Philosophy and Logical Syntax, London, 1935.
  The Logical Syntax of Language, London, 1937.

Daniel, G. E., *The Three Ages: An Essay on Archæological Method*, Cambridge, 1943.
Darwin, Charles, *The Formation of Vegetable Mould through the Action of Worms*, London, 1945.
Darwin, Francis, *More Letters of Charles Darwin*, Vol. I, London, 1903.

Eaton, R. M., *General Logic*, New York, 1931.

Eddington, A. S., "Indeterminacy and Indeterminism" (Symposium), *Proc. of the Arist. Soc.*, Sup. Vol. X, London, 1931.
Enc. Brit., 14th ed. Art. "Argon".
Ewing, A. C., *Idealism*, London, 1934.

George, W. H., *The Scientist in Action*, London, 1936.
Goodstein, R. L., "On von Mises' Theory of Probability", *Mind*, N.S. Vol. XLIX, No. 193, London, 1940.

Hume, David, *A Treatise of Human Nature*, Bk. I.
An Enquiry concerning Human Nature.
An Abstract of A Treatise on Human Nature, Cambridge, 1938.

James, William, *Pragmatism*, New York, 1928.
Japolsky, N. S., "A Theory of Elementary Particles" *London, Edinburgh, and Dublin Philosophical Magazine*, N.S. Vol. XX, London, 1935.
Jeffreys, Harold, *Scientific Inference*, Cambridge, 1931.
Theory of Probability, Oxford, 1939.
Jevons, W. S., *The Principles of Science*, London, 1924.
Johnson, W. E., *Logic*, Pt. II, Cambridge, 1922.
Joseph, H. W. B., *An Introduction to Logic*, Oxford, 1925.

Keynes, J. M., *A Treatise on Probability*, London, 1921.
Kneale, William, *Probability and Induction*, Oxford, 1949.

Lewy, Casimir, "On the 'Justification' of Induction", *Analysis*, Vol. VI, Nos. 5 and 6, Oxford, 1939.
Lindsay, R. B., and Margenau, H., *Foundations of Physics*, New York, 1936.

Mace, C. A., *The Principles of Logic*, London, 1933.
Mach, Ernst, *The Science of Mechanics*, Chicago, 1907.
Mill, J. S., *System of Logic*, London, 1919.
von Mises, Richard, *Probability, Statistics and Truth*, London, 1939.
Moore, G. E., *Philosophical Studies*, London, 1922.

Nagel, Ernest, *Principles of the Theory of Probability*, Inter. Enc. of Unified Science, Vol. I, No. 6, Chicago, 1939.
Newton, Isaac, *Philosophiae Naturalis Principia Mathematica*, ed. by Cajori, Cambridge, 1934.
Nicod, Jean, *The Logical Problem of Induction*, published in the Eng. trans. as part of *Foundations of Geometry and Induction*, London, 1930.

Ogden, C. K., *Bentham's Theory of Fictions*, London, 1932.

Pearson, Karl, *The Grammar of Science*, London, 1892.
Poincaré, Henri, *Science and Hypothesis*, London, 1905.
Popper, K. R., *Logik der Forschung*, Wien, 1935.
    "A Set of Independent Axioms for Probability", *Mind*,
    N.S. Vol. XLVII, No. 186, London, 1938.
    The Open Society and its Enemies, Vol. II, London, 1945.
    "The Poverty of Historicism (III)", *Economica*, N.S.
    Vol. XII, No. 46, London, 1945.
    "The Trivialisation of Mathematical Logic", *Proc. of*
    the Xth Inter. Cong. of Philosophy, Vol. I, Amsterdam,
    1948.
    "Indeterminism in Quantum Physics and in Classical
    Physics", *The British Journal for the Philosophy of Science*,
    Vol. I, Nos. 2 & 3, Edinburgh, 1950.

Rabaud, Etienne, *How Animals Find their Way about*, London, 1928.
Ramsey, F. P., *The Foundations of Mathematics and Other Logical Essays*,
    London, 1931.
Reichenbach, Hans, *Experience and Prediction*, Chicago, 1938.
    Philosophic Foundations of Quantum Mechanics, Ber-
    keley and Los Angeles, 1944.
Rowse, A. L., *The Use of History*, London, 1946.
Russell, Bertrand, *An Inquiry into Meaning and Truth*, London, 1940.
    Human Knowledge : its Scope and Limits, London, 1948.

Schlick, Moritz, "Meaning and Verification", Vol. XLV, No. 268,
    New York, 1936, p. 176.
Stace, W. T., "Positivism", *Mind*, N.S. Vol. LIII, No. 211, London,
    1944.
Stebbing, L. Susan, *A Modern Introduction to Logic*, London, 1933.
Strutt, R. J., *John William Strutt, 3rd Baron Rayleigh*, London, 1924.

Tchebysheff (Chebuishev), P. L., *Œuvres*, Tome I, St. Pétersbourg,
    1899.

Vaihinger, H., *The Philosophy of 'As If'*, London, 1924.
Valléry-Radot, René, *The Life of Pasteur*, London, 1919.

Whetham, W. C. D., and Whetham, M. D., *Cambridge Readings in the*
    Literature of Science, Cam-
    bridge, 1924.
Williams, Donald, *The Ground of Induction*, Cambridge (Mass.), 1947.

Wisdom, J. O., "The Methodology of the Psycho-Analytical Law of Mistakes", *The Egyptian Journal of Psychology*, Vol. I, No. 1, Cairo, 1945.

The Metamorphosis of Philosophy, Cairo (Al-Ma'aref and Basil Blackwell), 1947.

Wittgenstein, Ludwig, *Tractatus Logico-Philosophicus*, London, 1922.

von Wright, G. H., "On Probability", *Mind*, N.S. Vol. XLIX, No. 195, London, 1940.

The Logical Problem of Induction, Helsinki, 1941.

INDEX

Absolute zero, 21
Absolutes, 4, 6, 61, 76
Acceptability. *See* credibility
Accuracy. *See* exactitude, absolute
Acid, electric, 16, 17
Aether, 4, 31 f, 40
Alternative, negative. *See below*
   positive, 172
Analogy, argument by, Ch. XII, 118,
   130
   negative. *See* analogy, positive
   perfect, 116, 127 n
   positive, 108 f, 114, 115, 130, 135
   statistical, 108
   strength of, 108 f, 130
   types of, 104 f
Ants, orientation in, 11 f, 50
Argon, 15 f
Aristotle, 219, 222
Atoms, legal, 145
Attraction. *See* gravitation
Axiom, limit, 192
Ayer, A. J., 36, 158

Bacon, F., 85
Ball and ring, 19
Bayes's theorem. *See* theorem
Bees, orientation in, 11 f
Belief, rational, 186-9
   reasonable, 159, 160-2
Bentham, J., 74, 75
Berkeley, G., 36, 44, 74, 75, 77, 157,
   158
Bernoulli, Jac., *See* theorem
Boyle's law. *See* law
Bradley, F. H., 127 n
Braithwaite, R. B., 114 n, 124 n
Bridgman, P. W., 74, 76, 77, 82
Broad, C. D., 91 n, 123, 132-4, 142-8,
   149, 157, 162, 193, 201, 202 n,
   208

Carnap, R., 36, 158, 203
Catalyst, 160, 166
Causal relation, Ch. XI, 120, 121, 168-
   170, 219-21
Causation, as logical relation, 164
   horizontal, 147-8, 157, 165
   vertical, 147-8, 157, Ch. XVIII
Cause. *See* explanation
Causes, criteria for, *See* Criteria
Cavendish, H., 15
Change, qualitative and quantitative,
   19, 104, 106
Charles's law. *See* law
Chesterton, G. K., 66
Christadelphian, 95
Circumstances, varying the, 17 f, 118
Concepts, instances of. *See* hypothesis,
   non-instantial
   non-instantial. *See* hypothesis, non-
   instantial
   related to experience, 4, 8, 44-5
   unneeded, 4, 45
Conditions, identical and similar, 127 f
   varying the. *See* circumstances
Confirmable, weakly, 39
Confirmation, Ch. IV
   and falsification, asymmetry of, 57
   degree of, 57
Contraction, Lorentz-Fitzgerald, 53
Copeland & Wald, 190
Correlation, 22, 99
Credibility of hypothesis, 204
Criteria of Co-Variation, 98-9
   Explicitly Non-One-One Probable
   Causal Laws, 94-6
   Independence, 87, 88
   Probable Causal Laws, 89-94
Criterion of Counteracting Causes,
   96-8

Daniel, G. E., 41
Darwin, C., 9, 10, 49, 50, 91, 96

MADE AND PRINTED IN GREAT BRITAIN BY
EBENEZER BAYLIS AND SON, LTD., THE
TRINITY PRESS, WORCESTER, AND LONDON